The Non-Algebraic Elementary Functions

A Rigorous Approach

André L. Yandl

Department of Mathematics, Seattle University

The Non-Algebraic Elementary Functions

A Rigorous Approach

Prentice-Hall, Inc., Englewood Cliffs, N. J.

PRENTICE-HALL INTERNATIONAL, INC. *London*
PRENTICE-HALL OF AUSTRALIA, PTY., LTD. *Sydney*
PRENTICE-HALL OF CANADA, LTD. *Toronto*
PRENTICE-HALL FRANCE, S.A.R.L. *Paris*
PRENTICE-HALL OF JAPAN, INC. *Tokyo*
PRENTICE-HALL DE MEXICO, S.A. *Mexico City*

THE NON-ALGEBRAIC ELEMENTARY FUNCTIONS: A RIGOROUS APPROACH
by André L. Yandl.

Library of Congress Catalog Card Number: 63–17226.
Printed in the United States of America.   [C]

To My Teachers

Preface

To the Instructor: During the past few years, books called *Algebra Made Easy, Trigonometry Made Easy,* and *Calculus Made Easy* have been put on the market. To all appearances, they have been fairly successful with the general public. I have often wondered what would happen if someone wrote a book entitled *Trigonometry Made Difficult.* I must confess that I have been tempted to give that title to this book. My unusual approach makes some statements in justification seem appropriate.

The principal objective of this text is training the student for a rigorous calculus course. It is my conviction that a course in elementary functions or advanced trigonometry is the natural place to begin building the foundation for future rigorous mathematical studies. It is certainly the natural place to introduce the ideas of functions and limiting processes which the student will need not only in calculus but in much of his future mathematical work.

A certain number of theorems and proofs are usually omitted from elementary courses because they are too difficult. They do not appear in advanced courses, however; perhaps, because they are considered too elementary. I have included some of these theorems in the text.

Since some of the material introduced is quite modern and indeed very difficult, the presentation has been so arranged as to permit the omission of certain sections: The most difficult are double-starred and can be skipped without any loss in continuity. Single-starred material may be skipped without serious loss in continuity. The foregoing remarks apply to theorems, proofs, and problems which are starred but appear in non-starred sections.

In writing this book, I have been influenced by the material prepared by the School Mathematics Study Group, especially by the volumes on elementary functions, but the outline and arrangement of the material are mine.

vii

The text consists of three chapters. In the first chapter, the concepts of functions, properties of functions, inverse functions, and graphs of functions are thoroughly treated.

In the second chapter, the non-algebraic elementary functions are introduced, with a careful study of their properties based on the results of Chapter 1.

The notion of trigonometric angle is not introduced until Chapter 3 which includes applications of the elementary functions. This has been done in order to obviate the confusion which students usually encounter with regard to the difference between the trigonometric functions of angles and trigonometric functions of numbers. Postponing the first until the second has been mastered will, I believe, preserve clarity.

This text is unique because the following material is included.

1. The completeness property is introduced in order to permit precise statements for the definitions of arc length and the exponential function.

2. The proofs of three basic theorems (1.6.1., 1.6.4., and 1.6.5.) about least upper bounds of sets of real numbers are given, and these theorems are used consistently in proving most of the "hard theorems" included in the text.

3. A discussion of the determination of the points of intersection of curves whose equations are given in polar coordinates (Appendix A).

The numbering of the theorems and definitions is self-explanatory. For example, definition 2.5.1 is to be found in Chapter 2, section 5.

This book has been written for the benefit of the above-average student in his senior year of high school or his freshman year at college. I assume that you are an above-average student; otherwise, you would not be taking a course in elementary functions. I also assume that you are industrious, for such a course requires serious conscientious study. Even though these assumptions are true, you will discover that some of the proofs of some of the theorems are quite abstract and difficult. Most authors omit such proofs from their texts for this reason, but I believe that young students have the ability and desire to understand more material than is usually given them.

Mathematics is a discipline, and, like all other disciplines, it must be taught and learned early. If you intend to continue your work in mathematics, this book is meant not to discourage you, but to prepare you so that you can understand and therefore enjoy your future work in mathematics.

Basically, a mathematician's task consists of proving that certain statements are true within the logical system in which they have developed. Mathematicians begin with some undefined words and state some definitions and axioms in terms of these words. After that, they assert and prove propositions by using laws of logic which they have already carefully laid down.

Many of these propositions are hard to state and easy to prove; many are hard to state and hard to prove; others are easy to state and easy to prove; and some are easy to state and hard to prove. The last type is perhaps the most difficult which a student encounters. Because these propositions are easy to state and hard to prove, their statement is included in basic courses but their proofs are omitted. Often, such proofs are not readily available to the student in any of the standard textbooks. This, of course, need be no great loss so long as he understands that the statement does require a proof. Unfortunately, some of these statements seem to be true by nature. Many students pursue their courses through long years without realizing that such statements are not just true by nature, but that they can, and must, be proved. Who would doubt, for example, that a circle divides a plane into two regions, one inside and one outside the circle? This, however, is an example of a statement easy to understand intuitively, but to date, no easy proof has been found.

I have included in this text some of the proofs which are often postponed for advanced courses and which, to my knowledge, have not appeared in any of the standard textbooks. When you study this text, do not attempt to read the proof of any statement until you fully understand the meaning of every term involved in the statement and the meaning of the statement as a whole. Always study with a pencil and paper at hand; draw diagrams to illustrate geometrically the different concepts which you are studying; concentrate and think hard. Above all, do not get discouraged. Anything worth doing is worth doing well.

Acknowledgements: In writing this text, I have received much help and encouragement from many colleagues and friends.

I wish to acknowledge my debt to Professor Mary Turner who first suggested to me that I put my views and ideas about trigonometry into a book. Her interest and encouragement were a great influence in the writing of this text. The proof of theorem 1.6.5. is essentially hers.

I also wish to thank Professor T. S. Chihara, head of the Mathematics Department of Seattle University and all the members of his staff who read the manuscript and made many useful suggestions for improving it. I am particularly indebted to Professor C. C. Chang for his help in preparing the answers to the exercises.

Thanks are also due to Miss Kay Neff and Miss Veronica Miller for their excellent typing of the manuscript. I am especially thankful to Miss Miller for her competent editing in addition to the many hours of typing.

I am also deeply indebted to Professor Orval M. Klose. His influence on my teaching has been vital, and I owe him more than I can acknowledge.

I am indebted to the students of Seattle University who provided the original incentive for this text. I also owe many thanks to Mr. M. Pakulis who helped insert the symbols in the final manuscript. I wish to express my appreciation to the staff of Prentice-Hall for their help in producing the text. In particular, I wish to thank Mr. Richard Hansen and Mr. Robert Davis for their original interest in the manuscript.

Most of all, I want to give my thanks and love to my wife, Shirley, who spent endless hours inserting symbols and drawing diagrams through the various phases of the manuscript. I also owe her a great deal for being able to keep our three children relatively quiet during my many hours of writing.

ANDRÉ L. YANDL

Contents

The Non-Algebraic Elementary Functions

A Rigorous Approach

Chapter One

General Properties of Functions

Much of mathematics involves in some way the function concept. The present chapter will be devoted to topics which are closely related to that concept. We shall base our discussion of functions on sets. We must note, however, that the word "function" was first introduced in mathematics to refer to certain kinds of formulas. Mathematicians soon realized, however, that the meaning of the word could be generalized and their study of the topic made much clearer by formulating the function idea in terms of sets. Therefore, it seems natural to begin our discussion of the function concept with a brief introduction to the notions of sets.

1.1. Introduction In order to be able to give precise definitions in our future work, we introduce some very basic ideas about sets. We do not intend to give a rigorous treatment of set theory, for this topic has a place of its own in mathematics. We wish only to present some notions about sets which are easy to understand. These notions, however, are of great value in describing more complex ideas.

A *set* is a collection of certain objects. A description, or a property of the objects which belong to a set, must be clearly stated so that, given a certain object, there is no question as to whether or not it belongs to the set. Examples of sets are the following:

1. The set of all states in the United States in 1962

2. The set of all students who have attended Seattle University in 1962

3. The set of all monkeys in the world

4. The set of all positive integers (counting numbers)

5. The set of all married couples living in the United States in 1962

6. The set of all straight lines

We note that an object which belongs to a set may itself be a set. In example 5, each member of the set is a set consisting of two people; in example 6, each member of the set is a set of points (a line).

Definition 1.1.1. If some object belongs to a set, it is called an *element* or *member* of that set.

Usually, sets will be denoted by capital letters and elements of sets will be denoted by small letters. If A is a set and x is an element of A, we write $x \in A$ which is read "x is an element of A" or "x belongs to A." If x is not an element of A, we write $x \notin A$.

Definition 1.1.2. If A and B are sets and every element of A is also an element of B, we say that A is a *subset* of B, and we write $A \subset B$. If A is a subset of B and there is at least one element of B which is not an element of A, we say that A is a *proper subset* of B. Two sets A and B are equal ($A = B$) if and only if $A \subset B$ and $B \subset A$.

The two most common methods of describing a set are the roster method and the defining property method. The roster method lists the elements of the set, listing each element only once and enclosing the list in braces. The defining property method uses the following notational device:

$$A = \{x \mid x \text{ has the property } p\}$$

which is read "A equals (is) the set of all x which have property p" or "A is the set of x's such that x has property p."

Example 1. {1, 2, 3, 4} denotes the set whose four members are the first four counting numbers.

Example 2. $\{x \mid (x - 1)(x - 2) = 0\}$ denotes the set which consists of the numbers 1 and 2, since the statement $(x - 1)(x - 2) = 0$ becomes a true statement when x is replaced by 1 or by 2. We sometimes call this set the *solution set* of the equation $(x - 1)(x - 2) = 0$.

We note that

$$\{x \mid (x - 1)(x - 2) = 0\} = \{1, 2\}$$

Hence, it is sometimes possible to describe a set by either the roster method or the defining property method. On the other hand, one of the two methods is often much more efficient than the other.

Example 3. $S = \{x \mid x$ is a positive integer$\}$ cannot very well be written using the roster method although the symbol $\{1, 2, 3, \ldots\}$ is sometimes used for this set.

Definition 1.1.3. The *union* and *intersection* of the sets A and B are denoted by $A \cup B$ and $A \cap B$ respectively and are defined by the following:

$$A \cup B = \{x \mid x \in A \text{ or } x \in B \text{ or both}\}$$

$$A \cap B = \{x \mid x \in A \text{ and } x \in B\}$$

Example 4. If $A = \{1, 2, 3, 4\}$ and $B = \{3, 4, 5, 6\}$, then

$$A \cup B = \{1, 2, 3, 4, 5, 6\} \quad \text{and} \quad A \cap B = \{3, 4\}$$

Since it is desirable that the intersection of two sets be a set and since it is possible for two sets to have no element in common, we agree that any collection which has no member is a set. We further agree that there is only one such set and call it the *empty set*. We denote this set by $\emptyset$ and make the convention that it is a subset of any set.

Example 5. If $A = \{x \mid x$ is a positive even integer$\}$ and $B = \{x \mid x$ is a positive odd integer$\}$

then $A \cup B = \{x \mid x$ is a positive integer$\}$

and $A \cap B = \emptyset$

Definition 1.1.4. Two sets are said to be *disjoint* if and only if their intersection is the empty set.

If A and B are sets, $A \setminus B$ denotes the set whose elements are those elements of A which do not belong to B. Note that $A \setminus B$ is defined even if B is not a subset of A and that $A \setminus B = A$ whenever A and B are disjoint sets.

Example 6. If $A = \{1, 2, 3, 4\}$ and $B = \{1, 3\}$, then $A \setminus B = \{2, 4\}$.

Example 7.   If $S = \{x \mid (x - 1)(x - 2)(x - 5) = 0\}$

and $V = \{x \mid (x - 3)(x - 5) = 0\}$

then $S \setminus V = \{1, 2, 5\} \setminus \{3, 5\}$

$$= \{1, 2\}$$

We now illustrate how to prove some simple facts about sets with the following:

Example 8.   Show that for any two sets A and B, $A \cap B \subset A \cup B$.

Solution: If A and B are disjoint, $A \cap B = \emptyset$ and $A \cap B \subset A \cup B$, since by convention $\emptyset$ is a subset of any set.

In the case that $A \cap B \neq \emptyset$, we need to show that each element of $A \cap B$ is also an element of $A \cup B$. To this end, let x be an arbitrary member of $A \cap B$. Then $x \in A$ and $x \in B$. It is therefore true that $x \in A$ or $x \in B$. It follows that $x \in A \cup B$. Since x was arbitrary, we have proved that every element of $A \cap B$ is a member of $A \cup B$. Hence, $A \cap B \subset A \cup B$. ∎ *

The next basic concept about sets is that of cardinality.

Suppose that for a class of twenty students there are twenty seats available. Suppose, further, that on a certain day all students are present. Then, on that day, we have an obvious relationship between the set of twenty students and the set of twenty seats. To each student corresponds one seat and conversely. This is a special case of a very basic concept which we now define.

Definition 1.1.5.   Two sets A and B are said to be in a *one-to-one correspondence* when a rule can be given which associates each element of A with one and only one element of B and, conversely, associates each member of B with one and only one member of A. We sometimes say that A and B have the same *cardinality*. This is another way of saying that the two sets have the same "number of elements."

Example 9.   Establish a one-to-one correspondence between the sets $A = \{x \mid x$ is a positive integer$\}$ and $B = \{x \mid x$ is an even positive integer$\}$.

Solution: We can give the following rule: if $n \in A$, we associate with n the element $2n \in B$. It is clear that this association establishes a one-to-one correspondence between the elements of A and B. ∎

If A and B are two sets which have the same cardinality, the rule which associates each element of A with one and only one element of B and, with each element of B, one and only one element of A, is not in general unique, as is shown by the following:

* The symbol ∎ signalizes the end of a proof. This notation is due to P. R. Halmos.

Example 10. The sets $A = \{a, b, c\}$ and $B = \{1, 2, 3\}$ have the same cardinality. The one-to-one correspondence can be defined in any one of the following six ways:

1. $a \leftrightarrow 1$ $b \leftrightarrow 2$ $c \leftrightarrow 3$
2. $a \leftrightarrow 1$ $b \leftrightarrow 3$ $c \leftrightarrow 2$
3. $a \leftrightarrow 2$ $b \leftrightarrow 1$ $c \leftrightarrow 3$
4. $a \leftrightarrow 2$ $b \leftrightarrow 3$ $c \leftrightarrow 1$
5. $a \leftrightarrow 3$ $b \leftrightarrow 1$ $c \leftrightarrow 2$
6. $a \leftrightarrow 3$ $b \leftrightarrow 2$ $c \leftrightarrow 1$

Definition 1.1.6. If S is a set and if there exists a positive integer n such that S and the set $\{1, 2, 3, \ldots, n\}$ have the same cardinality, then we say that S is a *finite set*.

Definition 1.1.7. A set S is *infinite* if and only if it is not finite.

Exercises 1. Let $A = \{1, 2, 7, 9\}$ and $B = \{3, 4, 5, 6, 7\}$. Find $A \cup B$, $A \cap B$, and $A \setminus B$.

2. Write the following sets using the roster method:
   (a) $\{x \mid (x - 6)(x + 5)(x - 3) = 0\}$
   (b) $\{x \mid x^2 - 1 = 0\}$
   (c) $\{x \mid x$ is the first President of the United States$\}$
   (d) $\{x \mid x$ is a letter of the English alphabet$\}$

3. Describe the following, using the defining property method:
   (a) $\{a, e, i, o, u\}$
   (b) $\{$Glenn, Carpenter$\}$
   (c) $\{$"Prentice-Hall, Inc."$\}$

4. At a dance, how can one determine whether the set of men and the set of women have the same cardinality?

5. Give a rule that establishes a one-to-one correspondence between the sets $A = \{1, 3, 5, 7\}$ $B = \{2, 4, 6, 8\}$.

6. Show that for any two sets A and B it is true that $A \cap B \subset A$ and $A \subset A \cup B$.

7. Let $A = \{x \mid (x - 1)(x - 2)(x + 7) = 0\}$
   $B = \{1, 2\}$
   $C = \{1, 3, -7\}$
   $D = \{2, 4\}$.   Find:
   (a) $A \cup B$
   (b) $(A \cup B) \cap (C \cup D)$
   (c) $(A \cap B) \cup (C \cap D)$
   (d) $(A \cup C) \setminus B$
   (e) $(A \cup B) \cap C$ and $(A \cap C) \cup (B \cap C)$
   (f) $(A \cup D) \cup C$ and $A \cup (D \cup C)$
   (g) $(A \cap B) \cup C$ and $(A \cup C) \cap (B \cup C)$

8. For the sets described in exercise 7, which of the following statements are true?
   (a) $A \subseteq B$
   (b) $B \subset A$
   (c) $(A \cap D) \subseteq B$
   (d) $(A \cup B) \subseteq C$

1.2. The real numbers The number system used in this text is the system of real numbers. In more advanced courses in mathematics, an axiomatic treatment of the development of the real numbers is given.* For our purpose, it is sufficient to list a set of fundamental properties which are so chosen that *all* properties of the real numbers can be derived from them. In this section, we discuss the algebraic properties of the real numbers. In the following three sections, we shall present some deeper concepts about the real number system which are needed later in the text.

The real number system is a set R of objects, together with two basic operations, addition and multiplication, which satisfy certain properties. For convenience, these properties are separated into three groups: the *field properties*, the *order properties*, and the *completeness property*.

The following are the so-called field properties of the real numbers.

F_1 Closure under addition: If $x \in R$ and $y \in R$, then x and y have a unique sum $x + y$ and $x + y \in R$.

F_2 Closure under multiplication: If $x \in R$ and $y \in R$, then x and y have a unique product xy and $xy \in R$.

F_3 The associative law for addition: If x, y, and z are in R, then $(x + y) + z = x + (y + z)$.

F_4 The associative law for multiplication: If x, y, z are in R, then $x(yz) = (xy)z$.

F_5 There exists a number 0 (zero) such that, for any $x \in R$, $x + 0 = 0 + x = x$.

F_6 There exists a number 1 (one) such that $1 \neq 0$ and for any $x \in R$, $x \cdot 1 = 1 \cdot x = x$.

F_7 For any $x \in R$, there exists a number $-x$ such that $x + (-x) = -x + x = 0$.

F_8 For any non-zero real number x, there exists a number called the *reciprocal* of x and denoted by $1/x$ (or x^{-1}) such that $x \cdot x^{-1} = x^{-1} \cdot x = 1$.

* Edmund Landau, *Foundations of Analysis* (New York: Chelsea Publishing Company, 1960).

F_9 The commutative law for addition: If $x \in R$ and $y \in R$, then $x + y = y + x$.

F_{10} The commutative law for multiplication: If $x \in R$ and $y \in R$, then $xy = yx$.

F_{11} The distributive law: If x, y, and z are in R, then $x(y + z) = xy + xz$.

The following are the so-called order properties.

O_1 There exists a non-empty subset P of R such that, if we define $-P = \{-x \mid x \in P\}$, then $P \cup \{0\} \cup -P = R$ and $-P$, $\{0\}$ and P are mutually disjoint.

O_2 If $x \in P$ and $y \in P$, then $x + y \in P$.

O_3 If $x \in P$ and $y \in P$, then $xy \in P$.

Definition 1.2.1.   If $x \in P$, we say that x is a *positive* real number.

We shall state the completeness property in section 1.4. We do not intend to derive here all the algebraic properties of the real numbers which are undoubtedly familiar to the reader. We shall, however, give some examples to illustrate the techniques and leave the greatest part of the task for the exercises.

Example 1.   Show that for any $x \in R$, $x \cdot 0 = 0$.

Solution: Let $x \in R$.

By F_5, we have

$y + 0 = y$

Multiplying both sides by x, we get

$x(y + 0) = xy$

By F_{11}, we obtain

$xy + x \cdot 0 = xy$

Adding $-(xy)$ to both sides,

$-(xy) + (xy + x \cdot 0) = -(xy) + xy$

By F_3, we get

$[-(xy) + xy] + x \cdot 0 = -(xy) + xy$

By F_7, we obtain

$0 + x \cdot 0 = 0$

And the conclusion $x \cdot 0 = 0$ now follows by F_5. ∎

Example 2. Show that there is only one number having the property of the number 0 in F_5.

Solution: Suppose that there are two numbers 0 and 0′ having property F_5. Then by F_5, we have

$$0 + 0' = 0$$

and $0' + 0 = 0'$

But by F_9, we have

$$0 + 0' = 0' + 0$$

Hence, $0 = 0'$ ∎

Example 3. Show that $(-1)(-1) = 1$

Solution: $1 + (-1) = 0$

Hence, $(-1)[1 + (-1)] = (-1) \cdot 0 = 0$.

By F_{11}, we get

$$(-1)(1) + (-1)(-1) = 0$$

or $-1 + (-1)(-1) = 0$

Adding 1 to both sides

$$1 + [-1 + (-1)(-1)] = 1 + 0 = 1$$

Hence, by F_3,

$$[1 + (-1)] + (-1)(-1) = 1$$

and by F_7,

$$0 + (-1)(-1) = 1$$

The conclusion $(-1)(-1) = 1$ follows by F_5. ∎

We can now define two new operations, subtraction and division in terms of addition and multiplication.

Definition 1.2.2. If $x \in R$ and $y \in R$, the *difference* between x and y is defined to be the number $x + (-y)$. It is denoted by $x - y$. The operation of finding the difference between two numbers is called *subtraction*.

Definition 1.2.3. If $x \in R$, $y \in R$, and $y \neq 0$, the quotient of x and y is denoted by x/y and is defined by $x/y = x \cdot 1/y$. The operation of finding the quotient of two numbers is called *division*.

Definition 1.2.4. If $x \in R$ and $y \in R$, we say that x is *less* than y and write $x < y$ if and only if $y - x \in P$. ($y - x$ is positive).

Definition 1.2.5. If $x \in R$ and $y \in R$, we say that x is *greater* than y and we write $x > y$ if and only if $y < x$.

Definition 1.2.6. If $x \in R$ and $y \in R$, we say that x is *less than, or equal to*, y and we write $x \leq y$ if and only if either $x < y$ or $x = y$.

Greater than, or equal to, is defined similarly.

Definition 1.2.7. If $x \in R$, we say that x is *negative* if and only if $-x$ is positive.

The reader probably recalls many theorems from basic mathematics which involve concepts defined above. We illustrate how to prove some of these theorems in the following examples.

Example 4. Show that if x, y, z are in R, $x < y$ and $y < z$, then $x < z$.

Solution: $x < y$ implies $y - x \in P$

$y < z$ implies $z - y \in P$

By O_2, we get

$(y - x) + (z - y) \in P$

That is $(y + (-x) + z + (-y)) \in P$

By the associative law and commutative law for addition, F_7 and F_5, we see that

$z - x \in P$

Hence, $x < z$ ∎

Example 5. Show that if $x \in R$, then $-(-x) = x$.

Solution: By F_7, we have

$x + (-x) = 0$

Adding $-(-x)$ to both sides, we get

$[x + (-x)] + -(-x) = 0 + -(-x)$

Using the associative law for addition, we can write

$x + [(-x) + (-(-x))] = 0 + -(-x)$

that is, $\qquad x + 0 = 0 + -(-x)$

or $\qquad\qquad x = -(-x)$ ∎

Example 6. Show that $0 < 1$.

Solution: We want to show that $1 - 0 \in P$, that is, $1 \in P$. Since $R = P \cup \{0\} \cup -P$, it suffices to show that $1 \neq 0$ and $1 \notin -P$. The fact that $1 \neq 0$ is stated in F_6. We shall show that if we assume $1 \in -P$, a contradiction follows.

Suppose that $1 \in -P$. Then there exists some $x \in P$ such that $1 = -x$. Hence, $-1 = -(-x) = x$ and we conclude that $-1 \in P$. But $-1 \in P$ implies by O_3 that $(-1)(-1) \in P$. We know by example 3 that $(-1)(-1) = 1$. Hence, $1 \in P$. We now have shown that if we assume $1 \in -P$, then $1 \in P$ follows. This contradicts the fact that P and $-P$ are disjoint. Hence, we have proved that $1 \notin -P$ and we conclude that $1 \in P$. ∎

The following theorem will be of great value in the sections which follow.

Theorem 1.2.8. If $a \in R$, $b \in R$, $a \leq b$ and if for any positive number h it is true that $b - a \leq h$, then $a = b$.

Proof: We know that $a < b$ or $a = b$. Hence, it suffices to prove that $a < b$ is false. Suppose, on the contrary, that $a < b$. Then $b - a \in P$. It follows that $(b - a)/2 \in P$ also. Hence, from the hypothesis it follows that $b - a \leq (b - a)/2$, from which we get $2b - 2a \leq b - a$ and $b \leq a$. But $a < b$ and $b \leq a$ cannot both be true; hence, we must reject the assumption that $a < b$ and conclude that $a = b$. ∎

Exercises

1. Prove that if x, y, and z are in R and $x + y = x + z$, then $y = z$. This is often called *the left cancellation law for addition.*

2. State and prove the right cancellation law for addition.

3. State and prove the left and right cancellation laws for multiplication.

4. Prove that if $x \in R$, then the number $-x$ is unique.

5. Prove that if $x \in R$, $x \neq 0$, the number x^{-1} is unique.

6. Prove that if $x \in R$, then $x = -x$ if and only if $x = 0$.

7. Prove that if $x \in R$, $y \in R$ and $xy = 0$, then $x = 0$ or $y = 0$. (*Hint:* assume that $x \neq 0$, $y \neq 0$, and $xy = 0$. Then $(xy)y^{-1} = 0 \cdot y^{-1} = 0$, etc.)

8. Prove that if $x \in R$, then $-x = (-1)x$.

9. Prove that if $x \in R$ and $y \in R$, then $(-x)(-y) = xy$.

10. Prove that if x, y, and z are in R and $x < y$, then $x + z < y + z$.

11. Prove that if x, y, and z are in R and $x < y$, then $x - z < y - z$.

12. Prove that $x \in R$ and $x \neq 0$ implies $x^2 > 0$.

13. Prove that $x \in P$ implies $1/x \in P$.

14. Prove that $x \in -P$ implies $1/x \in -P$.

15. Prove that if $x \in R$, $y \in R$, $x < y$, and $z > 0$, then $xz < yz$.

16. Prove that if $x \in R$, $y \in R$, $x < y$, and $z < 0$, then $xz > yz$.

17. Prove that if x and y are in R such that $0 < x < y$, then $0 < 1/y < 1/x$.

18. Prove that if x, y, z, w are in R such that $x < y$ and $z < w$, then $x + z < y + w$.

19. Prove that if x, y, z, w are in R such that $0 < x < y$ and $0 < z < w$, then $0 < x \cdot z < y \cdot w$.

20. Prove that if x, y, z, w are in R such that $0 < x < y$ and $0 < z < w$, then $0 < x/w < y/z$.

21. Prove that if $x \in P \cup \{0\}$ and $y \in P \cup \{0\}$, then $x \leq y$ if and only if $x^2 \leq y^2$.

22. Prove that if $x \in R$, $y \in R$, and $x < y$, then $x < [(x + y)/2] < y$.

23. Prove that if x and y are real numbers such that $0 < x < y$, then $x < \sqrt{xy} < y$.

24. If x and y are real numbers and $0 < x < y$, which of the two numbers $[(x + y)/2]$ and $\sqrt{xy}$ is the larger? Give a proof for your answer. (The first number is called the *arithmetic average*; the second is the *geometric average*.)

*1.3. The well-ordering principle and mathematical induction In the last section, we introduced the real numbers by listing a set of properties which, together with the completeness property (which will be described in the next section), characterizes the system of real numbers. The reader is familiar with certain subsets of R. For example, the set N of *positive integers* (*natural numbers*) is the most basic subset of R. The set of *integers* is $N \cup \{0\} \cup -N$ where $-N = \{-n \mid n \in N\}$. The set $R^{\#}$ of *rational numbers* is the set of those real numbers which can be represented as fractions a/b where a and b are integers. Those real numbers which are not rational are called the *irrational numbers*.

There is a property of the positive integers which is so basic that the reader may have used it many times without being aware of its formal form. This property is called the *well-ordering principle* for the *positive integers*. We now introduce this principle.

Every non-empty set of positive integers has a least member.*

We shall use this principle to obtain theorem 1.3.2. which is the basis for proofs by mathematical induction.

Theorem 1.3.1. There does not exist an integer x with the property $0 < x < 1$.

---

* This principle is taken here as an axiom for the positive integers; however, it can be proved and is sometimes proved in more advanced texts.

Proof: Suppose, on the contrary, that the set $S = \{x \mid x$ is an integer and $0 < x < 1\}$ is not empty. Then by the well-ordering principle S has a least member, say y. Now we have $0 < y < 1$. Multiplying by y, it follows that $0 < y^2 < y$. Since y is a positive integer, y^2 is also a positive integer. Hence, $y^2 \in S$ and $y^2 < y$. Since y is the least member of S, we have obtained a contradiction which completes the proof of the theorem. ∎

Theorem 1.3.2. If $S \subset N$, $1 \in S$ and $k + 1 \in S$ whenever $k \in S$, then $S = N$.

Proof: We need only show that $N \setminus S = \emptyset$. Suppose, on the contrary, that $N \setminus S \neq \emptyset$. Hence, by the well-ordering principle, $N \setminus S$ has a smallest member, say x. Since $1 \in S$ and $x \in N \setminus S$, $1 \neq x$. By theorem 1.3.1., we know there is no positive integer between 0 and 1. Hence, $1 < x$ and $x - 1$ is a positive integer. Clearly, $x - 1 < x$; therefore, $x - 1 \in S$, for otherwise, x would not be the smallest member of $N \setminus S$. By hypothesis, $x - 1 \in S$ implies $(x - 1) + 1 = x \in S$. We have shown that if we assume $N \setminus S \neq \emptyset$, then we can find some integer x such that $x \in S$ and $x \in N \setminus S$. This is a contradiction, and we must conclude that $N \setminus S = \emptyset$. Therefore, $N = S$. ∎

We can now state the principle of finite induction.

Theorem 1.3.3. Let $S(n)$ be a statement which is either true or false when n is replaced by a specific natural number. If

1. $S(1)$ is true and
2. The truth of $S(k)$ implies the truth of $S(k + 1)$, then $S(n)$ is true for all natural numbers n.

Proof: Let $T = \{n \mid n$ is a natural number and $S(n)$ is true$\}$. Then $1 \in T$ and $k \in T$ implies $k + 1 \in T$. It follows by theorem 1.3.2. that $N = T$ and that $S(n)$ is true for all natural numbers.

Example 1. Prove that

$$1^2 + 2^2 + 3^2 + \ldots + n^2 = \frac{n(n + 1)(2n + 1)}{6}$$

is true for all natural numbers n.

Proof: Let $S(n)$ denote the foregoing equality. $S(1)$ is true, since

$$1^2 = \frac{(1)(1 + 1)(2 + 1)}{6} \text{ is true.}$$

Suppose now that $S(k)$ is true. That is, the equality

$$1^2 + 2^2 + \ldots + k^2 = \frac{k(k + 1)(2k + 1)}{6} \text{ is true.}$$

Adding $(k + 1)^2$ to both sides, we get

$$1^2 + 2^2 + \ldots + k^2 + (k + 1)^2 = \frac{k(k + 1)(2k + 1)}{6} + (k + 1)^2$$

$$= \frac{(k + 1)[k(2k + 1) + 6(k + 1)]}{6}$$

$$= \frac{(k + 1)(2k^2 + 7k + 6)}{6}$$

$$= \frac{(k + 1)(k + 2)(2k + 3)}{6}$$

Hence,

$$1^2 + 2^2 + \ldots + k^2 + (k + 1)^2 = \frac{(k + 1)[(k + 1) + 1][2(k + 1) + 1]}{6}$$

Hence, the statement $S(k + 1)$ is true whenever $S(k)$ is true. Therefore $S(n)$ is true for all natural numbers. ∎

Example 2. Prove that if $r \neq 1$, the statement

$$a + ar + ar^2 + \ldots + ar^n = \frac{a(1 - r^{n+1})}{1 - r}$$

is true for all natural numbers n.

Proof: Let $S(n)$ denote the given statement. Note that

$$\frac{a(1 - r^{1+1})}{1 - r} = \frac{a(1 - r^2)}{1 - r}$$

$$= \frac{a(1 - r)(1 + r)}{1 - r}$$

$$= a(1 + r)$$

$$= a + ar$$

Hence, $a + ar = \dfrac{a(1 - r^{1+1})}{1 - r}$

and we are satisfied that $S(1)$ is true.
Suppose $S(k)$ is true. That is, suppose that

$$a + ar + ar^2 + \ldots + ar^k = \frac{a(1 - r^{k+1})}{1 - r} \text{ is true.}$$

Adding ar^{k+1} to both sides, we get

$$a + ar + ar^2 + \ldots + ar^k + ar^{k+1} = \frac{a(1 - r^{k+1})}{1 - r} + ar^{k+1}$$

$$= \frac{a(1 - r^{k+1}) + ar^{k+1}(1 - r)}{1 - r}$$

$$= \frac{a[1 - r^{k+1} + r^{k+1} - r^{k+2}]}{1 - r}$$

Hence,

$$a + ar + ar^2 + \ldots + ar^k + ar^{k+1} = \frac{a[1 - r^{(k+1)+1}]}{1 - r}$$

and $S(k + 1)$ is true. It follows that $S(n)$ is true for all natural numbers n. ∎

It must be emphasized that the verification of the truth of a statement $S(n)$ for a few, or even for many natural numbers, does not guarantee the truth of the statement for all natural numbers. For example, the statement "$n^2 - n + 41$ is a prime number" (a natural number divisible only by itself and by 1) is true for $n = 1, 2, 3, \ldots, 40$. It is false, however, if we replace n by 41, since $41^2 - 41 + 41 = 41^2$ is divisible by 41 and hence is not a prime number.

In the first two examples, we carried out the second part of the proof by adding the same quantity to both sides of an equality. The following example illustrates that this is not always the technique to use.

Example 3. Prove that for all natural numbers n, $n(n + 1)(n + 2)$ is a multiple of three.

Solution: Let $S(n)$ denote the statement "$n(n + 1)(n + 2)$ is a multiple of three." Hence, $S(1)$ is true since $(1)(2)(3) = 6$ is divisible by 3.

Suppose now that $S(k)$ is true. That is, suppose that $k(k + 1)(k + 2)$ is divisible by three. We want to show that $S(k + 1)$ must be true. It suffices to show that

$$(k + 1)[(k + 1) + 1][(k + 1) + 2] = (k + 1)(k + 2)(k + 3)$$

is divisible by three.

The idea of this part of the proof is to find an integer N such that

$$(k + 1)(k + 2)(k + 3) = k(k + 1)(k + 2) + 3N$$

This would complete the proof, since we know that $k(k + 1)(k + 2)$ is divisible by three.

To this end, we use the distributive law and write

$$(k + 1)(k + 2)(k + 3) = (k + 1)(k + 2)k + (k + 1)(k + 2)3$$

Since both $k(k + 1)(k + 2)$ and $3(k + 1)(k + 2)$ are multiples of three, so is their sum and the proof that $(k + 1)(k + 2)(k + 3)$ is a multiple of three is complete. Hence, $S(n)$ is true for all natural numbers n. ∎

Exercises

1. Show that the square of any odd integer is odd. (*Hint:* any odd integer can be expressed as $2n + 1$ where n is some integer.)

2. Show that the sum of two odd integers is even and that their product is odd.

3. Show that the sum of two rational numbers is a rational number.

4. Is it possible for the product of two irrational numbers to be rational? Give an example to illustrate.

5. Is it possible for the sum of two irrational numbers to be rational? Give an example to illustrate.

   In exercises 6–16, prove by mathematical induction that the given statements are true for all natural numbers n.

6. $1 + 2 + 3 + \ldots + n = \dfrac{n(n + 1)}{2}$

7. $1^3 + 2^3 + 3^3 + \ldots + n^3 = \left[\dfrac{n(n + 1)}{2} \right]^2$

8. $1^4 + 2^4 + 3^4 + \ldots + n^4 = \dfrac{1}{30} n(n + 1)(2n + 1)(3n^2 + 3n - 1)$

9. $1 + 3 + 5 + \ldots + (2n - 1) = n^2$

10. $1 + 2 + 4 + \ldots + 2^{n-1} = 2^n - 1$

11. $\dfrac{1}{(1)(2)} + \dfrac{1}{(2)(3)} + \dfrac{1}{(3)(4)} + \ldots + \dfrac{1}{n(n + 1)} = \dfrac{n}{n + 1}$

12. $a + (a + d) + (a + 2d) + \ldots + a + (n - 1)d = \dfrac{n}{2}[2a + (n - 1)d]$

13. $x^n - y^n$ is divisible by $x - y$ (provided $x \neq y$).

14. $n^2 + n$ is a multiple of 2.

15. $2n^3 + 3n^2 + n$ is a multiple of 6.

16. $2n \leq 2^n$.

17. The binomial coefficients C_k^n are defined by $C_k^n = \dfrac{n!}{k!(n - k)!}$ where $n! = n(n - 1)(n - 2) \ldots (3)(2)(1)$ and $0! = 1$. Prove that given a natural number k, the statement $C_{k-1}^n + C_k^n = C_k^{n+1}$ is true for all natural numbers $n > k$. (*Hint:* Let $n = k + l$ and prove by mathematical induction that the statement is true for all natural numbers l.)

18. Let $S(n)$ denote the statement $2 + 4 + 6 + \ldots + 2n = n^2 + n + 1$. Prove that the truth of $S(k)$ implies the truth of $S(k + 1)$. There are, however, some natural numbers for which the statement is false. Does this contradict the induction principle? Are there any natural numbers for which $S(n)$ is true?

19. Show that the set of all positive rational numbers does not have a smallest member. (*Hint:* Suppose that there is a smallest positive rational number r. Arrive at a contradiction by finding a positive rational number smaller than r.)

20. Prove that $\sqrt{2}$ is irrational. (*Hint:* Show that assuming that $\sqrt{2} = m/n$ where m and n are integers and m/n in its lowest terms leads to a contradiction. Square both sides of $\sqrt{2} = m/n$ and use the fact that if the square of an integer is even, the integer itself must be even.)

1.4. The completeness property In this section, we shall introduce the completeness property. The field, order, and completeness properties completely characterize the system of real numbers. That is, any two sets with the same mathematical structure as that defined by the three groups of properties mentioned above are exactly alike (except possibly for the names and symbols used to denote the elements of the sets and the operations).

In order to be able to state the completeness property, we need the following definitions:

Definition 1.4.1. If S is a set of real numbers and b is a number such that for any $x \in S$ it is true that $x \le b$, then b is called an *upper bound* of S. On the other hand, if b' is a number such that for any $x \in S$ it is true that $b' \le x$, then b' is called a *lower bound* of S.

If c is an upper bound of S and for any upper bound d of S it is true that $c \le d$, we call c the *least upper bound* of S.* *Greatest lower bound* is defined similarly.

Example 1. Let $A = \{1, 2, 3, 4\}$.

The numbers 5, 10, $\frac{25}{3}$ are upper bounds of A (there are infinitely many upper bounds, for if b is an upper bound, so are $b + 1$, $b + 2$, $b + 3$, ...). Four is the least upper bound of A. Clearly, 1 is the greatest lower bound of A.

Example 2. Let N be the set of positive integers. 1 is the greatest lower bound (by theorem 1.3.1, there is no positive integer less than 1). N does not have an upper bound (see exercise 4 below).

Notation: Henceforth, l.u.b. S and g.l.b. S will denote respectively the least upper bound and the greatest lower bound of a set S of real numbers.

---

* See exercise 5 below.

A set of real numbers may or may not have an upper bound or a lower bound. Further, if a set of real numbers has a l.u.b., it may or may not be a member of the set. Similarly, the g.l.b. of a set may or may not be a member of that set. A very important property of the real number system is the following:

The completeness property: Every non-empty set of real numbers which has an upper bound has a least upper bound.

An immediate consequence of the property just stated is the following:

*Theorem 1.4.2. Every non-empty set of real numbers which has a lower bound has a greatest lower bound.

Proof: Let S be a set of real numbers and let l be a lower bound of S. Consider the set $-S = \{x \mid -x \in S\}$. $-l$ is an upper bound of $-S$. For, suppose that $x \in -S$; then, $-x \in S$ and $l \le -x$, from which we conclude $x \le -l$. By the axiom of completeness, $-S$ has a l.u.b., say b. Clearly $-b$ is the g.l.b. of the set S, for, if c were a lower bound of S with $-b < c$, then $-c < b$, and $-c$ would be an upper bound of $-S$, less than the least upper bound b. ∎

We may use the completeness property to prove the next theorem which is often called the *Archimedean principle*.

*Theorem 1.4.3. If a and b are positive real numbers, there exists some positive integer n such that $b < na$.

Proof: Let a and b be arbitrary positive numbers and suppose that there is no positive integer n for which it is true that $b < na$. Then, for all positive integers n, we have $na \le b$. Hence, b is an upper bound of the set $S = \{x \mid x = na, n$ a positive integer$\}$. By the axiom of completeness, S must have a least upper bound, say c. We note that for each positive integer n, $n + 1$ is also a positive integer. Hence, it is true that, for all positive integers n, $(n + 1)a \le c$. It follows that for all positive integers n, $na \le c - a$. Therefore, $c - a$ is an upper bound of the set S. Since a is a positive real number, $c - a$ is less than c. This contradicts the fact that c is the l.u.b. of the set S. Hence, we must reject the assumption that there is no positive integer n for which $b < na$ and conclude that for some positive integer n, we have $b < na$. ∎

A property of the real numbers which will be extremely useful in some of our future work has the following formal statement and proof:

**Theorem 1.4.4. If x and y are any two real numbers such that $x < y$, then there exists a rational number r with the property $x < r < y$.

Proof: *Case 1.* If x is negative and y is positive, take $r = 0$.

   Case 2. Suppose x and y are both positive. Since $x < y$, $y - x$ is positive. Hence, by theorem 1.4.3, there exists a positive integer n such that $1 < n(y - x)$. Therefore, $1/n < y - x$. The basic idea of the remaining part of the proof is to find a positive integer k such that $x < k/n < y$. Intuitively, we can see that if we considered the rational numbers $1/n$, $2/n$, $3/n$, etc., eventually we should find some integer k such that $[(k - 1)/n] \leq x < k/n < y$. To carry out the argument formally, consider the set $S = \{m \mid m$ is a positive integer and $nx < m\}$. S is not empty, since $nx > 0$ and $1 > 0$; therefore, by the Archimedean principle there exists some positive integer m such that $nx < m \cdot 1 = m$. It follows, by the well-ordering principle that S has a smallest member, say k. Hence, $k - 1 \leq nx < k$. Therefore, $x < k/n$. It remains to show that $k/n < y$. Using the fact that $k - 1 \leq nx$, we get $k/n - 1/n \leq x$.
But $1/n < y - x$
Adding the two preceding inequalities (see exercise 18, section 1.2), we get $k/n < y$
Hence, $x < k/n < y$

   Case 3. If both x and y are negative, then $-x$ and $-y$ are both positive and $-y < -x$. We can find a rational number k/n such that $-y < k/n < -x$ and multiplying throughout by -1, we get $x < -k/n < y$. ∎

Exercises
1. Name three different upper bounds and three different lower bounds for each of the following sets. Also name the l.u.b. and the g.l.b. in each case.
   (a) $\{x \mid 5 < x < 9\}$
   (b) $\{x \mid (x - 1)(x + 2)(x - 7) = 0\}$
   (c) $\{1, 2, 8, 25\}$
   (d) $\{x \mid 0 < x < 25\} \cap \{y \mid 10 < y < 30\}$

2. Give an example of a subset of R which
   (a) Has an upper bound but no lower bound
   (b) Has a lower bound but no upper bound
   (c) Has an upper bound and a lower bound and with both its l.u.b. and g.l.b. in the set
   (d) Has an upper bound and a lower bound but with neither its l.u.b. nor its g.l.b. in the set

3. Prove that the system of rational numbers does not satisfy the completeness property, i.e., show that there is a non-empty set of rational numbers which has a rational upper bound but no rational least upper bound. (See exercise 20, section 1.3.)

4. Prove that the set N of natural numbers has no upper bound. (*Hint:* Assume that N has an upper bound; then, by the axiom of completeness, N has a l.u.b. Then show that there is an upper bound less than the l.u.b. which is the desired contradiction.)

5. Prove that if S is a set of real numbers which has an upper bound, then it has a unique l.u.b. (*Hint:* By the axiom of completeness, we know the set has a l.u.b. Suppose b and c are both l.u.b. Show that $b \leq c$ and $c \leq b$ are both true.)

6. Prove that if S is a set of real numbers, then b is the l.u.b. of S if and only if the following two conditions are satisfied:
(a) For any $h > 0$, there exists some $x \in S$ such that $b - h < x$
(b) For any $x \in S$, $x < b + h$

7. State and prove a fact about g.l.b. similar to that given in exercise 5 for l.u.b.

8. State and prove a fact about g.l.b. similar to that given in exercise 6 for l.u.b.

9. Let x be any real number and let $S = \{r \mid r \text{ is rational and } r < x\}$. Prove that l.u.b. $S = x$. (*Hint:* Use theorem 1.4.4.)

10. Show that any finite set $\{a_1, a_2, \ldots, a_n\}$ of real numbers can be written as $\{b_1, b_2, \ldots, b_n\}$ where $b_1 < b_2 < \ldots < b_n$ and each b_i is one of the a_j's. Use this fact to show that any finite set of real numbers contains both its l.u.b. and g.l.b.

1.5. Absolute values Note that if a set of real numbers has only finitely many elements, then we can find the largest of these elements. (See exercise 10, section 1.4.) It is easy to show that this largest member of the set is its l.u.b. In this case, the l.u.b. is often called the *maximum* of the set. If the set is $\{x_1, x_2, \ldots, x_n\}$, and b is the largest member of that set, we write

$$b = \max \{x_1, x_2, \ldots, x_n\}$$

On the other hand, if c is the smallest member of the set, we write

$$c = \min \{x_1, x_2, \ldots, x_n\}$$

Hence, in the case of finite sets, we have

$$\text{l.u.b. } \{x_1, x_2, \ldots, x_n\} = \max \{x_1, x_2, \ldots, x_n\}$$

and g.l.b. $\{x_1, x_2, \ldots, x_n\} = \min \{x_1, x_2, \ldots, x_n\}$

We now give the following:

Definition 1.5.1. If x is a real number, the number $\max \{-x, x\}$ is called the *absolute value* of x and is denoted by $|x|$.

Theorem 1.5.2. If x and y are real numbers, then the following are true:

1. $|x| = |-x|$

2. $|x| = 0$ if and only if $x = 0$

3. If $x \neq 0$, $|x| = x$ if and only if $x > 0$

4. If $x \neq 0$, $|x| = -x$ if and only if $x < 0$

5. $|xy| = |x| \cdot |y|$

6. If $y \neq 0$, $\left|\dfrac{x}{y}\right| = \dfrac{|x|}{|y|}$

7. If $h > 0$, $|x| < h$ if and only if $-h < x < h$

8. If $h > 0$, $|x| \leq h$ if and only if $-h \leq x \leq h$

9. $-|x| \leq x \leq |x|$

10. $|x + y| \leq |x| + |y|$

Proof: 1. $|-x| = \max \{-(-x), -x\}$
$$= \max \{x, -x\}$$
$$= \max \{-x, x\}$$
$$= |x|$$

(2), (3), and (4) are proved trivially if we observe that if either of the two numbers $-x$, x is positive, the other is negative and vice versa, and of two numbers, a positive one and a negative one, the positive one is the larger.

5. (a) If $x \geq 0$ and $y \geq 0$, then $xy \geq 0$ and $|xy| = xy$. Also $|x| \cdot |y| = x \cdot y$. Hence, $|xy| = |x| \cdot |y|$

   (b) If $x \leq 0$ and $y \geq 0$, then $xy \leq 0$ and $|xy| = -xy$. Also $|x| \cdot |y| = -x \cdot y = -xy$. Hence, $|xy| = |x| \cdot |y|$.

   (c) If $x \geq 0$ and $y \leq 0$, then $xy \leq 0$ and $|xy| = -xy$. Also, $|x| \cdot |y| = x(-y) = -xy$. Hence, $|xy| = |x| \cdot |y|$.

   (d) If $x \leq 0$ and $y \leq 0$, then $-x \geq 0$ and $-y \geq 0$. Therefore, $|(-x)(-y)| = |-x| \cdot |-y|$, and $|xy| = |x| \cdot |y|$.

6. The proof is the same as for (5).

7. Suppose $h > 0$ and $|x| < h$. Hence, $\max \{-x, x\} < h$. Therefore, $x < h$ and $-x < h$. From the last inequality, we get $-h < x$. Hence, $-h < x < h$. Conversely, suppose $h > 0$ and $-h < x < h$. $-h < x$ implies $-x < h$. Hence, we have $x < h$ and $-x < h$. It follows that $\max \{-x, x\} < h$ and $|x| < h$.

8. The proof is exactly the same as the proof of (7), replacing each $<$ by $\leq$.

9. $|x| = \max\{-x, x\}$. Hence, $x \le |x|$ and $-x \le |x|$. The second inequality yields $-|x| \le x$. Therefore, $-|x| \le x \le |x|$.

10. By (9), we have

$$-|x| \le x \le |x|$$

and $-|y| \le y \le |y|$

Therefore, $-[|x| + |y|] \le x + y \le |x| + |y|$

If both x and y are zero, then $x + y = 0$ and $|x + y| = |x| + |y|$ since each side of the equality is zero. On the other hand, if either x or y (or both) is not equal to zero, then $|x| + |y| > 0$. Let $|x| + |y| = h$.

Then $-h \le x + y \le h$.

By (8), we get $|x + y| \le h$

That is, $|x + y| \le |x| + |y|$.

A different proof of part 10 of the theorem will be given in the next section.

Example 1. For which values of x is the following inequality satisfied? $|x - 3| < 5$

Solution: By part 7 of theorem 1.5.2, $|x - 3| < 5$ if and only if $-5 < x - 3 < 5$ or $-2 < x < 8$
Therefore, the solution of the given inequality is the set of all real numbers between -2 and 8.

Example 2. Solve the inequality $|2 - 3x| < 4$

Solution: By part 7 of theorem 1.5.2, $|2 - 3x| < 4$ if and only if $-4 < 2 - 3x < 4$ or $-6 < -3x < 2$
Multiplying by $-\frac{1}{3}$, we obtain

$2 > x > -\frac{2}{3}$

Therefore, the solution of the given inequality is the set of all real numbers between $-\frac{2}{3}$ and 2.

Remark: We recall from algebra that the principal square root of a non-negative real number b is the non-negative real number c such that $c^2 = b$. We write $c = \sqrt{b}$.
We know that for any $x \in R$, $x^2 \ge 0$. Hence, $\sqrt{x^2}$ is the non-negative real number y such that $y^2 = x^2$. We must be careful not to

state that $\sqrt{x^2} = x$, since x may be negative. Hence, we must have

$$\sqrt{x^2} = x \quad \text{if } x \geq 0$$

and $\sqrt{x^2} = -x \quad \text{if } x < 0$

In general, we write

$$\sqrt{x^2} = |x|$$

Exercises   1. Prove that $|x - y| \leq |x| + |y|$. (*Hint:* Use parts 1 and 10 of theorem 1.5.2.)

2. Prove that $|x| - |y| \leq |x + y|$. (*Hint:* Start with $x = (x + y) - y$ and use the result of exercise 1.)

3. Prove that $|x| - |y| \leq |x - y|$

Solve the following inequalities:

4. $|x - 5| < 2$

5. $|3x - 1| < \frac{1}{2}$

6. $|2 - 5x| < 3$

7. Prove that $|1/x - 4| < 2$ if and only if $1/6 < x < 1/2$

*8. Use mathematical induction to prove that
$$|x_1 + x_2 + \ldots + x_n| \leq |x_1| + |x_2| + \ldots + |x_n|$$

**1.6. More about the completeness property In this section, we discuss the relations between the least upper bounds of certain sets and give some indication of the connection between the completeness property and the decimal expansion of real numbers. We begin with some examples.

Example 1. If $A = \{0, 2, 4, 6\}$ and $B = \{-1, 0, 1, 2, 3, 4, 6\}$, A is a subset of B, but l.u.b. $A = $ l.u.b. B.

Example 2. If $A = \{x \mid x$ is a negative rational number$\}$ and $B = \{x \mid x$ is a negative irrational number$\}$, then A and B are disjoint, but

l.u.b. $A = $ l.u.b. B

since they are both zero.

Example 3. Let a and b be any two real numbers such that $a < b$. Let

$$A = \{x \mid a < x < b\} \quad \text{and} \quad B = \{x \mid x < b\}.$$

In this case, we have $A \subset B$ and l.u.b. $A = $ l.u.b. B, since they are both equal to b.

In all three examples, we had $A \neq B$, but in each case, we had l.u.b. $A = $ l.u.b. B. This raises the following interesting question: Under what conditions on two sets A and B can we be sure that l.u.b. $A = $ l.u.b. B? The answer is provided in the form of a theorem.

Theorem 1.6.1. Suppose that A and B are two non-empty sets of real numbers, each having an upper bound. Suppose, further, that for each $x \in A$ there is a $y \in B$ such that $x \le y$ and for each $u \in B$ there is some $v \in A$ such that $u \le v$. Then l.u.b. $A = $ l.u.b. B.

Proof: Since each set has an upper bound, each has a least upper bound. Let $\alpha = $ l.u.b. A and $\beta = $ l.u.b. B. Since α and β are real numbers, we must have

$$\alpha < \beta, \qquad \alpha = \beta, \qquad \text{or} \qquad \beta < \alpha$$

We shall show that $\alpha < \beta$ and $\beta < \alpha$ both lead to a contradiction.

Assume $\alpha < \beta$. Then there is an element x of B such that $\alpha < x \le \beta$. For, otherwise, α would be an upper bound of B less than the l.u.b. of B. By hypothesis, we know that $x \in B$ implies that there is some $y \in A$ such that $x \le y$. Hence, $\alpha < x \le y$. But this contradicts the fact that α is an upper bound of the set A since $\alpha < y$ and $y \in A$. Hence, it is false that $\alpha < \beta$.

Similarly, we can show that it is false that $\beta < \alpha$. Hence, we must conclude that $\alpha = \beta$. ∎

Theorem 1.6.2. If $A \subset B$ and B is a set of real numbers which has an upper bound, then l.u.b. $A \le $ l.u.b. B provided that $A \ne \varnothing$.

Proof: Let M be an upper bound of B. Since $x \in A$ implies $x \in B$ and $x \in B$ implies $x \le M$, M is also an upper bound of A. It follows that both A and B have least upper bounds.

Let l.u.b. $A = \alpha$ and l.u.b. $B = \beta$. The first part of the proof shows that any upper bound of B is also an upper bound of A. Since $\alpha = $ l.u.b. A, we have $\alpha \le \beta$. ∎

The next concept which we shall introduce will prove quite useful in some of the later proofs in this text.

Definition 1.6.3. If S and T are sets of real numbers, then $S + T$ and $S \cdot T$ are the sets defined by

$$S + T = \{x + y \mid x \in S \text{ and } y \in T\}$$

$$S \cdot T = \{xy \mid x \in S \text{ and } y \in T\}$$

Example 4. Let $S = \{2, 3\}$ and $T = \{1, 5\}$

then $S + T = \{2 + 1, 2 + 5, 3 + 1, 3 + 5\}$

$$= \{3, 7, 4, 8\}$$

and $\quad S \cdot T = \{(2)(1), (2)(5), (3)(1), (3)(5)\}$

$$= \{2, 10, 3, 15\}$$

We note that

l.u.b. $S = 3$, l.u.b. $T = 5$, l.u.b. $(S + T) = 8$ and

l.u.b. $(S \cdot T) = 15$.

Hence, in this case, it is true that

$$\text{l.u.b. } (S + T) = \text{l.u.b. } S + \text{l.u.b. } T$$

and that l.u.b. $(S \cdot T) = (\text{l.u.b. } S)(\text{l.u.b. } T)$

Example 5. Let $S = \{-3, 2\}$ and $T = \{-4, 1, 5\}$. It is easy to see that

$$S + T = \{-7, -2, 2, 3, 7\} \quad \text{and} \quad S \cdot T = \{-15, -8, -3, 2, 10, 12\}$$

Here l.u.b. $S = 2$, l.u.b. $T = 5$, l.u.b. $(S + T) = 7$ and l.u.b. $(S \cdot T) = 12$. We note that

$$\text{l.u.b. } (S + T) = \text{l.u.b. } S + \text{l.u.b. } T$$

but l.u.b. $(S \cdot T) \neq (\text{l.u.b. } S)(\text{l.u.b. } T)$

Hence, in general, we do not have l.u.b. $(S \cdot T) = (\text{l.u.b. } S)(\text{l.u.b. } T)$.

A natural question is under what conditions can we be sure that l.u.b. $(S \cdot T) = (\text{l.u.b. } S)(\text{l.u.b. } T)$. The answer will be provided by theorem 1.6.5.

Theorem 1.6.4. If S and T are non-empty sets of real numbers, each having an upper bound, then $S + T$ has an upper bound and

$$\text{l.u.b. } (S + T) = \text{l.u.b. } S + \text{l.u.b. } T$$

Proof: Let A and B be upper bounds of S and T respectively. Then $A + B$ is an upper bound of $S + T$. To see this, let $z \in S + T$. Then there is an $x \in S$ and a $y \in T$ such that $z = x + y$. But $x \leq A$ and $y \leq B$. Therefore $x + y \leq A + B$ and $z \leq A + B$

Since z was an arbitrary member of $S + T$, we see that $A + B$ is an upper bound of $S + T$.

Now, by the completeness property, each of the sets, S, T, and $S + T$ has a l.u.b. Let l.u.b. $S = a$, l.u.b. $T = b$, and l.u.b. $(S + T) = c$. We want to show that $c = a + b$.

We know by the previous argument that $a + b$ is an upper bound of $S + T$. Since c is the l.u.b. of $S + T$, we must have $c \leq a + b$.

Suppose now that we could show that for any $h > 0$, it is true that $(a + b) - c \leq h$. Then the conclusion $a + b = c$ would follow by theorem 1.2.8.

To this end, let h be an arbitrary positive number. There must exist some $x \in S$ such that

$$a - \frac{h}{2} < x \leq a$$

because, if that were not the case, then $a - h/2$ would be an upper bound of S which would be less than the least upper bound.

A similar argument shows that there exists some $y \in T$ such that

$$b - \frac{h}{2} < y \le b$$

Hence, $(a - h/2) + (b - h/2) < x + y \le a + b$

and $(a + b) - h < x + y \le a + b$

But $x + y \in S + T$

Since c is the l.u.b. of $S + T$, we must have

$x + y \le c$

which, together with $(a + b) - h < x + y$, gives

$(a + b) - h < c$ and $(a + b) - c < h$

Therefore, by theorem 1.2.8, it follows that $a + b = c$. ∎

Theorem 1.6.5. If S and T are non-empty sets of *positive* real numbers, each having an upper bound, then $S \cdot T$ has an upper bound and

l.u.b. $(S \cdot T) = ($l.u.b. $S)($l.u.b. $T)$

Proof: Let A and B be upper bounds of S and T respectively. Then $A \cdot B$ is an upper bound of $S \cdot T$. To see this, let $z \in S \cdot T$. Then there exists some $x \in S$ and some $y \in T$ such that $z = xy$. Now $0 < x \le A$ and $0 < y \le B$. Hence, $xy \le A \cdot B$ and $z \le A \cdot B$. Since z was arbitrary, we conclude that $A \cdot B$ is an upper bound of $S \cdot T$.

Let l.u.b. $S = a$, l.u.b. $T = b$, and l.u.b. $(S \cdot T) = c$

ab is an upper bound of $S \cdot T$.

Hence, $c \le ab$.

We want to show that $c = ab$. We shall prove that, if we assume that $c < ab$, we are led to a contradiction. Let

$$h = ab - c$$

Then, $h > 0$ (since we assumed that $c < ab$)

Hence, $\dfrac{h}{a + b} > 0$ (since a and b and, therefore, $a + b$ are positive)

We therefore know that there is an $x \in S$ and a $y \in T$ such that

$$a - \frac{h}{a + b} < x \le a$$

and $b - \dfrac{h}{a+b} < y \le b$

It follows that

$$a - x < \frac{h}{a+b} \tag{1}$$

and $b - y < \dfrac{h}{a+b}$ (2)

Now observe that

$$ab - xy = a(b - y) + y(a - x)$$

and that $0 < y \le b$ (3)

Using inequalities (1) and (3), we get

$$y(a - x) < \frac{hb}{a+b} \tag{4}$$

and from inequality (2), we obtain

$$a(b - y) < \frac{ha}{a+b} \tag{5}$$

Adding inequalities (4) and (5), we get

$$a(b - y) + y(a - x) < \frac{ha}{a+b} + \frac{hb}{a+b} = \frac{h(a+b)}{a+b} = h$$

Recalling that $ab - xy = a(b - y) + y(a - x)$ and $h = ab - c$, we can write $ab - xy < ab - c$ from which it follows that $c < xy$. But $xy \in S \cdot T$. Hence, c is less than some element of $S \cdot T$. This, however, contradicts the fact that c is the l.u.b. of $S \cdot T$. Hence, we must reject our assumption that $c < ab$ and conclude that $c = ab$. ∎

Using these concepts, we can give a simple proof of theorem 1.5.2 (part 10). We want to show that if x and y are real numbers, then $|x + y| \le |x| + |y|$

$|x| + |y| = \max \{-x, x\} + \max \{-y, y\}$ by definition

$\qquad = \max \{-x + (-y), -x + y, x + (-y), x + y\}$

$\qquad = \max \{-(x + y), -x + y, y - x, x + y\}$

$\qquad \ge \max \{-(x + y), (x + y)\}$ by 1.6.2

$\qquad = |x + y|$ by definition. ∎

Presently, we shall discuss briefly the connection between the completeness property and the decimal expansion of a real number.

We recall that a rational number is a real number which can be expressed as the ratio of two integers. The reader is undoubtedly familiar with the fact that, by carrying out the ordinary process of division, a rational number may be written as a decimal. For example,

$\frac{9}{4} = 2.25$ and $\frac{4193}{990} = 4.2353535\ldots = 4.2\underline{35}$

(where the part which is underscored is understood to be repeated indefinitely). A decimal is said to be *periodic* if and only if a digit, or a block of digits, is repeated indefinitely from the decimal (as in $2.314314\ldots = 2.\underline{314}$) or from a certain point (as in $21.052323\ldots = 21.05\underline{23}$) and no other digit appears between any two consecutive blocks of digits which repeat. The number of digits in one block is called the *length of the period*. We note that we can consider a terminating decimal to be periodic (as $2.25 = 2.25000\ldots = 2.25\underline{0}$).

It can be easily proved that a real number is rational if and only if it has a periodic decimal representation. (See exercises 5–9 below.)

We are now ready to show that any real number has a decimal representation and, therefore, that the irrational numbers are those real numbers whose decimal representations are non-periodic.

Let x be any positive real number. Let N be the largest integer such that $N \le x$. Having chosen N, let d_1 be the largest integer such that

$$N + \frac{d_1}{10} \le x$$

Clearly, $0 \le d_1 \le 9$, for, otherwise, N would not be the largest integer less than, or equal to, x. Then let d_2 be the largest integer such that

$$N + \frac{d_1}{10} + \frac{d_2}{10^2} \le x$$

Again, we must have $0 \le d_2 \le 9$.

Supposing now that $N, d_1, d_2, \ldots, d_k$ have been chosen by the foregoing process, we choose d_{k+1} to be the largest integer such that

$$N + \frac{d_1}{10} + \frac{d_2}{10^2} + \ldots + \frac{d_k}{10^k} + \frac{d_{k+1}}{10^{k+1}} \le x$$

We see that the integers $N, d_1, d_2, \ldots, d_n, \ldots$ have been described inductively. We first note that each number $N + d_1/10 + \ldots + d_n/10^n$ is rational. As a matter of fact, each can be written in the form $A/10^k$ where A and k are integers.

Consider the set S of all rational numbers just defined. S consists of N,

$$N + \frac{d_1}{10}, \qquad N + \frac{d_1}{10} + \frac{d_2}{10^2}, \qquad N + \frac{d_1}{10} + \frac{d_2}{10^2} + \frac{d_3}{10^3}, \qquad \text{etc.}$$

It is clear that x is an upper bound of S. To show that $x = \text{l.u.b. } S$, we shall assume that y is an upper bound of S with $y < x$ and arrive at a contradiction.

By theorem 1.4.4, there exists a rational number r such that $y < r < x$. If $r \in S$, we have the desired contradiction, since y is an upper bound of S and $y < r$. If $r \notin S$, it is easy to show (using a decimal expansion of the rational number r) that a number $r' \in S$ can be found such that $r < r'$. Hence, we have $y < r'$ which is the desired contradiction. Therefore, we must conclude that $x = \text{l.u.b. } S$.

The integers $N, d_1, d_2, \ldots, d_n, \ldots$ so obtained define a decimal representation of x and we write

$$x = N.d_1 d_2 d_3 \ldots d_n \ldots$$

We note that if x is irrational, there is no member of S which is equal to x and the set S is uniquely determined. It follows that the decimal representation of x is unique.

On the other hand, if x is a rational number, there may be two distinct decimal representations of x. (See exercise 10 below.)

Note: If x is negative, consider the positive number $-x$. By the above argument, $-x$ has a decimal representation $N.d_1 d_2 d_3 \ldots$. Then the decimal representation of x is $-N.d_1 d_2 d_3 \ldots$.

Exercises

1. If $S = \{x \mid x \text{ is an odd positive integer}\}$ and
   $T = \{x \mid x \text{ is an even positive integer}\}$
   (a) Find $S + T$ and $S \cdot T$
   (b) What are g.l.b. S, g.l.b. T, g.l.b. $(S + T)$ and g.l.b. $(S \cdot T)$?
   (c) Is it true that in this case
   g.l.b. $(S + T) = $ g.l.b. $S + $ g.l.b. T
   and g.l.b. $(S \cdot T) = $ (g.l.b. S)(g.l.b. T)?

2. Given $A = \{-1, 2, 3\}$ and $B = \{-2, -1, 0\}$, find $A + B$ and $A \cdot B$.

*3. State and prove a theorem similar to 1.6.2 for g.l.b.

*4. State and prove a theorem similar to 1.6.4 for g.l.b.

5. Show that $2.\overline{56}$ is rational. (*Hint:* Let $x = 2.\overline{56}$; then $100x = 256.\overline{56}$ and $100x - x = 26.5\overline{56} - 2.\overline{56}$, etc.)

6. Show that $12.1\overline{34}$ is rational.

*7. Prove that if x is a real number which has a periodic decimal representation, then x is rational. (*Hint:* Let
   $x = N.d_1 d_2 \ldots d_k \overline{a_1 a_2 \ldots a_e}$. Then
   $10^k x = N d_1 d_2 \ldots d_k . \overline{a_1 a_2 \ldots a_e}$ and
   $10^{k+e} x = N d_1 d_2 \ldots d_k a_1 a_2 \ldots a_e . \overline{a_1 a_2 \ldots a_e}$.
   Now consider $10^{k+e} x - 10^k x = \ldots$, etc.)

8. Carry out the division process for the following:
   (a) $\frac{2}{7}$ (b) $\frac{3}{8}$ (c) $\frac{5}{11}$
   In each step note
   (1) How many steps in the division process you have carried out until the decimals begin to repeat.
   (2) What the repeating block of decimals is.
   (3) How many digits are in this block and what the remainders are at each stage of the division process used in obtaining the first block of repeating digits.

*9. Explain why the division of a by b where a and b are integers always gives a repeating decimal. What is the maximum length of the period?

**10. In defining the decimal expansion of the positive real number x, we considered the integers N, d_1, d_2, ... such that for each n, d_n was the largest integer with the property $N + d_1/10 + d_2/10^2 + \ldots + d_n/10^n \le x$. If instead we require that each d_n be the largest integer such that $N + d_1/10 + d_2/10^2 + \ldots + d_n/10^n < x$, x is still the l.u.b. of the set of all rational numbers so obtained. Show, by considering the decimal expansions of $1/4$ (using both techniques) that the decimal expansions are not the same. For what kind of rational numbers can we have two different decimal representations?

1.7. Functions The study of functions is important because of the frequency with which they arise in mathematics. Modern trigonometry is basically the study of some special functions. The purpose of this present chapter is the study of some basic properties of functions. We shall stress those properties which are possessed by the trigonometric functions since these are the functions which we shall study in more detail later.

We first present the idea of a function informally, with some examples.

Example 1. The area of a square is given by the formula $A = s^2$. That is, if the side of the square has length s units, then the area of the square is s^2 square units. The formula $A = s^2$ assigns to each value of s a unique corresponding value of A.

Example 2. In physics, Hooke's law states that the force F needed to stretch a spring a distance x units beyond its natural length is given by $F = kx$ where k is a constant depending on the spring but not on x (provided $|x|$ is not too large). The formula assigns to each value of x a unique corresponding value of F.

Example 3. The table of multiplication of natural numbers assigns to each pair of natural numbers a unique natural number called their *product*.

Example 4. A program for a football game usually gives a list of the names of the players on a team, together with the numbers the players will wear on their jerseys. This list assigns to each player's name a unique corresponding number.

We see that, in each of the foregoing examples, we described a way of assigning to each element of some set an element of some other set. The reader can undoubtedly think of many examples of such pairings of elements of some set with elements of some other set. (See also examples 9 and 10, section 1.1.)

The idea of a function is essentially that of such an association or pairing of elements of two sets (not necessarily distinct). It is best described formally by making use of the idea of ordered pairs which we are about to introduce.

We know that the sets $\{a, b\}$ and $\{b, a\}$ are equal, since they have the same elements. Sometimes, however, it is desirable to distinguish one of the two elements of a pair as the first and the other as the second. In this case, we call the pair an *ordered pair* and we denote it by (a, b) (if a is the first element and b the second). It is useful to consider (a, a) an ordered pair, although $\{a, a\}$ is not a pair (since the statement $\{a, b\}$ is a pair implies $a \neq b$).

Definition 1.7.1. The ordered pairs (a, b) and (c, d) are *equal* if and only if $a = c$ and $b = d$.

Note: See exercise 7 below for a more abstract definition of ordered pairs.

Suppose now that S is a set of ordered pairs. Let us denote the set of all first elements of members of S by D_S and the set of all second elements of members of S by R_S.

If we pick an arbitrary $x \in D_S$, there is at least one $y \in R_S$ (there may be more than one) such that $(x, y) \in S$. In this case, we think of y as being assigned to x. It follows that S defines a way of assigning to each member of D_S one or more members of R_S. If this association is such that to each $x \in D_S$ only one $y \in R_S$ is assigned, then S is called a function. This concept is described formally in the following:

Definition 1.7.2. A *function* is a set of ordered pairs in which no two distinct members have the same first element.

In other words, if two ordered pairs (a, b) and (a, c) are in the set and have the same first element, then they cannot be distinct and must have the same second element.

Symbolically, if f is a function, then $(x, y) \in f$ and $(x, z) \in f$ implies $y = z$.

Definitions 1.7.3. Let f be a function. The set $\{x \mid (x, y) \in f$ for some $y\}$ is called the *domain* of f and is denoted by D_f. The *range* of f is the set $\{ \mid y (x, y) \in f$ for some $x\}$ and is denoted by R_f.

Note that if f is a function, then, for each $x \in D_f$, there is a unique corresponding $y \in R_f$ such that $(x, y) \in f$. Since y is uniquely determined by x and f, we introduce the symbol $f(x)$, read "f of x," and we write $y = f(x)$ to mean $(x, y) \in f$.

We call $f(x)$ the *image* of x under f or the *value* of the function f at x. A convenient notation is the following:

$f : x \to f(x)$, read "f sends x into $f(x)$" or "f takes x into $f(x)$." Pictorially, we may think of the function f as sending each $x \in D_f$ to its corresponding $f(x) \in R_f$ as illustrated in figure 1.

Figure 1.

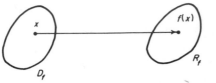

Definitions 1.7.4. A symbol which can be replaced by elements of a set of numbers is called a *variable*. The set is called the *replacement set* of the variable. If the replacement set of a variable x is the domain of a function f, x is called the *independent variable*, and if the replacement set is R_f, then the variable is called the *dependent* variable.

There are several methods for describing functions. It is sometimes possible to list all the ordered pairs which belong to the function. Tables are often useful for defining functions. Often one describes the domain of a function and then, for each x in the domain of that function, a rule is given to find the functional value $f(x)$. This rule is sometimes stated in words, but often it is an equation. We now proceed to give some examples to illustrate each of the methods.

Example 5. The set $F = \{(1, 2), (2, 5), (3, 6)\}$ is a function, since no two distinct members of F have the same first element.

Note that $D_f = \{1, 2, 3\}$ and $R_f = \{2, 5, 6\}$. Also $F(1) = 2$, $F(2) = 5$, and $F(3) = 6$.

Example 6. The following table was kept by a doctor to check on the success of the diet of one of his patients.

Date	Weight
November 19, 1961	235
January 22, 1962	210
March 27, 1962	180
April 15, 1962	171
May 28, 1962	160
June 29, 1962	157
July 22, 1962	152
August 24, 1962	148

This table describes a function whose domain is a set of dates and whose range is a set of measures of weights.

Example 7. Let $A = \{4, 5, 6, 7, 8, 9, 10\}$. Suppose that to each element of A we assign the smallest prime number which is greater than, or equal to, that element of A. This rule defines a function f. We easily see that $f(4) = 5$, $f(5) = 5$, $f(6) = 7$, $f(7) = 7$, $f(8) = 11$, $f(9) = 11$, and $f(10) = 11$. The domain of f is A and its range is the set $\{5, 7, 11\}$.

Example 8. Let the domain of a function g be the set R of real numbers and let

$$g : x \to x^2 + 1$$

We see, for example, that $g(-1) = (-1)^2 + 1 = 2, g(0) = 0^2 + 1 = 1$, and $g(\sqrt{2}) = (\sqrt{2})^2 + 1 = 3$.

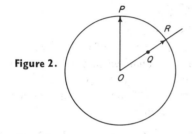

Figure 2.

Example 9. Let the set I be the interior of a given circle (see figure 2). Let C be the circle itself and let P be a fixed point on C. We shall now describe a rule which assigns to each point of I a unique point of C. If $O \in I$ is the center of the circle, assign to it the point P. If $Q \in I$ and $Q \neq O$, draw the ray starting at O and passing through Q. The intersection of the ray with the circle is the point R which we assign to Q. This rule defines a function F whose domain is I and range C. Note that an ordered pair of points (M, N) with $M \in I$ and $N \in C$ belongs to F if and only if either $M = O$ and $N = P$ or the ray starting at O and passing through M intersects the circle at N.

Sometimes a function is described by a formula without an explicit description of the domain of the function. In this text, we shall, in such cases, understand the domain to be the set of all real numbers for which the formula is defined and involves only real numbers.

Example 10. Let the function f be defined by $f(x) = 1/x$. This formula is defined for all real numbers $x \neq 0$. Hence, $D_f = R \setminus \{0\}$.
By definition,

$$R_f = \{y \mid (x, y) \in f \quad \text{for some } x\}$$

but $(x, y) \in f$ if and only if $y = 1/x$. If $y \neq 0$, there exists some value of x, namely $1/y$ for which $y = 1/x$. Hence $R_f = R \setminus \{0\}$ also.

Example 11. Let the function ϕ be defined by $\phi : x \to \sqrt{9 - x^2}$. Again it is understood $\phi(x) = \sqrt{9 - x^2}$ must be a real number for each $x \in D_\phi$. Hence, we must have

$$0 \leq 9 - x^2$$

Therefore, the domain of ϕ is the solution set of the foregoing inequality. That is, $D_\phi = \{x \mid -3 \leq x \leq 3\}$. It is an easy matter to verify that

$$R_\phi = \{y \mid 0 \leq y \leq 3\}$$

Example 12. Let a be a real number different from zero and let $g : x \to ax$. Show that for any x_1 and x_2 in D_g

$$g(x_1 + x_2) = g(x_1) + g(x_2)$$

Solution: $g(x_1) = ax_1,$ $g(x_2) = ax_2,$ and $g(x_1 + x_2) = a(x_1 + x_2)$

On the other hand,

$$g(x_1) + g(x_2) = ax_1 + ax_2$$
$$= a(x_1 + x_2)$$

Therefore, $g(x_1 + x_2) = g(x_1) + g(x_2)$ ∎

The last example suggests the following question: are there functions with the following properties?

1. $f(x_1 + x_2) = f(x_1) \cdot f(x_2)$

2. $\quad f(x_1 x_2) = f(x_1) + f(x_2)$

3. $\quad f(x_1 x_2) = f(x_1) \cdot f(x_2)$

We shall define later a function which possesses property 1 and another function which possesses property 2. It is easy to show that the function defined by $f : x \to |x|$ possesses property 3.

It must be emphasized that two functions f and g are equal if and only if their domains are equal and for x in their domains, $f(x) = g(x)$. (See exercise 8 below.)

For example, if $f : x \to x + 2$

and $g : x \to \dfrac{x^2 - 4}{x - 2}$

$f \neq g$, since $2 \in D_f$ but $2 \notin D_g$. However, $f(x) = g(x)$ for all real numbers $x \neq 2$.

Finally, we note that the domain of a function and the function itself have the same cardinality. For if, $x \in D_f$, $(x, y) \in f$ is uniquely determined and, conversely, if $(u, v) \in f$, $u \in D_f$ is uniquely determined. Hence, the correspondence $x \leftrightarrow (x, y)$ between the elements of D_f and those of f is a one-to-one correspondence.

In particular, if D_f has finitely many elements, then so does f. This is not necessarily true for the range of a function. As a matter of fact, the range may have only one element and the function infinitely many, as is the case for the constant function $f: x \to c$. Here we have $D_f = R$, the set of real numbers, $R_f = \{c\}$ where c is a constant and $f = \{(x, c) \mid x$ is a real number and c a given constant$\}$.

Exercises
1. Which of the following sets are functions?
   (a) $\{(-2, 3), (0, 1), (2, 5), (3,\frac{1}{2})\}$
   (b) $\{(0, 1), (1, 2), (3, 7), (1, 4)\}$
   (c) $\{(x, y) \mid y = 5x\}$
   (d) $\{(x, y) \mid x^2 + y^2 = 4\}$
   (e) $\{(x, y) \mid y = x^2 + 5x - 1\}$

2. Write the following in words (as you would read it).
   (a) $f(x) = x^2 + 1$
   (b) $g: x \to 3x^2 - 2x + 1$
   (c) $\phi = \{(x, y) \mid y = 3x - 5\}$

3. Which of the following tables define functions?
   (a)

x	-1	0	1
$f(x)$	5	3	$\frac{1}{4}$

   (b)

z	1	2	3	2
$g(z)$	5	1	2	1

   (c)

u	5	7	9	5
$\phi(u)$	2	3	4	5

4. Find the domains and ranges of the functions described by

   (a) $f: x \to \dfrac{1}{x + 1}$

   (b) $g: u \to \sqrt{16 - u^2}$

   (c) $\phi: z \to z^2 - 5$

5. Prove that the functions f and g defined by

   $$f: x \to \frac{x^2 - 1}{5x} \quad \text{and} \quad g: u \to \frac{u^2 - 1}{5u}$$

   are equal. (This shows that the symbol used in defining a function is only a "dummy variable" and has no effect on the function itself.)

6. In each case, tell whether or not the two functions described are equal. Justify your answers.

(a) $f : x \to (x + 1)(x - 2)$ and $g : u \to u^2 - u - 2$

(b) $\phi : x \to \dfrac{x^3 - 1}{x - 1}$ and $\mu : z \to z^2 + z + 1$

(c) $h : v \to v^2 - 4$ and $g : x \to (x + 2)(x - 2)$

**7. In more advanced texts, an ordered pair (a, b) is defined in the following way:

$(a, b) = \{\, \{a\}, \{a, b\} \,\}.$

Using this definition, prove the following theorem: $(a, b) = (c, d)$ if and only if $a = c$ and $b = d$. (*Hint:* Consider two cases, $a = b$ and $a \neq b$. Also you must make very strong use of the definition of equality of sets.)

*8. Show that two functions f and g are equal if and only if $D_f = D_g$ and for each x in their common domain, $f(x) = g(x)$. (*Hint:* Use the fact that f and g are sets and the definition of equality of sets.)

*9. Prove that $(a, b) = (b, a)$ if and only if $a = b$.

1.8. More about functions In this section, we give some examples of functions and show how under certain conditions we can manufacture new functions from old ones.

In the following three examples, we define some functions which have special names.

Example 1. The function defined by $I : x \to x$ is called the *identity function*. Clearly, $D_I = R_I = R$, where again R denotes the set of all real numbers.

Example 2. If $a \neq 0$ and b is any real number, then a function g defined by $g : x \to ax + b$ is called a *linear function*. It is easy to show that $D_g = R_g = R$.

Example 3. If $a_0, a_1, a_2, \ldots, a_n$ are real numbers, n is a positive integer and $a_0 \neq 0$, a function P defined by

$$P : x \to a_0 x^n + a_1 x^{n-1} + \ldots + a_n$$

is called a *polynomial function of degree n*. Clearly, $D_P = R$. The range of P depends on the a_i's. For example, if $n = 1$, then P is just a linear function and $R_P = R$. On the other hand,

if $n = 2, \qquad a_0 = 1, \qquad a_1 = 0, \qquad$ and $\qquad a_2 = 1$

then $R_P = \{y \,|\, y \geq 1\}$. (See example 8, section 1.7.)

By definition, a function f is a set of ordered pairs in which no two distinct members have the same first element. Suppose that g is a non-empty subset of f. Then g satisfies the definition of a function also. We give such a subset a special name which we introduce in the following:

Definition 1.8.1. Suppose that f is a function and that A is a non-empty subset of D_f. Then the non-empty subset g of f which has the property $(x, y) \in g$ if and only if $x \in A$ is called the *restriction* of f to A. It is sometimes denoted by $f \mid A$, read "f restricted to A."

Often, the restriction of a function may have a property which is not possessed by the function itself, as is illustrated by the following:

Example 4. Let the function f be defined by

$$f(x) = \begin{cases} 1 & \text{if } x \text{ is a rational number} \\ -1 & \text{if } x \text{ is an irrational number} \end{cases}$$

Then the statement "$f(x \cdot y) = f(x) \cdot f(y)$ for all x and y in the domain of f" is false. For example, $f(\sqrt{2} \cdot \sqrt{3}) = f(\sqrt{6}) = -1$ since $\sqrt{6}$ is irrational, but $f(\sqrt{2}) \cdot f(\sqrt{3}) = (-1)(-1) = 1$. Hence, $f(\sqrt{2}) \cdot f(\sqrt{3}) \neq f(\sqrt{2} \cdot \sqrt{3})$.

If, however, we consider the restriction g of f to the set of rational numbers, then the statement "$g(x \cdot y) = g(x) \cdot g(y)$ for every x and y in the domain of g" is true. To see this, we note that $D_g = R^\#$, the set of rational numbers. Hence, if x and y are in D_g, then they both are rational and so is xy. It follows that $g(x \cdot y) = 1$, $g(x) = 1$, $g(y) = 1$ and that $g(xy) = g(x) \cdot g(y)$.

Example 4 is somewhat artificial, but it does illustrate a very important point. We shall come back to this fact later when we define the inverse circular functions.

Definitions 1.8.2. If f and g are functions such that $D_f \cap D_g \neq \varnothing$ and both R_f and R_g are sets of real numbers, we define the functions $S = f + g$, $D = f - g$, $P = f \cdot g$, and $Q = f/g$ by

$$S(x) = f(x) + g(x) \quad \text{for every } x \in D_f \cap D_g$$

$$D(x) = f(x) - g(x) \quad \text{for every } x \in D_f \cap D_g$$

$$P(x) = f(x) \cdot g(x) \quad \text{for every } x \in D_f \cap D_g$$

$$Q(x) = f(x)/g(x) \quad \text{for every } x \in D_f \cap D_g \text{ and such that } g(x) \neq 0$$

Example 5. Suppose that $f : x \to x^2 + 1$ and $g : x \to (x - 1)/x$. Find equations defining the functions $S = f + g$, $D = f - g$, $P = f \cdot g$ and $Q = f/g$.

Solution: We first note that $D_f = R$ and $D_g = R \setminus \{0\}$. Hence, S, D, and P have the same domain, namely $D_f \cap D_g = R \setminus \{0\}$. Further, the domain of Q is $R \setminus \{0, 1\}$, since $g(0)$ is not defined and $g(1) = 0$. Therefore, $f(x)/g(x)$ is not defined for either $x = 0$ or $x = 1$.

Now, $S(x) = (x^2 + 1) + \dfrac{x - 1}{x}$

Therefore, $S(x) = \dfrac{x^3 + 2x - 1}{x}$ for every $x \in R \setminus \{0\}$

That is, $S : x \to \dfrac{x^3 + 2x - 1}{x}$

Similarly, $D(x) = (x^2 + 1) - \dfrac{x - 1}{x}$

Hence, $D(x) = \dfrac{x^3 + 1}{x}$ for every $x \in R \setminus \{0\}$

Further, $P(x) = f(x) \cdot g(x)$

$$= (x^2 + 1)\dfrac{(x - 1)}{x}$$

and $P(x) = \dfrac{x^3 - x^2 + x - 1}{x}$ for every $x \in R \setminus \{0\}$

Also, $Q(x) = \dfrac{x^2 + 1}{(x - 1)/x}$

$$= \dfrac{(x^2 + 1)x}{x - 1}$$

and $Q(x) = \dfrac{x^3 + x}{x - 1}$ for every $x \in R \setminus \{0, 1\}$ ∎

Under certain conditions, there is another way to form a new function from two given functions. Suppose that two functions f and g are given in such a way that $R_f = D_g$. Then, given $x \in D_f$, we can find a unique $f(x) \in R_f$. Since $R_f = D_g$, we also have $f(x) \in D_g$. Hence, we can find a unique $g[f(x)] \in R_g$. It follows that, given any $x \in D_f$, we have a way of finding a unique $g[f(x)] \in R_g$ corresponding to x. The set $\{(x, z) \mid z = g[f(x)]\}$ is a new function called the *composite* of g and f and denoted by $g \circ f$.

Remark: In order to be able to find $g[f(x)]$, it is not necessary to have $R_f = D_g$. We need consider only those x's in D_f for which $f(x) \in D_g$. Proceeding from the foregoing remark, we give the following:

Definition 1.8.3. Given two functions f and g such that $R_f \cap D_g \neq \varnothing$, the *composite* of g and f is the function $g \circ f = \{(x, z) \mid \text{for some } y \in R_f \cap D_g, (x, y) \in f \text{ and } (y, z) \in g\}$.

The reader should verify for himself that the set defined above is indeed a function. That is, it should be verified that $(x, z_1) \in g \circ f$ and $(x, z_2) \in g \circ f$ implies $z_1 = z_2$.

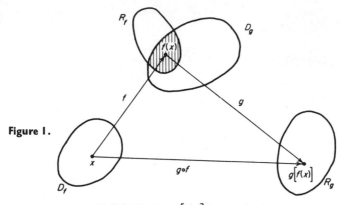

If $f(x) \notin D_g$, then $g[f(x)]$ is not defined.

Figure 1.

Figure 1 gives a pictorial representation of these functions. Equivalently, we can describe the composite of g and f by stating:

$$g \circ f : x \to g[f(x)] \quad \text{whenever } f(x) \in D_g.$$

Example 6. Given two functions f and g defined by the equations $f(x) = x^2 + 1$ and $g(x) = \sqrt{x}$, find a formula for $g \circ f(x)$.

Solution: Clearly, $R_f = \{y \mid y \geq 1\}$ and $D_g = \{x \mid x \geq 0\}$. Hence, $R_f \cap D_g \neq \varnothing$ and $g \circ f$ can be formed. Further, since $R_f \subset D_g$, we have
$$D_{g \circ f} = D_f = R.$$
Clearly,

$$g \circ f(x) = g[f(x)]$$
$$= g(x^2 + 1) \quad (\text{since } f(x) = x^2 + 1)$$
$$= \sqrt{x^2 + 1} \; \blacksquare$$

We conclude this section with a further remark on the notation.

Suppose that f is a function whose domain is a set of ordered pairs of real numbers. Then if $(x, y) \in f$, x must be an ordered pair (x_1, x_2) of real numbers. Using the notation already introduced, we should write

$$y = f(x) = f((x_1, x_2))$$

for the functional value of f at x. It is customary, however, to write $f(x_1, x_2)$ in lieu of $f((x_1, x_2))$. Such a function is called a *function of two variables.*

Example 7. Let f be defined by $f : (x, y) \to x^2 + y$. This can equivalently be written $f(x, y) = x^2 + y$. The domain of f is the set of all ordered pairs of real numbers and its range is the set of all real numbers.

Exercises 1. If $f : x \to x^2 - 2$ and $g : x \to \dfrac{1}{x - 3}$, find

(a) D_f, R_f, D_g, and R_g

(b) $f(1)$, $f(-3)$, $g(2)$, $g(7)$, $f \circ g(7)$

(c) Formulas for $S(x)$, $D(x)$, $P(x)$, and $Q(x)$.

2. The function f is defined by $f(x) = [x]$ where $[x]$ denotes the greatest integer which is less than, or equal to, x. (Examples: $[2.3] = 2$; $[-1.5] = -2$; and $[5] = 5$.)
Find

(a) D_f and R_f

(b) $f(2.6)$, $f(\sqrt{2})$, $f(7/13)$, $f(-2.3)$, and $f(0)$

(c) $f \circ f(x)$

3. Let the functions f and g be defined by $f(x) = 2x + 3$ and $g(x) = x + 2$. Show that $D_f = R_f = D_g = R_g$. Hence, the composite $f \circ g$ and $g \circ f$ are both defined. Use these functions to illustrate that $g \circ f \neq f \circ g$.

4. Suppose that $h : x \to 2x + 3$ and $g : x \to (x - 3)/2$. Find $h \circ g(1)$, $h \circ g(2)$, $g \circ h(3)$, $g \circ h(7)$, $h \circ g(x)$, and $g \circ h(x)$.

1.9. Coordinate system In this section, we describe a one-to-one correspondence between the set of ordered pairs of real numbers and the set of points of a plane. The method which we shall use is due to a French philosopher and mathematician, René Descartes (1596–1650). Among other things, this relationship between points of a plane and ordered pairs of real numbers provides a means for solving geometric problems algebraically, and the converse. It is the basis for a very important subject called *analytic geometry*.

It is indeed very difficult to describe axiomatically what is meant by "direction" on a line and "congruence of line segments."*

In this text, we shall not attempt to introduce those ideas in a very formal way. For our purpose, it will suffice to describe direction on the line by an arrow and to use the basic idea of congruence of line segments as described in basic geometry.

We begin by considering two perpendicular lines of infinite extent, one horizontal, the other vertical. We indicate direction on each line by an arrow, the horizontal one pointing from left to right, the vertical one from bottom up. (See figure 1.) The point O of intersection will be called the *origin*. Often, the horizontal line is called the *x axis* and the vertical line is called the *y axis*. On the *x* axis and to the right of the origin, pick a point P_1. Then pick a point P_2 on the *x* axis such that P_2 is to the right of P_1 and the segment $P_1 P_2$ is congruent to the segment OP_1. Continue the same process such that

---

* See, for example, Oswald Veblen, "The Foundations of Geometry", in *Monographs on Topics of Modern Mathematics*, ed. J. W. A. Young (New York: Dover Publications, Inc., 1955).

when P_k has been chosen, choose P_{k+1} on the x axis and to the right of P_k such that the segment $P_k P_{k+1}$ is congruent to the segment OP_1. We have described inductively how to pick a point P_n for each

Figure I.

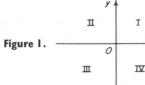

natural number n. Now for each natural number n, let us assign the ordered pair $(n, 0)$ to the point P_n. Also for each n, draw a circle with center at the origin and passing through P_n. (See figure 2.) This circle intersects the two axes at four points, one of which is P_n. Attach to the other three points the ordered pairs $(0, n)$, $(-n, 0)$, and $(0, -n)$ as indicated in figure 2. Henceforth, we shall use the expression "the point (x, y)" to mean the point to which we have assigned the ordered pair (x, y).

Figure 2.

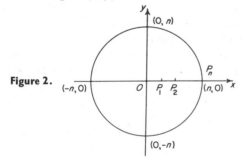

Now let r be a given positive rational number. We can find two positive integers p and q such that $r = p/q$ and p/q is in its lowest terms. (p and q have no common factor with the exception of the

Figure 3.

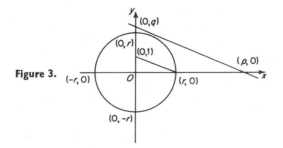

factor 1.) Consider the points $(p, 0)$ and $(0, q)$. Draw a straight line through these two points and draw a straight line parallel to this line and passing through the point $(0, 1)$. (See figure 3.) This parallel

intersects the x axis at a unique point to which we assign the ordered pair $(p/q, 0) = (r, 0)$. Draw a circle with center the origin and passing through the point $(r, 0)$. This circle intersects the two axes at three other points to which we assign the ordered pairs $(-r, 0)$, $(0, r)$, and $(0, -r)$ as indicated on figure 3. Thus we have shown that given any rational number $r > 0$, we can find uniquely four points on the axes to which we assign the ordered pairs $(r, 0)$, $(-r, 0)$, $(0, r)$, and $(0, -r)$. We now note the following:

1. Any point $(r, 0)$ is on the x axis. If $r > 0$, the point is to the right of the origin and if $r < 0$, the point is to the left of the origin.
2. Any point $(0, r)$ is on the y axis. If $r > 0$, the point is above the origin and if $r < 0$, the point is below the origin.
3. Since the origin is both on the x and y axes, we assign to it the pair $(0, 0)$.
4. There are points on each axis to which no pair of real numbers has been assigned. (See exercise 8 below.)

Assumption: Let S be the set of all ordered pairs of real numbers with the property that $(a, b) \in S$ implies $a = 0$ or $b = 0$. Then there is a one-to-one correspondence between S and the set of points on the two axes. Further, if one element of the ordered pair is zero and the other is rational, then the point corresponding to it is obtained as described previously. Also the one-to-one correspondence is such that if x is an irrational number and r_1, r_2 are rational numbers such that $r_1 < x < r_2$, then the point $(x, 0)$ is between $(r_1, 0)$ and $(r_2, 0)$. Similarly, the point $(0, x)$ is between $(0, r_1)$ and $(0, r_2)$.

Using the assumption stated above, we can now show that there is a one-to-one correspondence between the set of *all* points of the plane in which the two axes lie and the set of *all* ordered pairs of real numbers.

Figure 4.

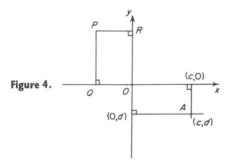

Let P be any point in the plane. If P is on either axis, we already have an ordered pair of real numbers assigned to it. So suppose that P does not lie on either axis. Draw perpendiculars from P to both the x and y axes. (See figure 4.) Let Q and R be the points of intersection of these perpendiculars with the x and y axes respectively. We know, by assumption, that there are unique ordered pairs of real numbers $(a, 0)$ and $(0, b)$ assigned to Q and R respectively. We now assign the ordered pair (a, b) to the point P. This pair is called the *coordinates* of the point P. The first element of the ordered pair (a, b) is called the *abscissa* (*first coordinate*, x *coordinate*); the second element is called the *ordinate* (*second coordinate*, y *coordinate*). Again the phrase "the point (a, b)" will mean "the point whose coordinates are the ordered pair (a, b)."

Conversely, suppose that an ordered pair (c, d) of real numbers is given. If $c = 0$ or $d = 0$, by assumption there is a unique point on one of the axes with coordinates (c, d). If both c and d are distinct from zero, consider the points $(c, 0)$ and $(0, d)$ on the x and y axes respectively. Through $(c, 0)$ and $(0, d)$ draw perpendiculars respectively to the x and y axes. These two perpendiculars intersect at a unique point A which we make correspond to the ordered pair (c, d). (See figure 4.)

Thus, we have established a one-to-one correspondence between all the points of the plane in which the two axes lie and the set of all ordered pairs of real numbers.

Example 1. Plot the points whose coordinates are $(-1, 3)$, $(5, 2)$, $(3, -1)$, $(-3, -2.5)$.

Solution: See figure 5.

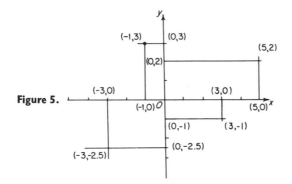

Figure 5.

Definitions 1.9.1. Let M_1 and M_2 be two points with coordinates $(x_1, 0)$ and $(x_2, 0)$ respectively. The *directed distance* from M_1 to M_2 is denoted by $\overline{M_1 M_2}$ and is defined by

$$\overline{M_1 M_2} = x_2 - x_1$$

The *distance* between the same two points is given by

$$|M_1 M_2| = |x_2 - x_1|$$

Remark: Since $|x_2 - x_1| = |x_1 - x_2|$, we have $|M_1 M_2| = |M_2 M_1|$. Distances between points which lie on the y axis are defined similarly.

Note: We must assume that the one-to-one correspondence of the assumption stated on page 43 is such that two segments $M_1 M_2$ and $N_1 N_2$, each lying on one of the axes, are congruent if and only if

$$|M_1 M_2| = |N_1 N_2|$$

Now, we can state the following:

Theorem 1.9.2. If P_1 and P_2 are two points with coordinates (x_1, y_1) and (x_2, y_2) respectively, the distance $|P_1 P_2|$ between P_1 and P_2 is given by

$$|P_1 P_2| = \sqrt{(x_2 - x_1)^2 + (y_2 - y_1)^2}$$

The proof is trivial, using the theorem of Pythagoras, and is left as an exercise for the reader.

Another interesting exercise for the reader is proving the following:

Theorem 1.9.3. 1. $|PQ| = 0$ if and only if P and Q coincide

2. For any two points P and Q, $|PQ| = |QP|$

3. Given any three points P, Q, and R, $|PQ| \le |PR| + |RQ|$

It should be clear that we have arrived at a formula for the distance between any two points in the plane in such a way that the segments $P_1 P_2$ and $Q_1 Q_2$ lying in the plane are congruent if and only if $|P_1 P_2| = |Q_1 Q_2|$. This fact will not be proved here since it depends very strongly on the one-to-one correspondence of the assumption on page 43 and on the axioms of euclidean geometry. A formal proof would take us too far afield.

Theorem 1.9.4. Let A and B be any two points with coordinates (x_1, y_1) and (x_2, y_2) respectively and let M be the midpoint of the segment AB. Then the coordinates of M are

$$\left(\frac{x_1 + x_2}{2}, \frac{y_1 + y_2}{2} \right)$$

Proof: Let M be the point with coordinates

$$\left(\frac{x_1 + x_2}{2}, \frac{y_1 + y_2}{2} \right)$$

We shall show that

$$|AM| = |MB| = (\tfrac{1}{2})|AB|$$

and therefore M will necessarily be the midpoint of the line segment AB.

$$|AM| = \sqrt{\left(\frac{x_1 + x_2}{2} - x_1\right)^2 + \left(\frac{y_1 + y_2}{2} - y_1\right)^2}$$

$$= \sqrt{\left(\frac{x_2 - x_1}{2}\right)^2 + \left(\frac{y_2 - y_1}{2}\right)^2}$$

$$|MB| = \sqrt{\left(x_2 - \frac{x_1 + x_2}{2}\right)^2 + \left(y_2 - \frac{y_1 + y_2}{2}\right)^2}$$

$$= \sqrt{\left(\frac{x_2 - x_1}{2}\right)^2 + \left(\frac{y_2 - y_1}{2}\right)^2}$$

Hence, $|AM| = |MB| = \frac{1}{2}\sqrt{(x_2 - x_1)^2 + (y_2 - y_1)^2} = (1/2)|AB|$. ∎

Exercises

1. Plot the points whose coordinates are
   (a) $(-1, 3), (2, 5), (-3, -5), (5, -3)$
   (b) $(1.2, 3.1), (3.2, -5.1), (-6.2, .5), (-3, -2.2)$

2. The two axes divide the plane into four quadrants numbered as on figure 1 of the preceding section. Indicate in which quadrant each of the following points lies
   (a) $(1, 3), (2, -5), (-3, -1), (-4, 7)$
   (b) (x, y) if $x < 0$ and $y > 0$

3. Find the distance between the following pairs of points:
   (a) $(1, 2)$ and $(-3, 7)$
   (b) $(-3, 5)$ and $(2, 6)$
   (c) $(2, -5)$ and $(-1, 0)$

4. Prove that the triangle with vertices $(5, 5), (2, 1)$, and $(-2, 4)$ is isosceles.

5. Prove that the triangle with vertices $(-1, 2), (3, 0)$, and $(3, 10)$ is a right triangle. (*Hint:* Use the converse of the Pythagorean theorem.)

6. Find the two points whose abscissas are 3 and which are at a distance 5 from the origin.

7. Show that the point $(5, 3)$ is on the perpendicular bisector of the line segment with end points $(-1, 1)$ and $(3, -3)$.

8. (a) Find the distance between the points $(1, 0)$ and $(0, 1)$.
   (b) Draw the circle with center $(1, 0)$ and passing through the point $(0, 1)$. Let $(x_1, 0)$ and $(x_2, 0)$ be the intersections of that circle with the x axis. Show that x_1 and x_2 are irrational numbers.

9. Suppose a and b are real numbers with $a \neq 0$. Let L be the set of points whose coordinates satisfy the equation $y = ax + b$. Show that L is a subset of a straight line. (*Hint:* Suppose A, B, and C are elements of L with coordinates $(x_1, y_1), (x_2, y_2), (x_3, y_3)$ respectively. Assume that $x_1 < x_2 < x_3$ and show that $|AB| + |BC| = |AC|$.) Later it will be shown that L is, in fact, a straight line.

10. Prove theorem 1.9.2.

*11. Prove theorem 1.9.3.

*12. Show that the sets $P_x = \{((x, y), x) \mid (x, y)$ is an ordered pair of real numbers$\}$ and $P_y = \{((x, y), y) \mid (x, y)$ is an ordered pair of real numbers$\}$ are functions. These functions are sometimes called *projection functions*. Discuss briefly the geometric interpretation of $P_x : (x, y) \to x$ and $P_y : (x, y) \to y$ and the analogy with the geometric expression, "projection of a point on a line."

*13. Suppose that r is a rational number and $r = p/q = p'/q'$ where p, q, p', q' are integers, p/q is in its lowest terms but p'/q' is not in its lowest terms. Show that if we carry out the construction of the point $(r, 0)$, using the points $(p', 0)$ and $(0, q')$ instead of the points $(p, 0)$ and $(0, q)$ as was done in section 1.9, we get exactly the same point.

*14. Show that the length of the segment joining the two midpoints of two sides of a triangle is equal to half the length of the third side. (*Hint:* Set the triangle so that the vertices are $(0, 0)$, $(a, 0)$, and (b, c). Then use theorem 1.9.4 and the distance formula.)

*15. Show that the diagonals of a parallelogram bisect each other.

1.10. Graphs In the preceding section, we asserted that a one-to-one correspondence exists between the set of all points of a plane and the set of all ordered pairs of real numbers. Furthermore, we arrived at a formula giving the distance between two points in terms of the coordinates of the two points. We pointed out that this formula was such that two line segments in the plane are congruent if and only if the distance between the two end points of one segment is equal to the distance between the two end points of the other. We are now ready to use these facts to introduce the idea of graphs and the equations of certain curves in the plane.

Definition 1.10.1. The *coordinate plane* is the plane which contains the two axes described in the preceding section.

Definition 1.10.2. Let S be a set of ordered pairs of real numbers. The *graph* of S is the set of points, in the coordinate plane, whose coordinates are members of S.

Figure 1.

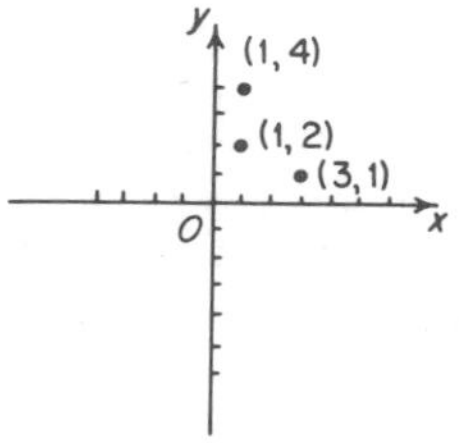

Example 1. If $S = \{(1, 2), (1, 4), (3, 1)\}$, the graph of S consists of the three points which are plotted on figure 1.

Note: The set S may be a function. In this case, we call its graph the *graph* of the *function S.*

Example 2. Let $f = \{(1, 3), (2, 5), (3, -4)\}$. Then the graph of the function f consists of the points whose coordinates are $(1, 3)$, $(2, 5)$, and $(3, -4)$. (See figure 2.)

Figure 2.

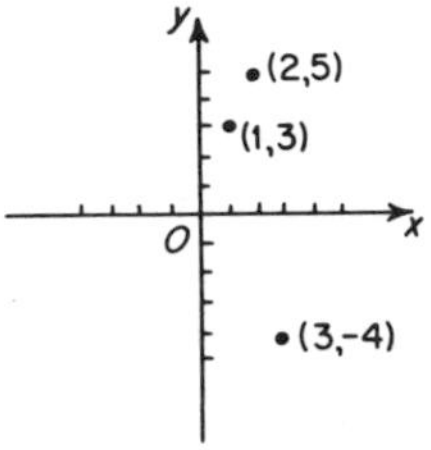

Remark: We note that in the foregoing two examples, the given sets of ordered pairs had only three members; hence, their graphs consisted of only three points. By definition, a set of ordered pairs and its graph have the same cardinality. We recall that a function and its domain have the same cardinality. (See the end of section 1.7.) Hence, the graph and the domain of a function have the same number of elements. It follows that if the domain of a function f is an infinite set, then the graph of f will have infinitely many points. In this case, we can sketch only an approximation of the graph. This is often done by finding a certain number of points of the graph and by assuming that the graph is a "smooth" curve. This is usually the case in our examples of functions whose domains have the following property. If two distinct numbers are in the domain, then so are all real numbers between them. Of course, the accuracy of the sketch depends largely on the number of points we first obtain.

Example 3. Sketch the graph of the function $g = \{(x, y) \,|\, y = x^2 + 1\}$.

Solution: We consider several convenient values of x and we find the corresponding values of $g(x)$. The results are tabulated below.

x	-3	-2	-1	0	1	2	3
$g(x)$	10	5	2	1	2	5	10

We now plot the points with coordinates $(-3, 10)$, $(-2, 5)$, etc. (See figure 3a) and sketch an approximation of the graph of g. (See figure 3b.) Later, using some techniques of calculus, the reader will be able to show that figure 3b is a better approximation than figure 3c. It must be kept in mind, however, that any sketch of a graph is always an approximation.

Often a set of ordered pairs of real numbers is defined by an equation. In this case, the graph of this set is also called the *graph of the equation.*

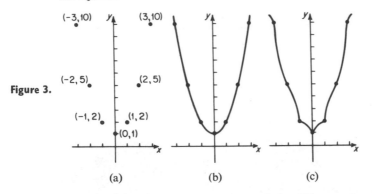

Figure 3.

(a)   (b)   (c)

Example 4. Let a and b be non-zero real numbers. Discuss the graph of the equation $y = ax + b$.

Solution: Let $S = \{(x, y) \mid y = ax + b\}$ and let G be the graph of S. Hence, G is also the graph of the equation $y = ax + b$. We first note that, by definition, $P \in G$ if and only if the coordinates of P satisfy the equation $y = ax + b$. Clearly, the points with coordinates $(-b/a, 0)$ and $(0, b)$ are in G. Consider the straight line L passing through these two points. We shall show that $L = G$. We know, by exercise 9 of the previous section, that $G \subset L$. We need only to show that $L \subset G$. Note that the line L intersects the x and y axes at $(-b/a, 0)$ and $(0, b)$ respectively and, hence, is not parallel to the y axis. It follows that any line parallel to the y axis will intersect the line L at exactly one point.

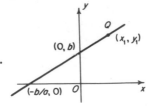

Figure 4.

Now let $Q \in L$. Suppose that Q has coordinates (x_1, y_1). By definition of G, the point (x_1, y_2) such that $y_2 = ax_1 + b$ is an element of G. By exercise 9 of the previous section, $G \subset L$. It follows that the point (x_1, y_2) is also an element of L. Both (x_1, y_1) and (x_1, y_2), however, are on the parallel to the y axis which passes through the point $(x_1, 0)$. Since they both are also on the line L, they must be the same point. Hence, $(x_1, y_2) = (x_1, y_1)$. Since (x_1, y_2) is in G, so is (x_1, y_1). Hence, $Q \in G$ and we have shown that $L \subset G$. It follows that $L = G$. ∎

We recall from basic geometry that a *locus* is a set of points, and only those points, which satisfy certain conditions. We now give the following:

Definition 1.10.3. The *equation of a locus* is the equation whose graph is the locus.

Recalling that a circle is the locus of points in a plane which are equidistant from a fixed point of that plane, we consider the following:

Example 5. Find the equation of the circle with radius r and center the point (h, k).

Solution: A point (x, y) is a point of the circle if and only if the distance from (h, k) to (x, y) is r. Hence (x, y) is on the circle if and only if

$$\sqrt{(x - h)^2 + (y - k)^2} = r$$

Therefore, the equation of the circle is

$$(x - h)^2 + (y - k)^2 = r^2 \quad \blacksquare$$

The circle with center at the origin and radius 1 will play a very important role in our future work. Its equation is

$$(x - 0)^2 + (y - 0)^2 = 1^2$$

That is, $x^2 + y^2 = 1$

Example 6. Find the center and radius of the circle whose equation is $x^2 + 2x + y^2 - 4y = 4$.

Solution: In order to complete the squares, we add 5 to both sides of the equation. (*Note* that $1 + 4 = 5$.)

$$x^2 + 2x + 1 + y^2 - 4y + 4 = 4 + 5$$

or $\quad (x + 1)^2 + (y - 2)^2 = 9$

which can be written

$$(x - (-1))^2 + (y - 2)^2 = 3^2$$

Hence, the center of the circle is the point $(-1, 2)$ and its radius is 3. $\blacksquare$

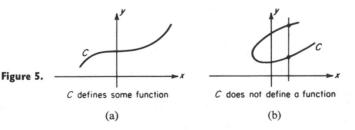

Figure 5.

C defines some function   *C* does not define a function

(a)   (b)

We note now that a locus (curve) in the plane defines a set of ordered pairs of real numbers. That is, if *C* is a curve in the coordinate plane, then we may consider the set

$S = \{(x, y) \mid \text{there is a point of } C \text{ with coordinates } (x, y)\}$

If $(x, y) \in S$ and $(x, z) \in S$ implies $y = z$, then S is a function. The geometric interpretation of the property that the set S must have in order to be a function is the following: If any perpendicular to the x axis intersects the curve C at no more than one point, then no two distinct members of S have the same first element and S is a function. (See figures 5a and 5b.)

Exercises

1. Sketch the graph of the function f of example 10, section 1.7.

2. Sketch the graph of the function ϕ of example 11, section 1.7.

3. Sketch the graph of the function g of example 12, section 1.7.

4. Sketch the graphs of the functions f, g, and h defined by the following:
   (a) $f : x \rightarrow 3x + 1$
   (b) $g : x \rightarrow 2x - 5$
   (c) $h : x \rightarrow -3x + 6$
   Do you notice anything significant common to each of the graphs?

5. Sketch the graphs of the functions f, g, and h defined by the following:
   (a) $f : x \rightarrow \sqrt{9 - x^2} \ (-3 \le x \le 3)$
   (b) $g : x \rightarrow \sqrt{25 - x^2} \ (-5 \le x \le 5)$
   (c) $h : x \rightarrow \sqrt{4 - x^2} \ (-2 \le x \le 2)$
   Do you notice anything significant common to each of the graphs?

6. Find the equations of the locus of all points in the coordinate plane which are equidistant from:
   (a) The points $(-1, 3)$ and $(2, 5)$
   (b) The points $(-3, 1)$ and $(0, 7)$

7. Find the equation of the locus of all points in the coordinate plane which are equidistant from the point $(0, 2)$ and the line parallel to the x axis and passing through the point $(0, -2)$.

8. Find the center and radius of the circle whose equation is $x^2 - 4x + y^2 + 8y = 5$.

9. Show that the graph of the equation $y = ax \ (a \neq 0)$ is a straight line. (*Hint:* Let b be any non-zero real number. Then, by example 4 of the previous section, the graph of the equation $y = ax + b$ is a straight line. Now show that the graph of $y = ax$ is a line parallel to the graph of $y = ax + b$.)

1.11. Inverse functions We begin our study of inverse functions with the following simple example:

Example 1. Let f and g be functions defined by $f : x \rightarrow x + 3$ and $g : x \rightarrow x - 3$. Find formulas defining the composites $g \circ f$ and $f \circ g$.

Solution: We first note that $D_f = R_f = D_g = R_g = R$ (the set of all real numbers). Now

$$f \circ g(x) = f[g(x)]$$
$$= f(x - 3)$$
$$= (x - 3) + 3$$
$$= x \quad \text{for every } x \in D_g$$

On the other hand,

$$g \circ f(x) = g[f(x)]$$
$$= f(x) - 3$$
$$= (x + 3) - 3$$
$$= x \quad \text{for every } x \in D_f$$

Hence, for all real numbers $x, f \circ g : x \to x$ and $g \circ f : x \to x$. ∎

It follows that $f \circ g = g \circ f = I$, where I denotes the identity function. We wish to study functions which have the properties described in the example.

We first note that if f is a function, f is a set of ordered pairs such that no two distinct members of f can have the same first element, but several members of f may have the same second element. Suppose, however, that a function f has the property that no two distinct members of f have the same second element. We may consider the set $\{(b, a) \mid (a, b) \in f\}$ and it is easy to show that this set is also a function. We denote it by f^{-1}.

Definition 1.11.1. Let f be a function with the property that no two distinct members of f have the same second element. Then $f^{-1} = \{(b, a) \mid (a, b) \in f\}$ is a function which we call the *inverse* of f.

Remark: The reader should not confuse the notation f^{-1} with the exponential notation ($a^{-1} = 1/a$ for any non-zero real number a). That is, f^{-1} is *not* $1/f$ but it is the inverse of f.

We note that if f has an inverse, we obtain f^{-1} simply by considering the set of all ordered pairs of f in the reverse order. Hence, it is clear that if f has an inverse, $D_f = R_{f^{-1}}$ and $R_f = D_{f^{-1}}$.

The property required of a function in the definition of its inverse is very closely related to the notion of a one-to-one correspondence between sets. Hence, we give the following:

Definition 1.11.2. A function f is said to be a *one-to-one function* if $(x_1, y) \in f$ and $(x_2, y) \in f$ implies $x_1 = x_2$.

Equivalently, a function f is one-to-one if whenever x_1 and x_2 are in the domain of f and $x_1 \neq x_2$, then $f(x_1) \neq f(x_2)$. We can now state the following:

Theorem 1.11.3. A function f has an inverse if and only if it is a one-to-one function.

Proof: Suppose that f has an inverse. Then, by definition,

$$f^{-1} = \{(b, a) \mid (a, b) \in f\}$$

is a function. We want to show that f is one-to-one. That is, we must show that $(a_1, b) \in f$ and $(a_2, b) \in f$ implies $a_1 = a_2$. Clearly, $(a_1, b) \in f$ and $(a_2, b) \in f$ implies $(b, a_1) \in f^{-1}$ and $(b, a_2) \in f^{-1}$, and since f^{-1} is a function, we must have $a_1 = a_2$.

Conversely, suppose f is one-to-one. Then we want to show that the set $f^{-1} = \{(b, a) \mid (a, b) \in f\}$ is indeed the inverse of f. Suppose that $(b, a_1) \in f^{-1}$ and $(b, a_2) \in f^{-1}$. Then $(a_1, b) \in f$ and $(a_2, b) \in f$. Since f is one-to-one, $a_1 = a_2$. Hence, we have shown that no two distinct members of f^{-1} have the same first element. It follows that the set f^{-1} is a function. ∎

Returning to the idea expressed in example 1, we consider a one-to-one function f. By theorem 1.11.3, f has an inverse f^{-1}. Since $D_f = R_{f^{-1}}$ and $D_{f^{-1}} = R_f$, both $f \circ f^{-1}$ and $f^{-1} \circ f$ can be formed. Further, by definition of composite functions,

$$f^{-1} \circ f = \{(x, z) \mid (x, y) \in f \text{ and } (y, z) \in f^{-1} \text{ for some } y \in R_f \cap D_{f^{-1}}\}.$$

But

$$R_f \cap D_{f^{-1}} = R_f = D_{f^{-1}}$$

Also, since f is one-to-one, $y \in R_f$ implies that there is a unique $x \in D_f$ such that $(x, y) \in f$. Then $(y, x) \in f^{-1}$. Since f^{-1} is a function $(y, z) \in f^{-1}$ and $(y, x) \in f^{-1}$ implies $x = z$. It follows that

$$f^{-1} \circ f = \{(x, x) \mid x \in D_f\}$$

Similarly, it can be shown that

$$f \circ f^{-1} = \{(x, x) \mid x \in D_{f^{-1}}\}$$

Note that, in general, $f^{-1} \circ f \neq f \circ f^{-1}$, since these two functions may have different domains. If $D_f = R_f$, however; then $D_f = D_{f^{-1}}$ and it is true that $f^{-1} \circ f = f \circ f^{-1}$.

Nevertheless, we always have

$$f \circ f^{-1} : x \to x \quad \text{for each } x \in D_{f^{-1}}$$

and $f^{-1} \circ f : x \to x \quad \text{for each } x \in D_f$

We are now ready to state the following theorem (the proof of which is left as an exercise):

Theorem 1.11.4. If f and g are two functions such that $f[g(x)] = x$ for every $x \in D_g$ and $g[f(x)] = x$ for every $x \in D_f$, then $g = f^{-1}$ and $f = g^{-1}$.

Remarks: The theorem above has very strong implications and it should be examined carefully.

Firstly, if two functions f and g have the properties stated in the hypothesis, then each has an inverse, and therefore, each must be one-to-one.

Secondly, it implies that, given a function f, there is at most one function, namely f^{-1} (if it exists), which has the two properties stated in the hypothesis.

Thirdly, it implies that if f has an inverse, so does f^{-1} and $(f^{-1})^{-1} = f$.

In connection with theorem 1.11.4, we note that it is not sufficient for f and g to be inverses of each other to have $f[g(x)] = x$ for every $x \in D_g$ or $g[f(x)] = x$ for every $x \in D_f$. We need *both* conditions satisfied. We illustrate this remark with the following:

Example 2. Let f and g be defined by $f(x) = x^2$ and $g(x) = \sqrt{x}$. Clearly $D_f = R$ (the set of real numbers); $R_f = R_+ \cup \{0\}$ (the set of non-negative real numbers); $D_g = R_+ \cup \{0\}$; and $R_g = R_+ \cup \{0\}$. It is easy to see that f is not one-to-one; hence, it does not have an inverse. However, we have $f \circ g(x) = f[g(x)] = [g(x)]^2 = (\sqrt{x})^2 = x$ for every $x \in D_g$. But $g \circ f(x) = g[f(x)] = \sqrt{f(x)} = \sqrt{x^2} = |x|$ for every $x \in D_f$.

Since $x = |x|$ whenever $x \geq 0$, it follows that g and the restriction of f to $R_+ \cup \{0\}$, satisfy the conditions of the hypothesis of theorem 1.11.4, and hence, they are inverses of each other.

This example illustrates why it is sometimes useful to consider a function which is the restriction of another function to a subset of the domain of that other function. It may happen that the restriction is one-to-one, hence, has an inverse, whereas the original function did not.

We shall now give some examples to illustrate how to find expressions for an inverse function when the original function is given.

Example 3. If $f = \{(1, 2), (2, 5), (3, -2)\}$, then it is trivial to express f^{-1}. Namely, $f^{-1} = \{(2, 1), (5, 2), (-2, 3)\}$.

Example 4. Suppose that f is defined by $f : x \to 2x + 5$. Find an expression for f^{-1}.

Solution: Clearly $(x, y) \in f$ if and only if $y = 2x + 5$. But $(x, y) \in f$ if and only if $(y, x) \in f^{-1}$. It follows that $(y, x) \in f^{-1}$ if and only if $y = 2x + 5$. Since it is customary to express the second element of the ordered pairs in terms of the first one, we solve for x and get $(y, x) \in f^{-1}$ if and only if $x = (y - 5)/2$. Hence, $f^{-1} : y \to (y - 5)/2$. It is common practice among mathematicians to use the symbol x for the independent variable of a function. Hence, we write

$$f^{-1} : x \to \frac{x - 5}{2}$$

Example 5. Let the domain of a function f be $D_f = \{x \mid -5 \le x \le 0\}$ and let f be defined by $f(x) = \sqrt{25 - x^2}$. Describe f^{-1}.

Solution: Clearly, $R_f = \{y \mid 0 \le y \le 5\}$. Hence,

$$D_{f^{-1}} = \{y \mid 0 \le y \le 5\} \quad \text{and} \quad R_{f^{-1}} = \{x \mid -5 \le x \le 0\}$$

since we always have $D_f = R_{f^{-1}}$ and $R_f = D_{f^{-1}}$.

Now $(x, y) \in f$ if and only if $y = \sqrt{25 - x^2}$. Hence, $(y, x) \in f^{-1}$ if and only if $y = \sqrt{25 - x^2}$.

Solving for x in terms of y, we get

$$x = \pm\sqrt{25 - y^2}$$

Since we know that $R_{f^{-1}} = \{x \mid -5 \le x \le 0\}$, we choose

$$x = -\sqrt{25 - y^2}$$

Hence, $f^{-1} : y \to -\sqrt{25 - y^2}$ and $D_{f^{-1}} = \{y \mid 0 \le y \le 5\}$.

Again, since it is customary to use x for the independent variable of a function, we write

$$f^{-1} : x \to -\sqrt{25 - x^2} \quad \text{and} \quad D_{f^{-1}} = \{x \mid 0 \le x \le 5\} \quad \blacksquare$$

Exercises

1. The function f is described by $f(x) = x/3 - 1$.
   (a) Show that f is a one-to-one function.
   (b) Describe f^{-1}.

2. The function f is defined by $f(x) = 1/(1 - x)$
   (a) Find D_f and R_f.
   (b) Show that f is one-to-one.
   (c) Describe f^{-1}.

3. The function g is defined by $g(x) = \sqrt{9 - x^2}$, $0 \le x \le 3$. Describe g^{-1}.

4. The function h is defined by

$$h(x) = \begin{cases} \sqrt{16 - x^2} & \text{if } -4 \le x \le 0 \\ -\sqrt{16 - x^2} & \text{if } 0 < x < 4 \end{cases}$$

   (a) Find D_h and R_h.
   (b) Describe h^{-1}.

5. Let $[x]$ denote the greatest integer less than, or equal to, x. Define the functions f and g by
   $f(x) = [x]$ for every real number x and
   $g(x) = x + 1/2$ for every *integer* x
   Show that $f \circ g(x) = x$ for all $x \in D_g$ and that the statement $g \circ f(x) = x$ for all $x \in D_f$ is false.

*6. Show that composition of functions is associative; i.e., $(f \circ g) \circ h = f \circ (g \circ h)$ whenever all the composites involved are defined.

**7. Prove theorem 1.11.4. (*Hint:* First prove that $D_f = R_g$ and $D_g = R_f$. Then show, using exercise 6, that if two functions g_1 and g_2 have the same properties as the function g in the hypothesis, then $g_1 = g_2$. Now show that f is one-to-one. Hence, f^{-1} exists and has the same properties as the function g in the hypothesis. Therefore, $g = f^{-1}$.)

1.12. Graphs of inverse functions We have seen that a function f has an inverse if and only if it is a one-to-one function. If f is a one-to-one function whose domain and range are subsets of the set of real numbers, we can consider its graph and the graph of its inverse. We shall show, in this section, that the two graphs are geometrically related. We begin by discussing briefly the geometric significance of one-to-oneness.

We recall that a curve C in the coordinate plane is the graph of some function f if and only if each perpendicular to the x axis does not intersect C at more than one point. Further, a function f is one-to-one if and only if no two distinct ordered pairs in f have the same second element. Hence, if C is the graph of some function, it will be the graph of a one-to-one function if and only if whenever (x_1, y)

Figure 1.

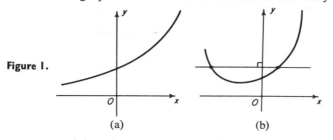

(a)   (b)

and (x_2, y) are points of C, we must have $x_1 = x_2$. That is to say, any perpendicular to the y axis must not intersect C at more than one point. Curve C (figure 1a) is the graph of a one-to-one function, whereas curve C' (figure 1b) is the graph of a function which is not one-to-one.

Figure 2.

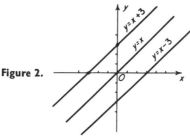

The graphs of a function and its inverse are geometrically related. We have seen that the functions f and g of example 1, section 1.11 have the property $f \circ g(x) = x$ for every $x \in D_g$ and $g \circ f(x) = x$ for every $x \in D_f$. Hence, by theorem 1.11.4, they are inverses of each other. The graphs of these functions are shown in figure 2, together with the graph of the equation $y = x$. (Note that the graph of the equation $y = x$ is a straight line; see section 1.10, exercise 9.) We observe that if we were to fold the paper along the graph of the equation $y = x$, the graphs of the functions f and g would match. This suggests some notion of symmetry and we make this notion precise by giving some definitions.

Definition 1.12.1. Given the points A, B, and a straight line L all in the same plane, we say that A and B are *symmetric with respect to L* if and only if the line L is the perpendicular bisector of the line segment AB.

Definition 1.12.2. The points A and B are *symmetric with respect to the point P* if and only if P is the midpoint of the line segment AB.

Definition 1.12.3. Suppose that S_1 and S_2 are two sets of points in a plane and L is a straight line lying in the same plane. We say that S_1 and S_2 are *symmetric with respect to L* if and only if for each $P \in S_1$, there is a $Q \in S_2$ such that P and Q are symmetric with respect to L, and for each $M \in S_2$, there is some $N \in S_1$ such that M and N are symmetric with respect to L.

Symmetry of sets S_1 and S_2 with respect to a point is defined similarly.

Theorem 1.12.4. If f and g are functions whose domains and ranges are subsets of the set of real numbers, then $g = f^{-1}$ if and only if the graphs of f and g are symmetric with respect to the graph of the equation $y = x$.

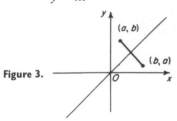

Figure 3.

Proof: We first remark that a very simple geometric argument (see figure 3) suffices to prove that two points A and B in the coordinate plane are symmetric with respect to the line $y = x$ if and only if the coordinates of A are the coordinates of B in reversed order.

Now suppose that $g = f^{-1}$. For convenience, denote the graphs of f and g by G_f and G_g respectively and the graph of the equation $y = x$ by L. Let $A \in G_f$. We want to show there is a $B \in G_g$ such that A and B are symmetric with respect to L. To that end, suppose that the coordinates of A are (a, b). Hence, $(a, b) \in f$. Therefore, $(b, a) \in f^{-1}$ and since $g = f^{-1}$, $(b, a) \in g$. If we let B be the point with coordinates

(b, a), $B \in G_g$, and A and B are symmetric with respect to L. A similar argument shows that if $C \in G_g$, we can find a $D \in G_f$ such that C and D are symmetric with respect to L.

Conversely, suppose that G_f and G_g are symmetric with respect to L. We note first that no perpendicular to the y axis intersects G_f at more than one point, for otherwise, the symmetry of G_f and G_g with respect to L would imply that some perpendicular to the x axis would intersect G_g at more than one point, and g would not be a function. Hence, f is one-to-one and f^{-1} exists. We want to show that $g = f^{-1}$. Recalling that g and f^{-1} are sets, we need to show $g \subset f^{-1}$ and $f^{-1} \subset g$. To this end, let $(a, b) \in g$. Then the point with coordinates (a, b) is in G_g and by symmetry the point with coordinates (b, a) is in G_f. It follows that $(b, a) \in f$ and that $(a, b) \in f^{-1}$. Therefore, $g \subset f^{-1}$. Starting with $(a, b) \in f^{-1}$, the foregoing argument in reverse leads to $(a, b) \in g$. Hence, $f^{-1} \subset g$ and we have proved that $g = f^{-1}$. ∎

Note: In view of theorem 1.12.4, if the graph of a function is symmetric with respect to the line L, then the function is its own inverse.

Figure 4.

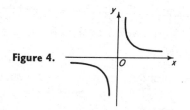

Example 1. The graph of the function f defined by the equation $f(x) = 1/x$ is symmetric with respect to L. (See figure 4.) Hence, f is its own inverse, a fact which is very easily verifiable by

$$f \circ f(x) = f[f(x)]$$

$$= \frac{1}{f(x)}$$

$$= \frac{1}{1/x}$$

$$= x$$

Therefore, $f \circ f(x) = x$, and using theorem 1.11.4, we get $f = f^{-1}$.

Exercises 1. Show (using elementary geometry) that two points A and B in the coordinate plane are symmetric with respect to the graph of the equation $y = x$ if and only if the coordinates of A are the coordinates of B in reversed order.

2. Draw the graphs of the functions f and g defined by

$$f(x) = 5x + 2 \quad \text{and} \quad g(x) = \frac{x - 2}{5}$$

Note the symmetry and prove that $g^{-1} = f$.

3. Find the equation defining f^{-1} if f is defined by $f(x) = 1/(1 - x)$. Draw the graphs of both f and f^{-1} on the same coordinate plane.

4. Let the function f be defined by

$$f(x) = \begin{cases} \sqrt{16 - x^2} & \text{if } 0 \leq x \leq 4 \\ -\sqrt{16 - x^2} & \text{if } -4 < x < 0 \end{cases}$$

(a) Give a geometric argument showing that f is its own inverse.
(b) Prove that $f^{-1} = f$.

1.13. Periodic functions Many events happen again and again at regular intervals of time. Examples of these are the celebration of your birthday (it happens every year, provided that you were not born on February 29), the passage of the second hand of your watch over the one o'clock mark (it happens once every minute), etc. Such events are said to be *periodic*. Often in physics and engineering, certain phenomena occur at regular intervals. In trying to give a mathematical formulation of these phenomena, physicists or engineers find that they need certain functions which can express this idea of recurrence at regular intervals. There are many such functions. We begin with an example.

Example 1. Consider the function f whose domain is the set of positive integers and whose range is the set $\{1, 2\}$ and which is defined by

$$f(n) = 1 \quad \text{if } n \text{ is even}$$

and $\quad f(n) = 2 \quad \text{if } n \text{ is odd}$

Note that $f(2) = f(4) = f(6) = f(8) = \ldots = f(26) = \ldots = 1$

and $\quad f(1) = f(3) = f(5) = f(7) = \ldots = f(25) = \ldots = 2.$

This function is somewhat uninteresting, but it provides a good example of a periodic function. We remark that if n is odd, so are $n + 2, n + 4, n + 6, n + 8$, etc., and if n is even, so are $n + 2, n + 4, n + 6, n + 8$, etc.

Hence, for the function f defined above, we can easily see that

$$f(n) = f(n + 2) = f(n + 4) = \ldots = f(n + 20) = \ldots$$

This example suggests the following definition:

Definition 1.13.1. If f is a function and if there exists a non-zero number p such that $f(x + p) = f(x)$ for all $x \in D_f$, then we say that f is *periodic* and the number p is called a *period*.

Remark: If there is a non-zero number p such that $f(x + p) = f(x)$ for all $x \in D_f$, then there are many other numbers with the same property as can be seen from the following:

Theorem 1.13.2. If f is a function and p is a non-zero number such that $f(x + p) = f(x)$ for all $x \in D_f$, then for any natural number n, $f(x + np) = f(x)$ for all $x \in D_f$.

Proof: We shall give a proof by induction. Let $S(n)$ denote the statement "$f(x + np) = f(x)$ for all $x \in D_f$." $S(1)$ is true by hypothesis. Suppose that $S(k)$ is true. Then,

$$f(x + kp) = f(x) \quad \text{for all } x \in D_f$$

Considering $f[x + (k + 1)p] = f(x + kp + p)$

$$= f(x + p + kp)$$
$$= f(x' + kp) \quad \text{(if we let } x' = x + p)$$
$$= f(x') \quad \text{(since } S(k) \text{ is true)}$$
$$= f(x + p)$$
$$= f(x)$$

Hence, we have shown that if $S(k)$ is true, $f[x + (k + 1)p] = f(x)$ is also true. That is, the truth of $S(k)$ implies that of $S(k + 1)$ and the statement $f(x + np) = f(x)$ for all $x \in D_f$ is true for all natural numbers n. ∎

It is now clear that a periodic function has many periods. If among all the non-zero numbers p, which have the property $f(x + p) = f(x)$ for all $x \in D_f$, there is one of smallest absolute value, then this smallest absolute value is called the *fundamental period* of the function f.

In example 1, the fundamental period of f was 2.

Remark: We have defined the fundamental period of a periodic function to be the smallest of all the numbers $|p|$, where $p \neq 0$ and p has the property $f(x + p) = f(x)$ for all $x \in D_f$. Can we be sure that such a smallest absolute value exists? The answer is no, as is shown in the following example.

Example 2. Let f be a function defined by $f(x) = 0$ if x is rational and $f(x) = 1$ if x is irrational. Now let p be any positive rational number. If x is rational, so is $x + p$; hence $f(x + p) = f(x)$ since they are both equal to zero. On the other hand, if x is irrational, so is $x + p$; hence $f(x + p) = f(x)$, since they are both equal to 1. Therefore, we have $f(x + p) = f(x)$ for all $x \in D_f$. It follows that f is periodic. Any positive rational number is a period of f. However, there is no smallest positive rational number. (See exercise 19, section 1.3.) ∎

The following theorem will become very useful when we discuss the properties of the trigonometric functions in Chapter 2.

Theorem 1.13.3. If f and g are periodic functions and p is a period of both f and g, then the functions $S = f + g$, $D = f - g$, $P = f \cdot g$ and $Q = f/g$ are all periodic with period p.

The proof is trivial and is left as an exercise for the reader.

Remark: In theorem 1.13.3, nothing is said about fundamental period. It is possible for both f and g to have the fundamental period k but for any one of the functions, $S, D, P,$ or Q not to have k as a fundamental period. We illustrate this fact with

Example 3. Suppose the functions f and g are defined by

$$f(x) = \begin{cases} 1 & \text{if } 2n \le x < 2n + 1 \\ 0 & \text{if } 2n + 1 \le x < 2n + 2 \end{cases}$$

and
$$g(x) = \begin{cases} -1 & \text{if } 2n \le x < 2n + 1 \\ 0 & \text{if } 2n + 1 \le x < 2n + 2 \end{cases}$$

for all integers n. It is easy to see that the fundamental periods of f and g are both 2. But $S(x) = f(x) + g(x) = 0$ for all x. Hence, S is periodic but has no fundamental period.

Theorem 1.13.4. If f and g are functions such that $R_f \subset D_g$ and f is periodic, then so is the composite $g \circ f$ of g and f.

Proof: Since f is periodic, there exists a non-zero number p such that $f(x + p) = f(x)$ for all $x \in D_f$. If we consider

$$g \circ f(x + p) = g[f(x + p)]$$
$$= g[f(x)]$$
$$= g \circ f(x)$$

We see that p is also a period of $g \circ f$. ∎

We again note that p need not be the fundamental period of $g \circ f$ even if it is the fundamental period of f.

Theorem 1.13.5. Let c be a non-zero constant. Suppose that f is a periodic function with period p and which has the property that $cx \in D_f$ whenever $x \in D_f$. Then the function g defined by $g(x) = f(cx)$ is periodic with period p/c.

Proof: We first note that $D_g = \{x \mid cx \in D_f\}$. We want to show that

$$g\left(x + \frac{p}{c}\right) = g(x) \quad \text{for all } x \in D_g$$

By the definition of the function g, we have

$$g\left(x + \frac{p}{c}\right) = f\left(c\left(x + \frac{p}{c}\right)\right)$$

$$= f(cx + p)$$
$$= f(cx) \quad \text{(since f has period p)}$$
$$= g(x) \quad \text{(by definition of g)}$$

Hence, $g\left(x + \dfrac{p}{c}\right) = g(x)$ for all $x \in D_g$ ∎

Exercises 1. Prove theorem 1.13.3.

2. Give five examples of periodic events from everyday life.

3. Suppose that a function f is periodic with period 2. Suppose also that if $0 \le x < 2$, we have $f(x) = x + 1$. Draw the graph of f. (Consider only values of x such that $-4 \le x \le 4$.)

4. Is it possible for a periodic function to have an inverse? Justify your answer.

1.14. Odd and even functions Let us consider the functions f and g defined by $f(x) = x^2$ and $g(x) = x^3$. For the first one, we note that $f(-x) = (-x)^2 = x^2$. Hence, $f(-x) = f(x)$ for all $x \in D_f$. On the other hand, for the second function, we have $g(-x) = (-x)^3 = -x^3$. Hence $g(-x) = -g(x)$ for all $x \in D_g$. If we consider the graphs of the

Figure I.

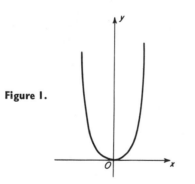

functions (see figures 1 and 2), we note that the graph of f is symmetric with respect to the y axis and that the graph of g is symmetric with respect to the origin. These symmetrical properties of the graphs of the functions f and g are very important, and functions which have these properties deserve special names. We first remark that each of the functions is a polynomial function. The degree of the only term in the polynomial x^2 is *even*, whereas the degree of the only term in the polynomial x^3 is *odd*. This suggests the following:

Definitions 1.14.1. A function f which has the property that $f(-x) = f(x)$ for all $x \in D_f$ is said to be an *even function*. On the other hand, any function g which has the property that $g(-x) = -g(x)$ for all $x \in D_g$ is said to be an *odd function*.

Figure 2.

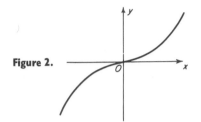

It is easy to verify that any polynomial function which has only terms of odd degrees is odd whereas any polynomial function which has only terms of even degrees is even. Polynomial functions, however, are not the only functions which can be either even or odd. As a matter of fact, we shall see in Chapter 2 that the trigonometric functions have these properties.

We observed earlier that the graphs of the functions f and g had certain symmetric properties. This observation can be extended to all odd and even functions, as is expressed in the next two theorems.

Theorem 1.14.2. A function f is even if and only if its graph is symmetric with respect to the y axis.

Proof: Suppose that the function f is even. We want to show that the graph of f, say G_f, is symmetric with respect to the y axis. We first note that two points (a, b) and (c, d) are symmetric with respect to the y axis if and only if $a = -c$ and $b = d$. Pick any point $A \in G_f$. Suppose that the coordinates of A are (x, y). Then $(x, y) \in f$ and $y = f(x)$. But f is even. Therefore, $f(-x) = f(x)$. It follows that $y = f(-x)$ and that $(-x, y) \in f$. Hence, the point B with coordinates $(-x, y)$ is in G_f. Since A and B are symmetric with respect to the y axis and since A was arbitrary, we have proved that G_f is symmetric with respect to the y axis.

Conversely, suppose that G_f is symmetric with respect to the y axis. Hence, if the point A with coordinates (x, y) is in G_f, so is the point B with coordinates $(-x, y)$. Therefore, $(x, y) \in f$ implies $(-x, y) \in f$. It follows that $f(-x) = f(x)$ for all $x \in D_f$. ∎

Theorem 1.14.3. A function f is odd if and only if its graph is symmetric with respect to the origin. The proof is left as an exercise.

Remark: It is possible for a function to be neither even nor odd as illustrated by the following:

Example I. Show that the function f defined by $f(x) = x^2 + x$ is neither even nor odd.

Solution: $f(x) = x^2 + x$

Hence, $f(-x) = (-x)^2 + (-x)$

$$= x^2 - x$$

But $x^2 - x \neq x^2 + x$ for some value of x, for example, $x = 1$

Hence, the statement "$f(-x) = f(x)$ for all $x \in D_f$" is false and f is not even.

Further, $-f(x) = -(x^2 + x)$

$$= -x^2 - x$$

But $x^2 - x \neq -x^2 - x$ for some value of x, for example, $x = 1$
Hence, the statement "$f(-x) = -f(x)$ for all $x \in D_f$" is false and f is not odd. ∎

We have therefore shown that this function is neither even nor odd. We notice in this example that the function is a sum of two functions, one of which is even and the other odd. You may wonder if this is always the case. The answer to this interesting question is provided by theorem 1.14.4.

Theorem 1.14.4. Any function f which has the property that $-x \in D_f$ whenever $x \in D_f$ can be expressed as a sum of two functions, one of which is even and the other odd.

Proof: It is easily verified that

$$f(x) = \frac{f(x) + f(-x)}{2} + \frac{f(x) - f(-x)}{2}$$

Let $\quad h(x) = \dfrac{f(x) + f(-x)}{2}$

and $\quad g(x) = \dfrac{f(x) - f(-x)}{2}$

Now $h(-x) = \dfrac{f(-x) + f(-(-x))}{2} = \dfrac{f(-x) + f(x)}{2}$

$$= \frac{f(x) + f(-x)}{2} = h(x)$$

Hence, the function h is even.

On the other hand,

$$g(-x) = \frac{f(-x) - f(-(-x))}{2} = \frac{f(-x) - f(x)}{2}$$

$$= -\frac{[f(x) - f(-x)]}{2} = -g(x)$$

Hence, the function g is odd. ∎

Theorem 1.14.5. Let the functions S, P, and Q be defined by

$$S(x) = f(x) + g(x) \quad \text{for every } x \in D_f \cap D_g$$

$$P(x) = f(x) \cdot g(x) \quad \text{for every } x \in D_f \cap D_g$$

$$Q(x) = \frac{f(x)}{g(x)} \quad \text{for every } x \in D_f \cap D_g \setminus \{x \mid g(x) = 0\}$$

Then,

1. If f and g are both even, it follows that S, P, and Q are also even.
2. If f and g are both odd, it follows that S is odd, but P and Q are even
3. If f is even and g is odd or vice versa, it follows that P and Q are odd.

The proof is easy and is left as an exercise.

Exercises

1. Prove theorem 1.14.3.

2. Prove theorem 1.14.5.

3. Verify that the function f defined by $f : x \rightarrow 2x^3 - 5x^2 + 1$ is neither odd nor even.

4. The function g defined by $g(x) = [(x - 1)/x]$ is neither odd nor even. Find formulas for functions f and h with the properties that f is even, h odd, and $g = f + h$.

5. Show that the only functions which are both even and odd are the functions f defined by $f(x) = 0$ for all $x \in D_f$ and with the property that $x \subset D_f$ implies $-x \in D_f$.

**6. Show that if f has the property that $-x \in D_f$ whenever $x \in D_f$, then the functions h and g, h even and g odd such that $f = h + g$ are unique. (*Hint:* Suppose that $f = h' + g'$ where h' is even and g' is odd. Subtract the two equalities and use the result of exercise 5.)

Chapter Two

The Non-Algebraic Elementary Functions

We now undertake the study of some very important functions. These functions are known in mathematical literature as the *non-algebraic elementary functions* or the *elementary transcendental functions*. They usually form the core of the topics covered in a basic trigonometry course. They are the trigonometric (circular) and inverse trigonometric functions, the exponential and logarithmic functions. Often, the trigonometric functions are introduced through the notion of angles. For our purpose, however, we find it best to use the notion of arc length. We shall discuss the relation between these two concepts in Chapter 3.

2.1. Arc length Consider a circle in a coordinate plane and two points A and B on that circle. These two points divide the circle into two arcs. Let C be a third point on the circle and let $\overset{\frown}{ACB}$ denote the arc of the circle which contains the point C. We shall give a precise definition for what we mean by the *length* of the arc $\overset{\frown}{ACB}$.

First suppose that a line through the point A and the center of the circle does not intersect the arc $\overset{\frown}{ACB}$ at any point distinct from A and B. Then the arc $\overset{\frown}{ACB}$ is called a *minor arc* of the circle. Otherwise, it is called a *major arc*. Note that our definition allows us to call a semi circle a minor arc. (See figure 1.)

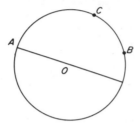

Figure I.

We begin by giving a naïve description of arc length which will lead to the formal definition. Whatever arc length is, our intuition tells us that we can approximate it by considering the length of broken lines in the following way:

Suppose that $\overset{\frown}{ACB}$ is a minor arc. Consider a set of points $(P_0, P_1, P_2, \ldots, P_{n-1}, P_n)$ with the following properties:

1. $P_0 = A$ and $P_n = B$.
2. Each P_i, $i = 0, 1, 2, \ldots, n$ is a point of the arc $\overset{\frown}{ACB}$.
3. If through each P_i a perpendicular to the chord AB is drawn and the intersection of that perpendicular with the chord AB is denoted by Q_i, then the following is true: if p, q, r are members of the set $\{0, 1, 2, \ldots, n-1, n\}$ and $p < q < r$, then

$$|Q_pQ_q| + |Q_qQ_r| = |Q_pQ_r|; \text{ i.e., } Q_q \text{ is between } Q_p \text{ and } Q_r. \text{ (See figure 2.)}$$

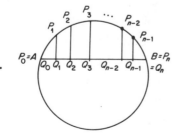

Figure 2.

Definition 2.1.1. The ordered set of points $(P_0, P_1, P_2, \ldots, P_n)$ described above is called an *inscripture* of the minor arc $\overset{\frown}{ACB}$ and is denoted by I.

We agree that the ordered pair (A, B) is also an inscripture of the arc $\overset{\frown}{ACB}$. We can now extend the definition of inscripture to major arcs in the following way: Suppose that the arc $\overset{\frown}{ACB}$ is a major arc. Then the line through A and the center of the circle intersects $\overset{\frown}{ACB}$ at a point D, distinct from A and B. The point D divides the arc $\overset{\frown}{ACB}$ into two minor arcs (one of which is a semicircle). Then the ordered set of points $(A, P_1, P_2, \ldots, P_{n-1}, B)$ is an inscripture of the arc $\overset{\frown}{ACB}$ if and only if exactly one of the following two conditions is satisfied:

1. For some i $(i = 1, 2, \ldots, n - 1)$, $D = P_i$ and the ordered sets of points $(A, P_1, P_2, \ldots, P_{i-1}, D)$ and $(D, P_{i+1}, \ldots, P_{n-1}, B)$ are inscriptures of the two minor arcs whose union is $\overset{\frown}{ACB}$.

2. $P_i \neq D$ for every i $(i = 0, 1, \ldots, n - 1, n)$ and there is a j $(0 \leq j < n)$ such that $(A, \ldots, P_j, D)$ and $(D, P_{j+1}, \ldots, P_{n-1}, B)$ are inscriptures of the two minor arcs.

We also denote an inscripture of a major arc $\overset{\frown}{ACB}$ by I.

Now if $I = (A, P_1, P_2, \ldots, P_{n-1}, B)$ is an inscripture of an arc $\overset{\frown}{ACB}$ (minor or major), then the length of the broken line

$$AP_1P_2 \ldots P_{n-1}B \quad \text{is} \quad |AP_1| + |P_1P_2| + \ldots + |P_{n-1}P_n|$$

and is denoted by $L(I)$. We use this notation because the length of the broken line is determined uniquely by the inscripture I. We see that we can take the length of the broken line as an approximation for the "length of the arc." If we want a better approximation, we consider a point P' on $\overset{\frown}{ACB}$ which is not a point of the inscripture I. Then we let $I' = (A, P_1, P_2, \ldots, P_i, P', P_{i+1}, \ldots, P_n)$ be a new inscripture of $\overset{\frown}{ACB}$. We see that $L(I')$ is a better approximation for the "length of the arc." Continuing in this way, we can get better and better approximations. We note that we still *do not know what arc length is*. We are willing to accept the fact that the length of the broken line approximates what we want to define. We do this on the basis that each point of that broken line is near a corresponding point of the arc $\overset{\frown}{ACB}$. We feel that if the inscripture has enough points, it is difficult to distinguish between the arc $\overset{\frown}{ACB}$ and the broken line $AP_1P_2 \ldots P_{n-1}B$ and therefore we *assume* that their lengths should be nearly equal.

We shall define arc length in such a way that the assumption that we made above is correct. Assumptions of this type, however, must be made with care, as we illustrate by the following example:

Example 1. Let ABC be an isosceles triangle with $|AB| = |AC|$. Let M_1, M_2, M_3 be the midpoints of AB, AC, and BC respectively. By a theorem of geometry, we know that M_1M_3 is parallel to AC and that $|M_1M_3| = $

$|AC|/2$. Similarly, M_2M_3 is parallel to AB and $|M_2M_3| = |AB|/2$. A simple argument suffices to show that

$$|BM_1| + |M_1M_3| + |M_2M_3| + |M_2C| = |AB| + |AC|.$$

Let M_4, M_5, M_6, M_7, M_8, M_9 be the midpoints of M_1B, M_1M_3, BM_3, M_2M_3, M_2C, and M_3C respectively. It is easy to show that the length of the broken line $BM_4M_6M_5M_3M_7M_9M_8C$ is equal to the length of the broken line $BM_1M_3M_2C$ and therefore is equal to $|AB| + |AC|$. (See figure 3.)

Figure 3.

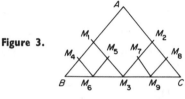

If we take the midpoints of the sides of the four smaller isosceles triangles, we obtain a new broken line whose length is equal to $|AB| + |AC|$. We can see now that it is possible to continue this process as long as we wish. Each time, the length of the broken line will be equal to $|AB| + |AC|$. After a certain number of steps, however, each point of the new broken line will be very near a point of the line segment BC. Further, because of the "thickness" of the lines drawn, it will be difficult to distinguish between the broken lines and the line segment BC. We cannot, however, assume that the lengths of the broken lines are nearly equal to $|BC|$, since we know that the length of each broken line is equal to $|AB| + |AC|$!

We now return to the intuitive description of arc length. We recall that an inscripture of the arc $\overset{\frown}{ACB}$ is a set of points $I = (A, P_1, P_2, \ldots, P_{n-1}, B)$, where each point is on the arc $\overset{\frown}{ACB}$ and the points are arranged in a certain way. We also recall that $L(I)$ denotes the length of the broken line $AP_1P_2 \ldots P_{n-1}B$ obtained by drawing line segments connecting consecutive points of the inscripture I. We note that we considered new inscriptures obtained from the inscripture I by adding points of the arc to I. We formalize this idea with the following:

Definition 2.1.2. If I_1 and I_2 are inscriptures of an arc $\overset{\frown}{ACB}$ and I_1 is a proper subset of I_2, then I_2 is called a *refinement* of I_1.

We now can state the following theorem:

Theorem 2.1.3. If I_1 and I_2 are inscriptures of an arc of a circle and if I_2 is a refinement of I_1, then $L(I_1) < L(I_2)$.

Proof: Suppose $I_1 = (A, P_1, P_2, \ldots, P_{n-1}, B)$.

We get the refinement I_2 by adding a finite number of points of the arc to the inscripture I_1. Suppose that the refinement I_2 has only one more point than I_1. Then,

$$I_2 = (A, P_1, \ldots, P_{j-1}, Q, P_j, P_{j+1}, \ldots, P_{n-1}, B)$$

and $L(I_2) = |AP_1| + P_1P_2| + \ldots + |P_{j-2}P_{j-1}| + |P_{j-1}Q| +$
$+ |QP_j| + |P_jP_{j+1}| + \ldots + |P_{n-1}B|$

But $L(I_1) = |AP_1| + |P_1P_2| + \ldots + |P_{j-2}P_{j-1}| + |P_{j-1}P_j| +$
$+ |P_jP_{j+1}| + \ldots + |P_{n-1}B|$

Figure 4.

Therefore, $L(I_2) - L(I_1) = |P_{j-1}Q| + |QP_j| - |P_{j-1}P_j|$.

But $|P_{j-1}Q| + |QP_j| - |P_{j-1}P_j| > 0$, since $P_{j-1}QP_j$ is a triangle.

Therefore, $L(I_1) < L(I_2)$. The proof can easily be generalized to the general case in which I_2 has k more points than I_1. ∎

Theorem 2.1.3 indicates that if $I_1, I_2, I_3, I_4, \ldots$ are inscriptures of the arc $\overset{\frown}{ACB}$, each, except for the first one, being a refinement of the previous one, then the numbers $L(I_1)\ L(I_2), L(I_3), L(I_4), \ldots$ are increasing. It can be shown that there is a number which is larger than any of the numbers $L(I_1), (L(I_2), \ldots$. That is to say, there is an upper bound for the set $\{L(I) | I$ is an inscripture of the arc $\overset{\frown}{ACB}\}$.

**Theorem 2.1.4. Let $\overset{\frown}{ACB}$ be an arc of a circle. Then the set $\{L(I)|I$ is an inscripture of the arc $\overset{\frown}{ACB}\}$ has an upper bound.

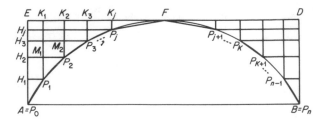

Figure 5.

Proof: Suppose that the arc is a minor arc. Then we can construct a rectangle $ABDE$ with the side ED tangent to the arc at the point F. (See figure 5.) Consider any inscripture I of the arc $\overset{\frown}{AFB}$. We shall show that $L(I) < |AE| + |ED| + |DB|$. We note first that F may not be a point of the inscripture I. Let I' denote either I (in the case that F is a point of the inscripture I) or the inscripture obtained by adding to I the point F. In any case, we have

$$L(I) \leq L(I')$$

Suppose that the points $P_1, P_2, \ldots, P_j$ of the inscripture are on the arc $\overgroup{AF}$ and that the points $P_{j+1}, P_{j+2}, \ldots, P_n$ are on the arc $\overgroup{FB}$. Construct the perpendiculars $P_1H_1, P_2H_2, \ldots, P_jH_j$ to the line segment AE and the perpendiculars $P_1K_1, P_2K_2, \ldots, P_jK_j$ to the line segment EF.

In this way, we form the right triangle $AH_1P_1, P_1M_1P_2, \ldots, P_jK_jF$. (See figure 5.) Since the length of the hypotenuse of a right triangle is less than the sum of the lengths of the other two sides, we obtain

$$|AP_1| < |AH_1| + |H_1P_1|$$
$$|P_1P_2| < |P_1M_1| + |M_1P_2|$$
$$\vdots \qquad\qquad \vdots$$
$$|P_jF| < |P_jK_j| + |K_jF|$$

Hence,

$$|AP_1| + |P_1P_2| + \ldots + |P_jF| < |AH_1| + |P_1M_1| + \ldots + |P_jK_j| +$$
$$+ |H_1P_1| + |M_1P_2| + \ldots + |K_jF|$$

But $|P_1M_1| = |H_1H_2|, |P_2M_2| = |H_2H_3|, \ldots, |P_jK_j| = |H_jE|$

and $|H_1P_1| = |EK_1|, |M_1P_2| = |K_1K_2|, \ldots, |K_jF| = |K_jF|$

It follows that

$$|AP_1| + |P_1P_2| + \ldots + |P_jF| <$$
$$|AH_1| + |H_1H_2| + \ldots + |H_jE| + |EK_1| + |K_1K_2| + \ldots + |K_jF|$$

and $|AP_1| + |P_1P_2| + \ldots + |P_jF| < |AE| + |EF|$

Exactly the same argument leads to the result

$$|FP_{j+1}| + |P_{j+1}P_{j+2}| + \ldots + |P_{n-1}B| < |FD| + |DB|$$

It follows that

$$|AP_1| + |P_1P_2| + \ldots + |P_jF| + |FP_{j+1}| + \ldots + |P_{n-1}B| < |AE| +$$
$$+ |EF| + |FD| + |DB|$$

Hence, $L(I') < |AE| + |ED| + |DB|$

Since we have shown

$$L(I) \leq L(I')$$

we get $L(I) < |AE| + |ED| + |DB|$ \hfill (1)

We now recall that the inscripture I was an arbitrary inscripture of the arc $\overset{\frown}{ACB}$. Hence, inequality (1) is true which ever inscripture we choose. Therefore, $|AE| + |ED| + |DB|$ is an upper bound for the following set $\{L(I)\,|\,I$ is an inscripture of the arc $\overset{\frown}{ACB}\}$. ∎

By the completeness property, this set must have a least upper bound. We call this least upper bound the *length* of the arc $\overset{\frown}{ACB}$.

Note: If the arc $\overset{\frown}{ACB}$ is a major arc, a very similar argument can be given. (See exercise 1 below.) We are now ready to give the following:

Definition 2.1.5. Let $\overset{\frown}{ACB}$ be an arc of a circle. The *length of the arc* is the least upper bound of the set whose elements are the real numbers $L(I)$ obtained by considering all possible inscriptures I of the arc $\overset{\frown}{ACB}$.

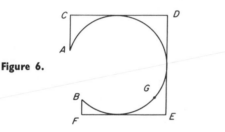

Figure 6.

Exercise 1. Show that for any inscripture I of the arc $\overset{\frown}{AGB}$ shown on figure 6, it is true that $L(I) < |AC| + |CD| + |DE| + |EF| + |FB|$. (*Hint:* Use theorem 2.1.4 twice.)

**2.2. Some important theorems In this section, we shall prove two basic theorems from geometry.

Theorem 2.2.1. Consider two concentric circles with center A and radii r_1 and r_2. Let Ax and Ay be two rays intersecting the circle with radius r_1 at B and C, and the circle with radius r_2 at D and E such that B and D are on Ax and C and E are on Ay. Let a third ray Az intersect the circle with radius r_1 at F and the circle with radius r_2 at G. If s_1 and s_2 denote the lengths of the arcs $\overset{\frown}{BFC}$ and $\overset{\frown}{DGE}$ respectively, then $s_2/s_1 = r_2/r_1$. (See figure 1.)

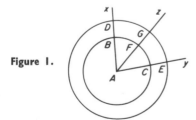

Figure 1.

Proof: Let $I = (B, P_1, P_2, \ldots, P_{n-1}, C)$ be any inscripture of the arc $\overset{\frown}{BFC}$. (See figure 2.) We obtain an inscripture of the arc $\overset{\frown}{DGE}$ by drawing $n-1$ rays starting at A and passing through $P_1, P_2, \ldots, P_{n-1}$ respectively. The intersections of these rays with the arc $\overset{\frown}{DGE}$ are denoted by $Q_1, Q_2, \ldots, Q_{n-1}$, where we require for each i that P_i and Q_i be on the same ray. (See figure 2.) Let J denote the inscripture

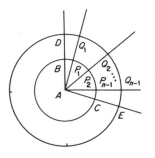

Figure 2.

$(D, Q_1, Q_2, \ldots, Q_{n-1}, E)$. (See exercise 1 below.) We can show that $L(J) = (r_2/r_1) \cdot L(I)$. To this end, consider the triangles ABP_1 and ADQ_1. Clearly, these two triangles are similar and we have

$$\frac{|DQ_1|}{|BP_1|} = \frac{r_2}{r_1} \quad \text{and} \quad |DQ_1| = \frac{r_2}{r_1} \cdot |BP_1|$$

Noticing that the pairs of triangles AP_1P_2 and AQ_1Q_2, AP_2P_3 and AQ_2Q_3, etc., are also pairs of similar triangles, we obtain the following:

$$|DQ_1| = \frac{r_2}{r_1} \cdot |BP_1| \tag{1}$$

$$|Q_1Q_2| = \frac{r_2}{r_1} \cdot |P_1P_2| \tag{2}$$
$$\vdots \qquad\qquad \vdots$$
$$|Q_{n-1}E| = \frac{r_2}{r_1} \cdot |P_{n-1}C| \tag{n}$$

and, adding, we get

$$|DQ_1| + |Q_1Q_2| + \cdots + |Q_{n-1}E|$$

$$= \frac{r_2}{r_1} (|BP_1| + |P_1P_2| + \cdots + |P_{n-1}C|)$$

Hence, $L(J) = \frac{r_2}{r_1} \cdot L(I)$

Note that we started with an arbitrary inscripture I of the arc $\overset{\frown}{BFC}$ and found an inscripture J of the arc $\overset{\frown}{DGE}$ such that $L(J) = (r_2/r_1) \cdot L(I)$. We could have started with any inscripture K of the arc $\overset{\frown}{DGE}$ and found, in exactly the same fashion, an inscripture H of the arc $\overset{\frown}{BFC}$ such that $L(K) = (r_2/r_1) \cdot L(H)$. Hence, it is true that

if we let $S_1 = \{L(I) \,|\, I$ is an inscripture of $\overset{\frown}{BFC}\}$

and $S_2 = \{L(J) \,|\, J$ is an inscripture of $\overset{\frown}{DGE}\}$

then $S_2 = \left\{\dfrac{r_2}{r_1}\right\} \cdot S_1$

Since the elements of each of the sets above are positive, we can use theorem 1.6.5 and conclude that

$$\text{l.u.b. } S_2 = \left(\text{l.u.b. } \left\{\frac{r_2}{r_1}\right\}\right) \cdot (\text{l.u.b. } S_1)$$

But, by definition

$$\text{l.u.b. } S_2 = s_2 \quad \text{and} \quad \text{l.u.b. } S_1 = s_1$$

Hence, $s_2 = \dfrac{r_2}{r_1} \cdot s_1$

and $\dfrac{s_2}{s_1} = \dfrac{r_2}{r_1}$ ∎

Note: If the rays Ax and Ay coincide, then each arc is the whole circle and s_1 and s_2 are respectively the circumferences of the circles with radii r_1 and r_2. We therefore get the following:

Corollary 2.2.2. The circumference of any circle is proportional to the radius of that circle.

Now the following definition can be given.

Definition 2.2.3. The ratio of the circumference of any circle to its diameter is a real number universally denoted by π.

One of the important properties of arc length is that it is additive. This fact is expressed in the next theorem:

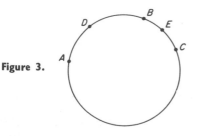

Figure 3.

Theorem 2.2.4. Let $\overset{\frown}{ABC}$ be an arc of a circle and let D and E be points such that (A, D, B, E, C) is an inscripture of the arc $\overset{\frown}{ABC}$. If s_1, s_2, and s_3 denote the lengths of the arcs $\overset{\frown}{ADB}$, $\overset{\frown}{BEC}$, and $\overset{\frown}{ABC}$ respectively, then

$$s_1 + s_2 = s_3$$

Proof: Let

$$U = \{L(I) \mid I \text{ is an inscripture of } \overset{\frown}{ADB}\}$$

$$V = \{L(J) \mid J \text{ is an inscripture of } \overset{\frown}{BEC}\}$$

$$W = \{L(K) \mid K \text{ is an inscripture of } \overset{\frown}{ABC}\}$$

Then, $s_1 = \text{l.u.b. } U$; $\qquad s_2 = \text{l.u.b. } V$; $\qquad$ and $\qquad s_3 = \text{l.u.b. } W$

We claim that

1. For each $x \in W$, there exists a $y \in U + V$ such that $x \leq y$ and
2. For each $x \in U + V$, there exists a $y \in W$ such that $x \leq y$.

Hence, by theorem 1.6.1, l.u.b. $W = \text{l.u.b. } (U + V)$

But by theorem 1.6.4, l.u.b. $(U + V) = \text{l.u.b. } U + \text{l.u.b. } V$.

Hence, l.u.b. $W = \text{l.u.b. } U + \text{l.u.b. } V$.

That is, $\qquad s_3 = s_1 + s_2$

Therefore, to complete the proof, we need only verify the foregoing two claims.

Consider $x \in W$. There exists an inscripture K of ABC such that $x = L(K)$.

Case 1. B is a point of K. That is,

$$K = (A, P_1, P_2, \ldots, P_i, B, P_{i+1}, P_{1+2}, \ldots, P_{n-1}C)$$

Then, let

$$I = (A, P_1, P_2, \ldots, P_i, B) \quad \text{and} \quad J = (B, P_{i+1}, P_{i+2}, \ldots, P_{n-1}, C)$$

Clearly, $L(K) = L(I) + L(J)$ and I is an inscripture of $\overset{\frown}{ADB}$ whereas J is an inscripture of $\overset{\frown}{BEC}$. Let $y = L(I) + L(J)$ and we have $x = y$ with $y \in U + V$.

Case 2. B is not a point of K. Then consider the inscripture $K' = (A, P_1, P_2, \ldots, P_j, B, P_{j+1}, \ldots, P_{n-1}, C)$. K' is a refinement of K, and by theorem 2.1.3, $L(K) < L(K')$.

Again, we let

$$I = (A, P_1, P_2, \ldots, P_j, B) \quad \text{and} \quad J = (B, P_{j+1}, \ldots, P_{n-1}, C)$$

As before we get $L(K') = L(I) + L(J)$, and denoting $L(I) + L(J)$ by y

we have $x < y$ and $y \in U + V$. In both cases, given $x \in W$, we can find a $y \in U + V$ such that $x \leq y$.

To prove claim 2, let $x \in U + V$. Then there exists an inscription I of $\overset{\frown}{ADB}$ and an inscription J of $\overset{\frown}{BEC}$ such that $x = L(I) + L(J)$.

If $I = (A, P_1, P_2, \ldots, P_k, B)$ and $J = (B, Q_1, Q_2, \ldots, Q_e, C)$

then $K = (A, P_1, P_2, \ldots, P_k, B, Q_1, Q_2, \ldots, Q_e, C)$

is an inscription of $\overset{\frown}{ABC}$ and $L(K) = L(I) + L(J)$. If we let $y = L(K)$ we have $x = y$ and $y \in W$. Hence, claim 2 has been verified and the proof of the theorem is complete. ∎

Exercises   1. Show that $(D, Q_1, Q_2, \ldots, Q_{n-1}, E)$ obtained in the proof of theorem 2.2.1 is indeed an inscription of the arc $\overset{\frown}{DGE}$. (Verify that the set of points satisfies the conditions listed in defining an inscription in section 2.1.)

2. Give a proof of theorem 2.2.4 which does not make use of theorems 1.6.1 and 1.6.4. (*Hint:* Define U, V, W as in the proof given in the text. Show that $s_1 + s_2$ is an upper bound of W, and therefore, that $s_3 \leq s_1 + s_2$, since s_3 is l.u.b. W. Further, show that for a fixed inscription J of $\overset{\frown}{BEC}$, $s_3 - L(J)$ is an upper bound of the set U. Hence, $s_1 \leq s_3 - L(J)$ from which conclude that $L(J) \leq s_3 - s_1$. Since J was arbitrary, conclude that $s_3 - s_1$ is an upper bound of V; hence, $s_2 \leq s_3 - s_1$ and $s_1 + s_2 \leq s_3$. Therefore, $s_1 + s_2 = s_3$.)

2.3. Paths Suppose we are given a circle of radius r. Then its circumference is $2\pi r$. (See definition 2.2.3.) Suppose now that a point Q starts at a fixed point P on the circle and travels on the circle without reversing its direction. If we agree that the counterclockwise and clockwise directions are the positive and negative directions respectively, then knowing that the point Q started at P, it is sufficient to know the distance α traveled by Q to know exactly where it stopped.

Note: α may be positive or negative, depending on whether the point travels counterclockwise or clockwise. We also note that $|\alpha|$ may be greater than $2\pi r$. The motion of the point just described is called a *directed path*; the point P is called the *initial point* of the path; and the position where Q stops is called the *terminal point* of the path.

Observe that there is a one-to-one correspondence between the set of paths on a given circle and the set of ordered pairs

$\{(P, \alpha) \,|\, P$ belongs to the circle and α is a real number$\}$

That is to say, given (P, α), there is a unique path on the given circle whose initial point is P with the point traveling a directed distance α on the circle. Conversely, given a path with initial point P, there is a unique ordered pair (P, α) corresponding to it. Because of this one-to-one correspondence, we shall not distinguish between the path and the pair (P, α). We shall write "the path (P, α)" meaning "the path which is the motion of a point Q starting at P and traveling a directed distance α on a given circle."

Definition 2.3.1. On a given circle, two paths (P_1, α_1) and (P_2, α_2) are *equal* if and only if $P_1 = P_2$ and $\alpha_1 = \alpha_2$.

Note: It is possible for two paths to be distinct but for the distances traveled by each point on the circle to be equal. In this case, we say that the paths are equivalent.

Figure 1.

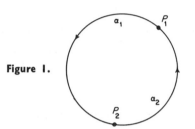

Definition 2.3.2. On a given circle, two paths (P_1, α_1) and (P_2, α_2) are *equivalent* if and only if $\alpha_1 = \alpha_2$. We remark that two equal paths are equivalent but two equivalent paths are not necessarily equal. (See figure 1.) We recall that, given an arc $\overset{\frown}{ABC}$ on a circle, the line segment AC is called the *chord* of the arc $\overset{\frown}{ABC}$. We state the following theorem the proof of which can be supplied by the reader. (See exercise 5 below.)

Theorem 2.3.3. If in the same circle the lengths of two arcs are equal, then the lengths of their chords are equal.

We see immediately from theorem 2.3.3 that if the paths (P_1, α_1) and (P_2, α_2) are equivalent, and if Q_1 and Q_2 are their respective terminal points, then $|P_1 Q_1| = |P_2 Q_2|$. The converse is not necessarily true. However, if $|P_1 Q_1| = |P_2 Q_2|$ where Q_1 and Q_2 are respectively the terminal points of two paths (P_1, α_1) and (P_2, α_2) on the same circle, then there is an integer n such that $\alpha_1 = \alpha_2 + 2n\pi r$ or there is an integer k such that $\alpha_1 = -\alpha_2 + 2k\pi r$. (See exercise 6 below.)

Definition 2.3.4. Given two paths (P_1, α_1) and (P_2, α_2) on the same circle, the sum $(P_1, \alpha_1) + (P_2, \alpha_2)$ is the path $(P_1, \alpha_1 + \alpha_2)$.

We remark that the addition of paths is not commutative

since $(P_1, \alpha_1) + (P_2, \alpha_2) = (P_1, \alpha_1 + \alpha_2)$

and $(P_2, \alpha_2) + (P_1, \alpha_1) = (P_2, \alpha_2 + \alpha_1)$

but $(P_1, \alpha_1 + \alpha_2) \neq (P_2, \alpha_2 + \alpha_1)$

unless $P_1 = P_2$.

Since, however, $\alpha_1 + \alpha_2 = \alpha_2 + \alpha_1$, the two sums are equivalent paths.

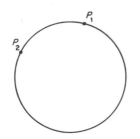

Figure 2.

Example 1. Consider a circle of radius 2 as shown in figure 2. Draw diagrams to show the following paths:

1. $\left(P_1, \dfrac{\pi}{2}\right)$

2. $\left(P_2, -\dfrac{\pi}{6}\right)$

3. $\left(P_1, \dfrac{\pi}{2}\right) + \left(P_2, \dfrac{\pi}{3}\right)$

4. $\left(P_2, -\dfrac{\pi}{3}\right) + \left(P_1, \dfrac{\pi}{2}\right)$

5. $\left(P_1, \dfrac{\pi}{4}\right) + \left(P_2, -\dfrac{\pi}{4}\right)$

Solution: 1. Since the radius of the circle is 2, the circumference is 4π. Hence, $\pi/2$ is $\frac{1}{8}$ of the circumference. The path $(P_1, \pi/2)$ is shown on figure 3.

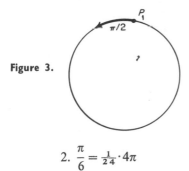

Figure 3.

2. $\dfrac{\pi}{6} = \frac{1}{24} \cdot 4\pi$

Hence, for the path $(P_2, -\pi/6)$, the point traveled a distance which is one twenty-fourth of the circumference in the clockwise direction. (See figure 4.)

Figure 4.

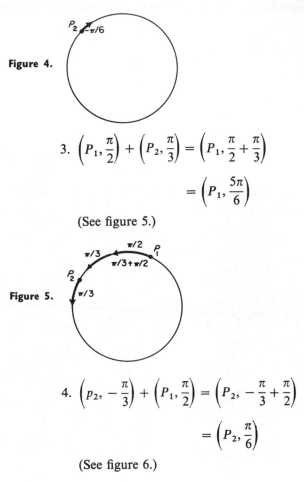

3. $\left(P_1, \dfrac{\pi}{2}\right) + \left(P_2, \dfrac{\pi}{3}\right) = \left(P_1, \dfrac{\pi}{2} + \dfrac{\pi}{3}\right)$

$$= \left(P_1, \dfrac{5\pi}{6}\right)$$

(See figure 5.)

Figure 5.

4. $\left(p_2, -\dfrac{\pi}{3}\right) + \left(P_1, \dfrac{\pi}{2}\right) = \left(P_2, -\dfrac{\pi}{3} + \dfrac{\pi}{2}\right)$

$$= \left(P_2, \dfrac{\pi}{6}\right)$$

(See figure 6.)

Figure 6.

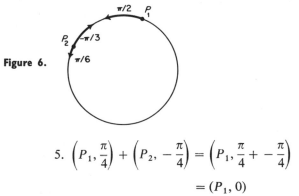

5. $\left(P_1, \dfrac{\pi}{4}\right) + \left(P_2, -\dfrac{\pi}{4}\right) = \left(P_1, \dfrac{\pi}{4} + -\dfrac{\pi}{4}\right)$

$$= (P_1, 0)$$

We note that the symbol $(P_1, 0)$ corresponds to the path in which the point does not move from P_1. ∎

Exercises

1. Consider a circle of radius 4. Pick two distinct points P_1 and P_2 on that circle. Draw diagrams to show the following paths:

   (a) $\left(P_1, \dfrac{\pi}{4}\right)$

   (b) $(P_2, -5\pi)$

   (c) $(P_1, 6\pi) + \left(P_2, \dfrac{25\pi}{2}\right)$

   (d) $(P_2, -8\pi) + (P_1, 2\pi)$

2. Show that the addition of paths is associative; i.e., for any three paths on the same circle we have
$(P_1, \alpha_1) + [(P_2, \alpha_2) + (P_3, \alpha_3)] = [(P_1, \alpha_1) + [(P_2, \alpha_2)] + (P_3, \alpha_3)$

*3. Let a circle with radius r be given. Suppose that A and B are two points of the circle which do not lie on the same diameter. Let s_1 and s_2 be the respective lengths of the two arcs determined by A and B on the circle. Prove that min $\{s_1, s_2\} \le \pi r$. (*Hint:* Note that $s_1 + s_2 = 2\pi r$.)

*4. Given a circle and two points A and B on the circle but not lying on the same diameter, the arc with smaller length determined by the points A and B is called the *minor arc subtended* by the chord AB. Prove that if A, B, C, and D are on the circle and $|AB| = |CD|$, then the length of the minor arc subtended by AB is equal to the length of the minor arc subtended by CD. (*Hint:* Show that for each inscripture I of one minor arc, there is an inscripture J of the other minor arc such that $L(I) = L(J)$.)

**5. Prove theorem 2.3.3. (*Hint:* Assume that the theorem is not true and arrive at a contradiction, using exercise 4.)

6. Show that if (P_1, α_1) and (P_2, α_2) are two paths on a circle with respective terminal points Q_1 and Q_2 and if $|P_1 Q_1| = |P_2 Q_2|$, then there exists some integer n such that either $\alpha_1 = \alpha_2 + 2n\pi r$ or $\alpha_1 = -\alpha_2 + 2n\pi r$ where r is the radius of the circle.

7. Show that if two paths (P_1, α_1) and (P_2, α_2) on the same circle are equivalent and if Q_1 and Q_2 are their respective terminal points, then $|P_1 Q_1| = |P_2 Q_2|$. (*Hint:* Use theorem 2.3.3.)

8. Show that if (P_1, α_1) is a given path on a circle and P_2 is a point of the circle, then there is one and only one path (P_2, α_2) which is equivalent to (P_1, α_1).

2.4. A more formal approach to the notion of paths Suppose that a circle with radius r is given. Let P be a fixed point on that circle. In section 2.3, we described a directed path as the motion of a point starting at P and traveling on the circle.

This description is sufficient for a basic course in mathematics. It depends very heavily, however, on the *intuitive* concept of motion of a point. It is extremely difficult to describe the concept of paths rigorously. Hence, in this section, we shall indicate only briefly the basic idea underlying a more rigorous approach.

Basically, a directed path is a function with domain the set $[0, 1] = \{t \mid 0 \le t \le 1\}$ and with range an arc of the circle. This function is required to have certain properties.

We begin by describing a special function (path) with domain $[0, 1]$ and range the whole circle. Let the circle with radius r be given and on it a fixed point P. Consider two perpendicular diameters, one of which has P as one of its end points. Denote one of the end points of

Figure I.

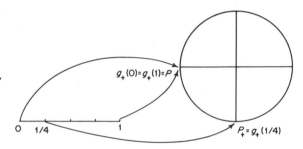

the other diameter by P_+. (See figure 1.) We describe a function g_+ by requiring it to have the following properties:

1. $g_+(0) = g_+(1) = P$

2. $g_+(\tfrac{1}{4}) = P_+$

3. If $t_1 \ne t_2$ and t_1 and t_2 are both between 0 and 1, then $g_+(t_1) \ne g_+(t_2)$ (i.e., the restriction of g_+ to $\{t \mid 0 < t < 1\}$ is one-to-one).

4. For any x such that $0 < x \le 1$, the set $\{g_+(t) \mid 0 \le t \le x\}$ is an arc which we denote by A_x.

5. If $0 < x < y \le 1$ and A_x, A_y denote two arcs as described in property 4, and if the lengths of these arcs are s_x and s_y respectively, then it is true that $s_y/s_x = y/x$.

The difficulty in this more formal approach is in proving the existence of such a function g_+. A proof would take us too far afield.

Intuitively, the reader may well think of the function g_+ as describing the motion of a point moving at constant speed once around the circle in a unit of time. Think of $g_+(t)$ as giving the position of the point at instant t.

Condition 1 states that the point starts and ends at P, since it is at P at instants $t = 0$ and $t = 1$.

Condition 2 specifies the positive direction since, when $t = \tfrac{1}{4}$, the point (by condition 5) has covered a distance which is equal to one-fourth of the circumference. Hence, the direction in which it must have traveled in order to be at P_+ when $t = \frac{1}{4}$ is unique.

Condition 3 states that the point does not reverse its direction, since, at different instants, it is at different locations.

Condition 4 states that the moving point travels "continuously" through every point of the circle.

Condition 5 indicates that the point is moving at a constant speed. A pictorial representation of the function g_+ is given in figure 1.

The motion of a point in the negative direction can be best described by defining g_- with domain $[0, 1]$ and range the circle such that

$$g_-(t) = g_+(1 - t) \quad \text{for every } t \in [0, 1]$$

Now suppose that we want to describe the motion of a point traveling only a distance α on the circle ($0 \le \alpha \le 2\pi r$). If this point is to travel the distance α in a unit of time, we need what we might call a *slowing down* function so that in a unit of time the point will travel only a distance α.

Let this slowing down function be defined by

$$S(t) = \frac{\alpha}{2\pi r} \cdot t \quad (0 \le t \le 1)$$

Then we define the path $p_{(P,\alpha)}$ to be the composite function $g_+ \circ S$.

The reader may verify that the range of the function $g_+ \circ S$ is an arc of length α. (See figure 2.)

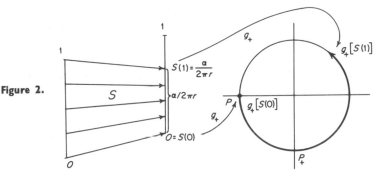

Figure 2.

In the case $\alpha < 0$ and $0 < -\alpha \le 2\pi r$, define S by

$$S(t) = -\frac{\alpha}{2\pi r} \cdot t$$

and the path $p_{(P,\alpha)}$ is defined to be the function $g_- \circ S$.

Suppose now that $2\pi r < \alpha$. Hence, we must describe the motion of a point which travels completely around the circle once or more times. We therefore need what we might call a *speeding up* function. Suppose that the motion which we try to describe is that of a point which has traveled a distance $\alpha = n \cdot 2\pi r + \beta$, where n is a positive integer and $0 \leq \beta < 2\pi r$. First, we note that if the point moved at a constant speed, then it must have passed over the same point at regular intervals (each interval of time being the time needed for one complete revolution). The idea is indicated pictorially in figure 3 for $n = 3$.

Figure 3.

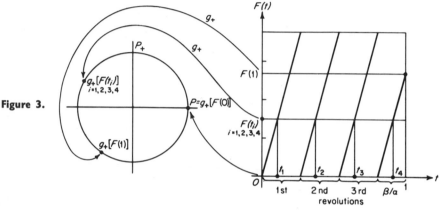

We now proceed to define the function F in the following way: Suppose $2\pi r < \alpha$. Let $u = (2\pi r / \alpha)$. Then $u < 1$, and for each t $(0 \leq t \leq 1)$, there exists a unique non-negative integer k such that $ku \leq t < (k + 1)u$. We now define the function F as follows. For each t, $0 \leq t \leq 1$, consider the unique k such that $ku \leq t < (k + 1)u$. Then let $F(t) = (t/u) - k$. Now the path $p_{(P,\alpha)}$ is defined to be the composite function $g_+ \circ F$.

The reader may verify that $g_+ \circ F(0)$ is the point P and that the point $g_+ \circ F(1)$ is the same point as the terminal point of the path (P, α) as described in section 2.3.

If $2\pi R < -\alpha$, then we can define the path $p_{(P,\alpha)}$ as the composite function $g_- \circ F$ where F is defined in a similar way.

We conclude this section with a remark. The most important thing to notice about the approach we outlined in this section is that a *path is a function* with domain [0, 1] and range an arc of a circle. In more advanced texts, in which more of the theory of functions is presented, this approach is by far the most appropriate. The knowledge which one has about functions can then be used to advantage in proving certain theorems in which paths are involved.

Exercises 1. If $0 \leq \alpha \leq 2\pi R$ and P is a point of a circle of radius R, show that the range of the path (function) $p_{(P,\alpha)} = g_+ \circ S$ is an arc of length α.

2. (a) Consider a circle of radius 4. Pick a point P on the circle and let $\alpha = 25\pi/2$. Draw a diagram to illustrate the path $(P, 25\pi/2)$ as described in section 2.3.

   (b) Pick the point P_+ on the circle so that the positive direction is counterclockwise. Show that $g_+ \circ F(0) = P$ and $g_+ \circ F(1)$ is the terminal point of the path described in part (a). (F is a function defined as described in section 2.4.)

3. Show that for the function $g_+ \circ F$ described in section 2.4,

$$g_+ \circ F\left(\frac{u}{4}\right) = g_+ \circ F\left(\frac{5u}{4}\right) = \ldots = g_+ \circ F\left(\frac{u}{4} + nu\right) = P_+$$

where n is an integer such that $nu \le 1 < (n+1)u$.

4. Consider a coordinate plane and a circle C in that plane with radius R and with center at the origin. Denote the points $(R, 0)$ and $(0, R)$ by P and P_+ respectively. Define a function h with domain $[0, 1]$ and with range C as follows:

$$h : t \to (x, y)$$

where for each t,

$$0 \le t \le \tfrac{1}{2}; \quad x = R - 4Rt; \quad \text{and } y = \sqrt{R^2 - x^2}$$

and for each t,

$$\tfrac{1}{2} < t \le 1; \quad x = 4Rt - 3R; \quad \text{and } y = -\sqrt{R^2 - x^2}$$

Show that the function h has the same properties as the function g_+ defined in section 2.4 except property 5.

2.5. The trigonometric functions

In this section, we introduce the six trigonometric functions. Since the circle plays such an important role in the definitions, these functions are often called the *circular functions*.

In order to simplify the statements of future definitions and theorems, we agree to the following convention. Henceforth, unless otherwise specified, C_0 will denote a circle of radius 1 with center at the origin of a cartesian coordinate system. P_0 will denote the point $(1, 0)$, and a path (P_0, α) on C_0 will be called a *standard path*. (See figure 1.)

Figure 1.

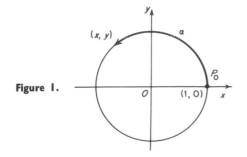

We now define the sine, cosine, tangent, cotangent, secant, and cosecant functions.

Definitions 2.5.1. The six *trigonometric (circular) functions* are defined by the following equations

$$\sin(\alpha) = y$$

$$\cos(\alpha) = x$$

$$\tan(\alpha) = \frac{y}{x} \quad (x \neq 0)$$

$$\cot(\alpha) = \frac{x}{y} \quad (y \neq 0)$$

$$\sec(\alpha) = \frac{1}{x} \quad (x \neq 0)$$

$$\csc(\alpha) = \frac{1}{y} \quad (y \neq 0)$$

where (x, y) are the coordinates of the terminal point of the standard path (P_0, α).

We can immediately make the following remarks: The sine and cosine functions are defined for any value of α. Hence, the domain of these functions is the set of all real numbers. The tangent and secant functions are not defined, however, if $x = 0$. That is, they are not defined if (P, α) has terminal point on the y axis. It is clear that this will be the case if $\alpha = \pm\pi/2, \pm 3\pi/2, \pm 5\pi/2, \pm 7\pi/2, \ldots$, i.e., if α is an odd multiple of $\pi/2$, Hence, the domain of the tangent and secant function is the set of all real numbers with the exception of the odd multiples of $\pi/2$. A similar argument shows that the domain of the cotangent and cosecant functions is the set of all real numbers with the exception of the numbers of the form $n\pi$, for $n = 0, \pm 1, \pm 2, \pm 3$, etc.

Notation: We shall not always follow the convention of using parentheses in denoting the functional values; i.e., we shall write $\sin \alpha$ for $\sin(\alpha)$, $\cos \alpha$ for $\cos(\alpha)$, etc.

Example 1. Find the values of those trigonometric functions which are defined at $\pi/2$.

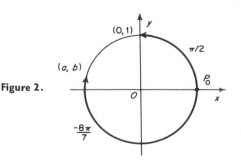

Figure 2.

Solution: Consider the standard path $(P_0, \pi/2)$. (See figure 2.) Its terminal point is the point $(0, 1)$. Hence,

$$\sin \frac{\pi}{2} = 1$$

$$\cos \frac{\pi}{2} = 0$$

$$\tan \frac{\pi}{2} = \tfrac{1}{0} \quad \text{not defined}$$

$$\cot \frac{\pi}{2} = \tfrac{0}{1} = 0$$

$$\sec \frac{\pi}{2} = \tfrac{1}{0} \text{ is not defined and } \csc \frac{\pi}{2} = \tfrac{1}{1} = 1 \quad \blacksquare$$

Example 2. Determine which of the six trigonometric functional values at $-8\pi/7$ are positive and which are negative.

Solution: Consider the standard path $(P_0, -8\pi/7)$. (See figure 2.) Since $-3\pi/2 < -8\pi/7 < -\pi$, its terminal point (a, b) is in the second quadrant. Hence, $a < 0$ and $b > 0$. It follows that $\sin(-8\pi/7) > 0$ (since $\sin(-8\pi/7) = b$); $\cos(-8\pi/7) < 0$ (since $\cos(-8\pi/7) = a$); $\tan(-8\pi/7) < 0$ (since $\tan(-8\pi/7) = b/a$, and $b/a < 0$).

Further,

$$\cot\left(-\frac{8\pi}{7}\right) < 0; \qquad \sec\left(-\frac{8\pi}{7}\right) < 0; \qquad \text{and} \qquad \csc\left(-\frac{8\pi}{7}\right) > 0$$

Since

$$\cot\left(-\frac{8\pi}{7}\right) = \frac{a}{b}; \qquad \sec\left(-\frac{8\pi}{7}\right) = \frac{1}{a}; \qquad \text{and} \qquad \csc\left(-\frac{8\pi}{7}\right) = \frac{1}{b}$$

$$\text{and } \frac{a}{b} < 0; \qquad \frac{1}{a} < 0; \qquad \text{and} \qquad \frac{1}{b} > 0 \quad \blacksquare$$

Example 3. Write the six trigonometric functional values at $22\pi/3$ as functional values at a number α such that $0 < \alpha < \pi/2$.

Solution: Consider the standard path $(P_0, 22\pi/3)$. (See figure 3.) Since $22\pi/3 = 7\pi + \pi/3$ and since half of the circumference has length π, the paths $(P_0, 22\pi/3)$ and $(P_1, \pi/3)$ have the same terminal point T with coordinates (a, b). Draw a straight line through T and the origin. This straight line intersects the circle C_0 at a point T'. By symmetry, we see that T' is the terminal point of the standard path $(P_0, \pi/3)$. Also by symmetry we see that if (c, d) are the coordinates of T', then we must have $|a| = |c|$ and $|b| = |d|$. But the point T is in the third quadrant; hence, both a and b are negative. T' is in the first quadrant;

Figure 3.

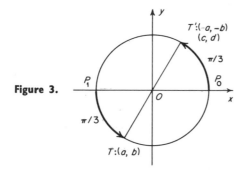

therefore, both c and d are positive. It follows that we must have $c = -a$ and $d = -b$. Hence, the coordinates of T' are $(-a, -b)$. We now get directly from the definitions

$$\sin \frac{22\pi}{3} = b \quad \text{and} \quad \sin \frac{\pi}{3} = -b$$

Therefore, $$\sin \frac{22\pi}{3} = -\sin \frac{\pi}{3}$$

$$\cos \frac{22\pi}{3} = a \quad \text{and} \quad \cos \frac{\pi}{3} = -a$$

Hence, $$\cos \frac{22\pi}{3} = -\cos \frac{\pi}{3}$$

$$\tan \frac{22\pi}{3} = \frac{b}{a} \quad \text{and} \quad \tan \frac{\pi}{3} = \frac{-b}{-a} = \frac{b}{a}$$

It follows that $\tan \dfrac{22\pi}{3} = \tan \dfrac{\pi}{3}$

Similarly, we show that

$$\cot \frac{22\pi}{3} = \cot \frac{\pi}{3}; \quad \sec \frac{22\pi}{3} = -\sec \frac{\pi}{3}; \quad \csc \frac{22\pi}{3} = -\csc \frac{\pi}{3}. \ \blacksquare$$

Example 4. Which of the trigonometric functions have the property $f(\pi - \alpha) = f(\alpha)$ for all α in the domain of the function?

Solution: Let α be an arbitrary real number and consider the standard paths (P_0, α) and $(P_0, \pi - \alpha)$. (See figure 4.) It is clear that

$$(P_0, \pi - \alpha) = (P_0, \pi) + (P_1, -\alpha)$$

Hence, by symmetry, if the coordinates of the terminal point of the path (P_0, α) are (a, b) the coordinates of the terminal point of the path $(P_0, \pi - \alpha)$ will be $(-a, b)$. Hence, the abscissas of the two terminal points differ, but the ordinates are equal.

Figure 4.

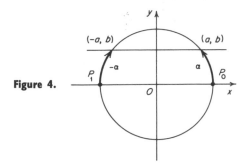

Hence, the trigonometric functions which have the property $f(\pi - \alpha) = f(\alpha)$ are those functions defined only in terms of the ordinate of the terminal point, namely the sine and cosecant functions. We have

$$\sin (\pi - \alpha) = \sin \alpha \quad \text{for all } \alpha$$

and $\csc (\pi - \alpha) = \csc \alpha \quad \text{for all } \alpha \in D_{\text{csc}}$. ∎

Exercises 1. Find the values of those trigonometric functions which are defined at

(a) $-\dfrac{3\pi}{2}$ (b) $\dfrac{5\pi}{2}$ (c) $-2,251\pi$

2. Determine which of the six trigonometric functional values are positive and which are negative at

(a) $\dfrac{6\pi}{5}$ (b) $\dfrac{15\pi}{7}$ (c) $-\dfrac{5\pi}{7}$

3. Write the six trigonometric functional values at $29\pi/4$ as trigonometric functional values at a number α such that $0 < \alpha < \pi/2$.

4. Which of the trigonometric functions have the property
   (a) $f(\alpha + \pi) = f(\alpha)$ for all $\alpha \in D_f$
   (b) $f(\alpha + 2\pi) = f(\alpha)$ for all $\alpha \in D_f$
   (c) $f(\alpha) = f(-\alpha)$ for all $\alpha \in D_f$
   (d) $f(-\alpha) = -f(\alpha)$ for all $\alpha \in D_f$

2.6. Functional values for special numbers Certain trigonometric functional values can be determined using only the definitions and basic plane geometry. We shall discuss briefly the techniques used in finding such functional values. First, we consider the following two right triangles ACB and $A'B'C'$. (See figure 1.)

Figure I.

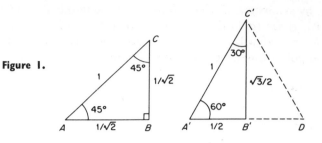

In both cases, the hypotenuse is 1. We note that triangle ABC is isosceles; hence, $|AB| = |BC|$. Using this fact and the theorem of Pythagoras, we have

$$|AB|^2 + |BC|^2 = 1^2$$

$$2|AB|^2 = 1$$

$$|AB|^2 = \tfrac{1}{2}$$

$$|AB| = \frac{1}{\sqrt{2}}$$

We also note that triangle $A'B'C'$ is half of an equilateral triangle. Hence, by symmetry, we get

$$|A'B'| = \tfrac{1}{2}|A'D|$$

$$|A'B'| = \tfrac{1}{2}$$

Using the fact that $|A'B'|^2 + |B'C'|^2 = |A'C'|^2$, we obtain

$$\left(\frac{1}{2}\right)^2 + |B'C'|^2 = 1$$

$$|B'C'|^2 = 1 - \frac{1}{4}$$

$$|B'C'|^2 = \frac{3}{4}$$

$$|B'C'| = \frac{\sqrt{3}}{2}$$

Consider the points, $P_0, P_1, P_2, \ldots, P_{15}$ on the circle C_0 which have the following property: Either P_i is on one of the axes (as P_0, P_4, P_8, and P_{12}), or by drawing the perpendicular P_iH_i to the x axis, we obtain a right triangle OH_iP_i congruent to one of the triangles of figure 1. (See figure 2.)

It is easy to obtain the coordinates of each one of the points $P_0, P_1, \ldots, P_{15}$. We give one example and leave the determination of the other coordinates to the reader.

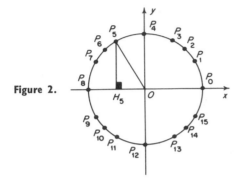

Figure 2.

Example 1. Find the coordinates of the point P_5 given that the triangle OH_5P_5 is congruent to triangle $A'B'C'$ of figure 1. (See figure 2.)

Solution: Clearly, $|OH_5| = 1/2$ and $|H_5P_5| = \sqrt{3}/2$. Since the point P_5 is in the second quadrant, its abscissa must be negative and its ordinate positive. Hence, the coordinates of P_5 are $(-1/2, \sqrt{3}/2)$. ∎

Definition 2.6.1. A real number α is called a *special number* if the standard path (P_0, α) has for its terminal point one of the points $P_0, P_1, \ldots, P_{15}$ described above.

Example 2. Find the six trigonometric functional values at $-\pi/6$.

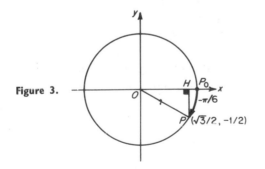

Figure 3.

Solution: We must consider the standard path $(P_0, -\pi/6)$. (See figure 3.) First note $\pi/6 = 2\pi \cdot 1/12$. From basic geometry, we know that a complete revolution is $360°$; therefore, $\frac{1}{12}$th of a complete revolution is $30°$. Hence, the angle P_0OP is a $30°$ angle and the right triangle PHO is congruent to triangle $A'B'C'$ of figure 1. Hence, the co-ordinates of the point P are $(\sqrt{3}/2, -1/2)$ where we take the abscissa positive and ordinate negative since the point P is in the fourth quadrant. It follows that

$$\sin\left(-\frac{\pi}{6}\right) = -\frac{1}{2}$$

$$\cos\left(-\frac{\pi}{6}\right) = \frac{\sqrt{3}}{2}$$

$$\tan\left(-\frac{\pi}{6}\right) = -\frac{1/2}{\sqrt{3}/2} = -\frac{1}{\sqrt{3}}$$

$$\cot\left(-\frac{\pi}{6}\right) = \frac{\sqrt{3}/2}{-1/2} = -\sqrt{3}$$

$$\sec\left(-\frac{\pi}{6}\right) = \frac{1}{\sqrt{3}/2} = \frac{2}{\sqrt{3}}$$

$$\csc\left(-\frac{\pi}{6}\right) = \frac{1}{-1/2} = -2 \ \blacksquare$$

Exercises 1. Find the coordinates of the terminal points of the following standard paths:

(a) $(P_0, 0)$ (b) $(P_0, \pi/6)$
(c) $(P_0, \pi/4)$ (d) $(P_0, \pi/3)$
(e) $(P_0, \pi/2)$ (f) $(P_0, 2\pi/3)$
(g) $(P_0, 3\pi/4)$ (h) $(P_0, 5\pi/6)$
(i) (P_0, π) (j) $(P_0, 7\pi/6)$
(k) $(P_0, 5\pi/4)$ (l) $(P_0, 4\pi/3)$
(m) $(P_0, 3\pi/2)$ (n) $(P_0, 5\pi/3)$
(o) $(P_0, 7\pi/4)$ (p) $(P_0, 11\pi/6)$

2. Fill in the blank spaces in the following table. (The given values are taken from example 1.) Use the results of exercise 1.

	sin	cos	tan	cot	sec	csc
0						
$\dfrac{\pi}{6}$						
$\dfrac{\pi}{4}$						

	sin	cos	tan	cot	sec	csc
$\dfrac{\pi}{3}$						
$\dfrac{\pi}{2}$						
$\dfrac{2\pi}{3}$	$\dfrac{\sqrt{3}}{2}$	$-\dfrac{1}{2}$	$-\sqrt{3}$	$-\dfrac{1}{\sqrt{3}}$	-2	$\dfrac{2}{\sqrt{3}}$
$\dfrac{3\pi}{4}$						
$\dfrac{5\pi}{6}$						
π						
$\dfrac{7\pi}{6}$						
$\dfrac{5\pi}{4}$						
$\dfrac{4\pi}{3}$						
$\dfrac{3\pi}{2}$						
$\dfrac{5\pi}{3}$						
$\dfrac{7\pi}{4}$						
$\dfrac{11\pi}{6}$						

3. Find the following numbers:

(a) $\sin\left(\dfrac{14\pi}{3}\right)$

(b) $\cos\left(-\dfrac{29\pi}{4}\right)$

(c) $\tan\left(\dfrac{11\pi}{6}\right)$

(d) $\cot\left(-\dfrac{5\pi}{2}\right)$

(e) $\sec\left(\dfrac{13\pi}{2}\right)$

(f) $\csc\left(-\dfrac{23\pi}{4}\right)$

2.7. Properties of trigonometric functions We shall show in this section that the trigonometric functions possess some of the properties discussed in Chapter 1.

Recalling that D_f denotes the domain of a function f and R_f denotes its range, we note that

$$D_{\cos} = D_{\sin} = R \quad \text{(the set of all real numbers)}$$

$$D_{\tan} = D_{\sec} = R \backslash \left\{ (2n+1)\frac{\pi}{2} \mid n \text{ is an integer} \right\}$$

and $\qquad D_{\cot} = D_{\csc} = R \backslash \{ n\pi \mid n \text{ is an integer} \}$

These observations were made and justified immediately following the definitions of the trigonometric functions in section 2.5. The reader should return to that section and review it.

By definition, $\sin \alpha = y$ where y is the ordinate of the terminal point of the standard path (P_0, α). It is clear that $-1 \leq y \leq 1$, and for each y, such that $-1 \leq y \leq 1$, there is at least one α such that $\sin \alpha = y$. Therefore, the range of the sine function is the set $\{ y \mid -1 \leq y \leq 1 \}$. Similarly,

$$R_{\overline{\cos}} = \{ y \mid -1 \leq y \leq 1 \}$$

because $\cos \alpha = x$ is the abscissa of the terminal point of the path (P_0, α).

In order to discuss the range of the tangent function, we first note that by the similarity of the right triangles in figure 1, we have

$$\tan \alpha = \frac{y}{x} = \frac{\overline{P_0 Q}}{\overline{O P_0}}$$

But $\overline{OP_0} = 1$. Therefore,

$$\tan \alpha = \overline{P_0 Q}$$

Hence, from figure 1, we conclude that as α ranges from 0 to $\pi/2$, $\overline{P_0 Q}$ assumes every non-negative real number and as α ranges from 0 to $-\pi/2$, $\overline{P_0 Q}$ assumes every non-positive real number; hence, the

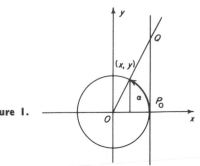

Figure 1.

range of the tangent function is the set of all real numbers. Similarly, we can see that the range of the cotangent function is the set of all real numbers.

We note that $\sec \alpha = 1/x$ and $\csc \alpha = 1/y$ where (x, y) are co-ordinates of the terminal point of the standard path (P_0, α). Further, $|x| \leq 1$ and $|y| \leq 1$. It follows that $1/|x| \geq 1$ and $1/|y| \geq 1$. Therefore, $|\sec \alpha| \geq 1$ and $|\csc \alpha| \geq 1$. We can conclude that

$$R_{\sec} = R_{\csc} = \{z \mid |z| \geq 1\}.$$

One of the most important properties of the trigonometric functions is the content of the next theorem.

Theorem 2.7.1. All six trigonometric functions are periodic. The fundamental period of the tangent and cotangent functions is π, that of the other four functions is 2π.

Proof: (a) We want to show that for any α

$$\sin (\alpha + 2\pi) = \sin \alpha$$

and that of all numbers $|p|$ which have the property $p \neq 0$ and

$$\sin (\alpha + p) = \sin \alpha \quad \text{for all } \alpha \in D_{\sin}, \, 2\pi \text{ is the smallest.}$$

We note that, given α, the standard paths (P_0, α) and $(P_0, \alpha + 2\pi)$ have the same terminal point, say (x, y).

Then $$\sin \alpha = y$$

$$\sin (\alpha + 2\pi) = y$$

Therefore, $\sin (\alpha + 2\pi) = \sin \alpha$

Now let p be a number which has the property $\sin (\alpha + p) = \sin \alpha$ for all $\alpha \in D_{\sin}$. Then the statement

$$\sin (0 + p) = \sin 0$$

must be true.

But $\sin 0 = 0$

Hence, we must have

$$\sin p = 0$$

But by definition of the sine function, $\sin p = 0$ if and only if $p = 0, \pm\pi, \pm 2\pi, \pm 3\pi$, etc. Of all these numbers, the non-zero ones with smallest absolute value are $\pm\pi$. But π cannot be the fundamental period since π and $-\pi$ are not periods of the sine function. This fact is easily verified if we note that

$$\sin \frac{\pi}{2} = 1; \qquad \sin \left(\frac{\pi}{2} + \pi\right) = \sin \frac{3\pi}{2} = -1$$

and $$\sin \left(\frac{\pi}{2} + (-\pi)\right) = \sin \left(-\frac{\pi}{2}\right) = -1$$

Hence, $$\sin \left(\frac{\pi}{2}\right) \neq \sin \left(\frac{\pi}{2} + \pi\right)$$

and $$\sin \left(\frac{\pi}{2}\right) \neq \sin \left(\frac{\pi}{2} + (-\pi)\right)$$

It follows that 2π is the fundamental period of the sine function.

(b) We shall show that

$$\tan (\alpha + \pi) = \tan \alpha \quad \text{for all } \alpha \in D_{\tan}$$

Let $\alpha \in D_{\tan}$, but otherwise arbitrary. Consider the standard paths (P_0, α) and $(P_0, \alpha + \pi)$. It is clear, since π is half of the circumference, that the terminal points of the two given paths are symmetric

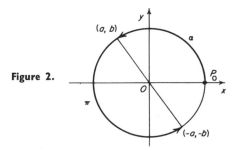

Figure 2.

with respect to the origin. Hence, if the terminal point of (P_0, α) is (a, b) the terminal point of $(P_0, \alpha + \pi)$ must be $(-a, -b)$. (See figure 2.) By definition,

$$\tan \alpha = \frac{b}{a} \quad \text{and} \quad \tan (\alpha + \pi) = \frac{-b}{-a} = \frac{b}{a}$$

Therefore, $\tan \alpha = \tan (\alpha + \pi)$ for any $\alpha \in D_{\tan}$.

The proof that π is the fundamental period of the tangent function is similar to the proof that 2π is the fundamental period of the sine function and will not be given. ∎

The proof that the cosine, secant, cosecant, and cotangent functions are periodic is left as an exercise.

Theorem 2.7.2. The cosine and secant functions are even; the other four trigonometric functions are odd.

Proof: Let α be any number. (It is understood that α is restricted to the domain of whatever function is discussed in the proof, but otherwise arbitrary.) Consider the standard paths (P_0, α) and $(P_0, -\alpha)$. The

Figure 3.

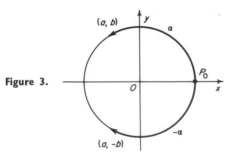

terminal points of these paths are symmetric with respect to the x axis. Hence, if the coordinates of the terminal point of (P_0, α) are (a, b), the coordinates of the terminal point of $(P_0, -\alpha)$ will be $(a, -b)$. (See figure 3.) By definition, we have

$$\sin (-\alpha) = -b \quad \text{and} \quad \sin (\alpha) = b$$

Therefore, $-\sin (\alpha) = -b$

from which it follows that

$$\sin (-\alpha) = -\sin \alpha$$

Since α was arbitrary, we conclude that the sine function is an odd function.

From the definitions, we also get

$$\cos(-\alpha) = a = \cos\alpha$$

$$\tan(-\alpha) = \frac{-b}{a} = -\left(\frac{b}{a}\right) = -\tan\alpha$$

$$\cot(-\alpha) = \frac{a}{-b} = -\left(\frac{a}{b}\right) = -\cot\alpha$$

$$\sec(-\alpha) = \frac{1}{a} = \sec\alpha$$

$$\csc(-\alpha) = \frac{1}{-b} = -\left(\frac{1}{b}\right) = -\csc\alpha$$

We can therefore conclude that, in addition to the sine function, the tangent, cotangent, and cosecant functions are odd, but the cosine and secant functions are even. ∎

The reader may have already noticed a peculiarity about the names of the circular functions. They are the sine and *co*sine, the tangent and *co*tangent, the secant and *co*secant. We have therefore grouped the six functions into three groups of two functions: {sin, cos}, {tan, cot}, {sec, csc}, and we now agree that each function is the *cofunction* of that function which is in the same group. We remark that not only is cosine the cofunction of sine, but the sine is the cofunction of cosine.

We now state another property of the circular functions.

Theorem 2.7.3. The value of any circular function at α is equal to the value of its cofunction at $\pi/2 - \alpha$.

Proof: Let α be any number. (Again it is understood that α is restricted to the domain of whatever function is discussed in the proof.) Consider the standard paths (P_0, α) and $(P_0, (\pi/2) - \alpha)$. It is clear that

$$\left(P_0, \frac{\pi}{2} - \alpha\right) = \left(P_0, \frac{\pi}{2}\right) + (P_1, -\alpha)$$

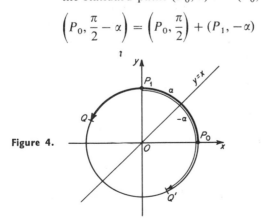

Figure 4.

(See figure 4.) Let Q and Q' be the terminal points of the paths (P_0, α) and $(P_0, (\pi/2) - \alpha)$ respectively. Then the lengths of the arcs $\overset{\frown}{P_0 Q}$ and $\overset{\frown}{P_1 Q'}$ are equal. A simple geometric argument, using theorem 2.3.3, suffices to show that the points Q and Q' are symmetric with respect to the graph of the equation $y = x$. Hence, if the coordinates of Q are (a, b), those of Q' will be (b, a).

Using the definitions of the circular functions, we obtain

$$\sin \alpha = b \qquad \sin \left(\frac{\pi}{2} - \alpha \right) = a$$

$$\cos \alpha = a \qquad \cos \left(\frac{\pi}{2} - \alpha \right) = b$$

$$\tan \alpha = \frac{b}{a} \qquad \tan \left(\frac{\pi}{2} - \alpha \right) = \frac{a}{b}$$

$$\cot \alpha = \frac{a}{b} \qquad \cot \left(\frac{\pi}{2} - \alpha \right) = \frac{b}{a}$$

$$\sec \alpha = \frac{1}{a} \qquad \sec \left(\frac{\pi}{2} - \alpha \right) = \frac{1}{b}$$

$$\csc \alpha = \frac{1}{b} \qquad \csc \left(\frac{\pi}{2} - \alpha \right) = \frac{1}{a}$$

It follows that

$$\sin \alpha = \cos \left(\frac{\pi}{2} - \alpha \right) \qquad \cot \alpha = \tan \left(\frac{\pi}{2} - \alpha \right)$$

$$\cos \alpha = \sin \left(\frac{\pi}{2} - \alpha \right) \qquad \sec \alpha = \csc \left(\frac{\pi}{2} - \alpha \right)$$

$$\tan \alpha = \cot \left(\frac{\pi}{2} - \alpha \right) \qquad \csc \alpha = \sec \left(\frac{\pi}{2} - \alpha \right) \quad ∎$$

Remark: Two numbers whose sum is $\pi/2$ are said to be *complements* of each other.

We note that $(\pi/2) - \alpha$ is the complement of α, since

$$(\pi/2) - \alpha + \alpha = \pi/2$$

Hence, theorem 2.7.3 can be restated in the following way:
"The value of any function at any number is equal to the value of its cofunction at the complement of that number."

Example 1. Find a value of α for which

$$\tan \left(\frac{\pi}{6} + \alpha \right) = \cot \left(2\alpha - \frac{\pi}{4} \right)$$

Solution: The equation will certainly be satisfied if $(\pi/6) + \alpha$ and $2\alpha - (\pi/4)$ are complements of each other.

Hence, it suffices to have

$$\left(\frac{\pi}{6} + \alpha\right) + \left(2\alpha - \frac{\pi}{4}\right) = \frac{\pi}{2}$$

$$3\alpha = \frac{\pi}{2} - \frac{\pi}{6} + \frac{\pi}{4}$$

$$3\alpha = \frac{7\pi}{12}$$

$$\alpha = \frac{7\pi}{36}$$

Example 2. Tell in each case whether the function f defined by the given equation is odd or even. Justify your answer in each case.

(a) $f(x) = x^2 + 5\cos x$

(b) $f(x) = (x^2 + 1)\csc x$

(c) $f(x) = \dfrac{\cos x + \sec x}{\tan x + \cot x}$

Solution: (a) Clearly, if we define functions g and h by $g(x) = x^2$ and $h(x) = 5\cos x$, both functions g and h are even. Further, the function f is the sum of two even functions; hence, by theorem 1.14.5, f must be even.

(b) If we define the function g by $g(x) = x^2 + 1$, we note that g is an even function. Since csc is odd, we conclude that f is the product of an even function by an odd function; hence, it is odd.

(c) In this case, it is easy to see that f is the quotient of an even function by an odd function; hence, it is odd. ∎

Exercises 1. Show that the cosine function is periodic, with fundamental period 2π.

2. Show that the cotangent function is periodic, with fundamental period π.

3. Show that the secant and cosecant functions are periodic, with fundamental period 2π.

4. Show that the function f defined by $f(x) = \sin 3x$ is odd.

5. Tell in each case whether the function f defined by the given equation is odd or even. Justify your answer in each case.

(a) $f(x) = x + \sin x$ (b) $f(x) = x \cdot \tan x$

(c) $f(x) = x^2 \cdot \csc x$ (d) $f(x) = \dfrac{\sin x + \tan x}{2x^3 + 5x}$

6. Find a value of α which satisfies the given equation

(a) $\sin\left(\dfrac{\pi}{6} - \alpha\right) = \cos\left(3\alpha - \dfrac{\pi}{5}\right)$

(b) $\sec\left(\dfrac{\pi}{3} + 2\alpha\right) = \csc\left(-\alpha - \dfrac{\pi}{3}\right)$

(c) $\tan(\alpha - 22\pi) = \cot\left(\dfrac{3\pi}{4} - 4\alpha\right)$

2.8. Basic identities An *identity* is a statement of equality, usually denoted by $\equiv$ which is true for all permissible values of the variables. In this text, by a *permissible value*, we mean a real value of the variable for which the statement has meaning.

For example,

$$(x + y)^2 \equiv x^2 + 2xy + y^2$$

and $\dfrac{1}{(x - 1)(x + 1)} \equiv \dfrac{1}{2(x - 1)} - \dfrac{1}{2(x + 1)}$

are identities.

Note that, in the second identity, 1 and -1 are not permissible values of the variable, since, if we replace x by either 1 or -1, the statement is meaningless because it involves division by zero.

We have already stated and proved some trigonometric identities; i.e.,

$$\tan \alpha \equiv \cot\left(\dfrac{\pi}{2} - \alpha\right), \qquad \sin(\alpha + 2\pi) \equiv \sin \alpha, \text{ etc.}$$

We shall derive a few identities in this section. We shall call them *basic identities* because they follow almost immediately from the definitions of the trigonometric functions.

Perhaps the most basic of all trigonometric identities is the following:

$$\cos^2 \alpha + \sin^2 \alpha \equiv 1 \tag{1}$$

To prove this, let α be any real number. Consider the standard path (P_0, α) with terminal point (a, b). Then $\cos \alpha = a$ and $\sin \alpha = b$. Since the point (a, b) is on the circle C_0 whose equation is $x^2 + y^2 = 1$, we have $a^2 + b^2 = 1$.

Hence, $\cos^2 \alpha + \sin^2 \alpha = 1$. Since α was arbitrary, identity 1 has been proved.

We shall recall that the six trigonometric functions are defined by

$$\sin \alpha = b, \quad \cos \alpha = a, \quad \tan \alpha = \frac{b}{a}$$

$$(a \neq 0), \quad \cot \alpha = \frac{a}{b} \quad (b \neq 0),$$

$$\sec \alpha = \frac{1}{a} \quad (a \neq 0); \quad \text{and} \quad \csc \alpha = \frac{1}{b} \quad (b \neq 0)$$

where (a, b) are coordinates of the terminal point of the path (P_0, α). We note the following

$$\sin \alpha \cdot \csc \alpha = b \cdot \frac{1}{b} = 1$$

$$\cos \alpha \cdot \sec \alpha = a \cdot \frac{1}{a} = 1$$

$$\tan \alpha \cdot \cot \alpha = \frac{b}{a} \cdot \frac{a}{b} = 1$$

Since α was arbitrary, we have obtained the following identities:

$$\sin \alpha \cdot \csc \alpha \equiv 1 \tag{2}$$

$$\cos \alpha \cdot \sec \alpha \equiv 1 \tag{3}$$

$$\tan \alpha \cdot \cot \alpha \equiv 1 \tag{4}$$

Identities 2, 3, and 4 are often called the *reciprocal relations* since they indicate that certain functions are reciprocal of other functions. We also get, directly from the definitions, that

$$\tan \alpha \equiv \frac{\sin \alpha}{\cos \alpha} \tag{5}$$

$$\text{and } \cot \alpha \equiv \frac{\cos \alpha}{\sin \alpha} \tag{6}$$

Further, dividing both sides of identity 1 by $\cos^2 \alpha$, we obtain

$$1 + \frac{\sin^2 \alpha}{\cos^2 \alpha} \equiv \frac{1}{\cos^2 \alpha}$$

$$\text{or } 1 + \left(\frac{\sin \alpha}{\cos \alpha}\right)^2 \equiv \left(\frac{1}{\cos \alpha}\right)^2$$

$$1 + \tan^2 \alpha \equiv \sec^2 \alpha \tag{7}$$

Similarly, dividing both sides of identity 1 by $\sin^2 \alpha$, we get

$$\cot^2 \alpha + 1 \equiv \csc^2 \alpha \tag{8}$$

Example 1. Use the basic identities to derive the trigonometric functional values at $\pi/4$.

Solution: We first note that $\pi/4 = (\pi/2) - (\pi/4)$. Hence $\pi/4$ is its own complement and we can write

$$\sin \frac{\pi}{4} = \cos \frac{\pi}{4}$$

Hence, using identity 1, we get

$$\sin^2 \frac{\pi}{4} + \sin^2 \frac{\pi}{4} \equiv 1$$

$$2 \sin^2 \frac{\pi}{4} \equiv 1$$

$$\sin^2 \frac{\pi}{4} = \frac{1}{2}$$

$$\sin \frac{\pi}{4} = \frac{1}{\sqrt{2}}$$

where we choose the positive square root for $\frac{1}{2}$ since $0 < \pi/4 < \pi/2$ and therefore the terminal point of the standard path $(P_0, \pi/4)$ is in the first quadrant.

We also have

$$\cos \frac{\pi}{4} = \frac{1}{\sqrt{2}}$$

Hence,

$$\tan \frac{\pi}{4} = \frac{\sin \pi/4}{\cos \pi/4} = \frac{1/\sqrt{2}}{1/\sqrt{2}} = 1$$

$$\cot \frac{\pi}{4} = \frac{1}{\tan \pi/4} = \frac{1}{1} = 1$$

$$\sec \frac{\pi}{4} = \frac{1}{\cos \pi/4} = \frac{1}{1/\sqrt{2}} = \sqrt{2}$$

$$\csc \frac{\pi}{4} = \frac{1}{\sin \pi/4} = \frac{1}{1/\sqrt{2}} = \sqrt{2} \quad \blacksquare$$

Example 2. Given that $\sin \alpha = 3/5$ and that $\pi/2 < \alpha < \pi$, find $\cos \alpha$ and $\tan \alpha$.

Solution: Since $\pi/2 < \alpha < \pi$, the terminal point of the standard path (P_0, α) is in the second quadrant. Hence, $\cos \alpha$ and $\tan \alpha$ will be negative.

Using identity 1, we get

$$\cos^2 \alpha + (\tfrac{3}{5})^2 = 1$$

$$\cos^2 \alpha = 1 - \frac{9}{25}$$

$$\cos^2 \alpha = \frac{16}{25}.$$

$$\cos \alpha = -\frac{4}{5}$$

where we took the negative square root of 16/25 because we knew that $\cos \alpha < 0$. Now we get

$$\tan \alpha = \frac{\sin \alpha}{\cos \alpha} = \frac{3/5}{-4/5} = \frac{3}{5} \cdot \frac{5}{-4} = \frac{-3}{4} \quad \blacksquare$$

Exercises 1. Given that $\sin \alpha = -5/13$ and $\pi < \alpha < 3\pi/2$, find $\cos \alpha$, $\tan \alpha$, $\cot \alpha$, $\sec \alpha$, and $\csc \alpha$.

2. Given that $\tan \alpha = 10/3$ and $-\pi < \alpha < -\pi/2$, find $\sin \alpha$, $\cos \alpha$, $\cot \alpha$, $\sec \alpha$, and $\csc \alpha$.

3. Find the six trigonometric functional values at $5\pi/6$, using the definitions of the trigonometric functions. Then check that identities 1–8 of this section are satisfied by your results.

4. Find the six trigonometric functional values at $-3\pi/4$, using the definitions of the trigonometric functions. Then check that the identities 1–8 of this section are satisfied by your results.

5. Write the expression $2 \tan \alpha + 3 \sec \alpha - 5(\cot \alpha) \cdot (\csc \alpha)$ as an equivalent expression involving only sines and cosines.

2.9. The addition formulas In section 1.7, example 12, we observed that the function g defined by $g : x \rightarrow ax$ has the property $g(x_1 + x_2) = g(x_1) + g(x_2)$. Obviously, the trigonometric functions do not have this property, as can readily be seen in the case of the sine function. Since

$$\sin\left(\frac{\pi}{2} + \frac{\pi}{2}\right) = \sin \pi = 0 \quad \text{and} \quad \sin \frac{\pi}{2} + \sin \frac{\pi}{2} = 1 + 1 = 2$$

we therefore have that

$$\sin\left(\frac{\pi}{2} + \frac{\pi}{2}\right) \neq \sin \frac{\pi}{2} + \sin \frac{\pi}{2}$$

We shall, however, be able to derive some relationships giving the trigonometric functional values at $\alpha + \beta$ in terms of trigonometric functional values at α and β. For any real numbers α and β, consider the standard paths (P_0, α), $(P_0, \alpha + \beta)$, and $(P_0, -\beta)$. Let their terminal points be T_1, T_2, and T_3 respectively. Using the definitions of the trigonometric functions, we observe that the coordinates of T_1 are $(\cos \alpha, \sin \alpha)$, those of T_2 are $(\cos (\alpha + \beta), \sin (\alpha + \beta))$, and those of T_3 are $(\cos (-\beta), (\sin (-\beta)) = (\cos \beta, -\sin \beta)$.

Figure 1.

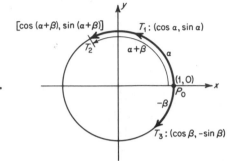

Now consider the paths $(P_0, \alpha + \beta)$ and $(T_3, \alpha + \beta)$. Clearly the terminal points of these paths are T_2 and T_1 respectively. Since these two paths are equivalent, we have (by exercise 7, section 2.3) that

$$|P_0 T_2| = |T_3 T_1|$$

By the distance formula, we have

$$|P_0 T_2| = \sqrt{[\cos (\alpha + \beta) - 1]^2 + [\sin (\alpha + \beta) - 0]^2}$$

$$|T_3 T_1| = \sqrt{[\cos \alpha - \cos \beta]^2 + [\sin \alpha - (-\sin \beta)]^2}$$

Therefore,

$$[\cos (\alpha + \beta) - 1]^2 + \sin^2 (\alpha + \beta)$$
$$= (\cos \alpha - \cos \beta)^2 + (\sin \alpha + \sin\beta)^2$$

From which it follows that

$$\cos^2 (\alpha + \beta) - 2 \cos (\alpha + \beta) + 1 + \sin^2 (\alpha + \beta)$$
$$= \cos^2 \alpha - 2 \cos \alpha \cos \beta + \cos^2 \beta + \sin^2 \alpha + 2 \sin \alpha \sin \beta + \sin^2 \beta$$

Using the facts that

$$\cos^2 (\alpha + \beta) + \sin^2 (\alpha + \beta) = 1; \qquad \cos^2 \alpha + \sin^2 \alpha = 1;$$

and $\qquad \cos^2 \beta + \sin^2 \beta = 1$

we obtain

$$2 - 2 \cos (\alpha + \beta) = 2 - 2 \cos \alpha \cos \beta + 2 \sin \alpha \sin \beta$$

and $\qquad \cos (\alpha + \beta) = \cos \alpha \cos \beta - \sin \alpha \sin \beta$

Since α and β were arbitrary real numbers, the foregoing equality is an identity and we write

$$\cos(\alpha + \beta) \equiv \cos\alpha\cos\beta - \sin\alpha\sin\beta \tag{1}$$

We can now easily obtain the other addition formulas in the following way:

$$\cos(\alpha - \beta) \equiv \cos(\alpha + (-\beta))$$

$$\equiv \cos\alpha\cos(-\beta) - \sin\alpha\sin(-\beta)$$

$$\equiv \cos\alpha\cos\beta - \sin\alpha(-\sin\beta)$$

Hence, $\cos(\alpha - \beta) \equiv \cos\alpha\cos\beta + \sin\alpha\sin\beta \tag{2}$

We recall now that the value of a trigonometric function at a number is equal to the value of the cofunction at the complement of that number. We shall use this fact to derive a formula for $\sin(\alpha + \beta)$.

$$\sin(\alpha + \beta) \equiv \cos\left(\frac{\pi}{2} - (\alpha + \beta)\right)$$

$$\equiv \cos\left(\frac{\pi}{2} - \alpha - \beta\right)$$

$$\equiv \cos\left(\left(\frac{\pi}{2} - \alpha\right) - \beta\right)$$

$$\equiv \cos\left(\frac{\pi}{2} - \alpha\right)\cdot\cos\beta + \sin\left(\frac{\pi}{2} - \alpha\right)\cdot\sin\beta \quad \text{by (2)}$$

Hence, $\sin(\alpha + \beta) \equiv \sin\alpha\cos\beta + \cos\alpha\sin\beta \tag{3}$

Now we write

$$\sin(\alpha - \beta) \equiv \sin[\alpha + (-\beta)]$$

$$\equiv \sin\alpha\cos(-\beta) + \cos\alpha\sin(-\beta)$$

$$\equiv \sin\alpha\cos\beta + (\cos\alpha)(-\sin\beta)$$

Hence,

$$\sin(\alpha - \beta) \equiv \sin\alpha\cos\beta - \cos\alpha\sin\beta \tag{4}$$

Further,

$$\tan(\alpha + \beta) \equiv \frac{\sin(\alpha + \beta)}{\cos(\alpha + \beta)}$$

$$\equiv \frac{\sin\alpha\cos\beta + \cos\alpha\sin\beta}{\cos\alpha\cos\beta - \sin\alpha\sin\beta}$$

$$\equiv \frac{[\sin\alpha\cos\beta/\cos\alpha\cos\beta] + [\cos\alpha\sin\beta/\cos\alpha\cos\beta]}{[\cos\alpha\cos\beta/\cos\alpha\cos\beta] - [\sin\alpha\sin\beta/\cos\alpha\cos\beta]}$$

Hence,

$$\tan(\alpha + \beta) \equiv \frac{\tan\alpha + \tan\beta}{1 - \tan\alpha\tan\beta} \tag{5}$$

From identity 5, we get an expression for $\tan(\alpha - \beta)$ in the following way:

$$\tan(\alpha - \beta) \equiv \tan[\alpha + (-\beta)]$$

$$\equiv \frac{\tan\alpha + \tan(-\beta)}{1 - (\tan\alpha)(\tan(-\beta))}$$

$$\equiv \frac{\tan\alpha - \tan\beta}{1 - (\tan\alpha)(-\tan\beta)}$$

Hence, $\tan(\alpha - \beta) \equiv \dfrac{\tan\alpha - \tan\beta}{1 + \tan\alpha\tan\beta}$ $\tag{6}$

It is now easy to determine the trigonometric functional values at certain numbers.

Example 1. Compute $\sin(7\pi/12)$.

Solution: Since $\dfrac{7\pi}{12} = \dfrac{\pi}{3} + \dfrac{\pi}{4}$, we can use identity 3

and get $\sin\dfrac{7\pi}{12} = \sin\left(\dfrac{\pi}{3} + \dfrac{\pi}{4}\right)$

$$= \sin\frac{\pi}{3}\cos\frac{\pi}{4} + \cos\frac{\pi}{3}\sin\frac{\pi}{4}$$

$$= \frac{\sqrt{3}}{2}\cdot\frac{1}{\sqrt{2}} + \frac{1}{2}\frac{1}{\sqrt{2}}$$

$$= \frac{\sqrt{3} + 1}{2\sqrt{2}} \quad \blacksquare$$

Example 2. Compute $\tan(\pi/12)$.

Solution: Note first that $\dfrac{\pi}{12} = \dfrac{\pi}{3} - \dfrac{\pi}{4}$

Hence, we can use identity 6 and obtain

$$\tan\frac{\pi}{12} = \tan\left(\frac{\pi}{3} - \frac{\pi}{4}\right)$$

$$= \frac{\tan(\pi/3) - \tan(\pi/4)}{1 + (\tan\pi/3)\cdot\tan(\pi/4)}$$

$$= \frac{\sqrt{3} - 1}{1 + \sqrt{3}} \quad \blacksquare$$

Example 3. We have shown, using the definitions, that $\sin(\pi - \alpha) = \sin\alpha$. (Section 2.5, example 4.) Prove the same result using a different method.

Solution: $\sin(\pi - \alpha) = \sin\pi\cos\alpha - \cos\pi\sin\alpha$

$$= 0\cdot\cos\alpha - (-1)\sin\alpha$$

$$= 0 + \sin\alpha$$

$$= \sin\alpha \quad\blacksquare$$

Example 4. Prove the identity $\sin[\alpha + (3\pi/2)] = -\cos\alpha$

Solution: $\sin\left(\alpha + \dfrac{3\pi}{2}\right) = \sin\alpha\cos\dfrac{3\pi}{2} + \cos\alpha\sin\dfrac{3\pi}{2}$

$$= (\sin\alpha)\cdot 0 + (\cos\alpha)(-1)$$

$$= 0 - \cos\alpha$$

$$= -\cos\alpha \quad\blacksquare$$

Example 5. We have stated in section 2.7 that the tangent function is periodic with fundamental period π. Prove the same result using a different technique.

Solution: The fundamental period of the tangent function is the smallest of all numbers $|p|$ which have the property $p \neq 0$

and $\tan(\alpha + p) = \tan\alpha$ for all $\alpha \in D_{\tan}$

But $\tan(\alpha + p) = \dfrac{\tan\alpha + \tan p}{1 - \tan\alpha\tan p}$

Hence, we must have

$$\dfrac{\tan\alpha + \tan p}{1 - \tan\alpha\tan p} = \tan\alpha$$

or $\tan\alpha + \tan p = \tan\alpha(1 - \tan\alpha\tan p)$

$$\tan\alpha + \tan p = \tan\alpha - \tan^2\alpha\tan p$$

$$\tan p + \tan^2\alpha\tan p = 0$$

$$\tan p(1 + \tan^2\alpha) = 0$$

The last equality will be true only if $\tan p = 0$. It is clear that the smallest $|p|$ which has the property $\tan p = 0$ and $p \neq 0$ is π. $\blacksquare$

Example 6. Derive a formula expressing $\tan(\alpha/2)$ in terms of trigonometric values at α.

Solution: First note that $\dfrac{\alpha}{2} = \alpha - \dfrac{\alpha}{2}$

Then
$$\sin \frac{\alpha}{2} = \sin \left(\alpha - \frac{\alpha}{2} \right)$$

$$\sin \frac{\alpha}{2} = \sin \alpha \cos \frac{\alpha}{2} - \cos \alpha \sin \frac{\alpha}{2}$$

Hence, $\sin \dfrac{\alpha}{2} + \cos \alpha \sin \dfrac{\alpha}{2} = \sin \alpha \cos \dfrac{\alpha}{2}$

$$\sin \frac{\alpha}{2} (1 + \cos \alpha) = \sin \alpha \cos \frac{\alpha}{2}$$

Dividing both sides by $(1 + \cos \alpha) \cos (\alpha/2)$ we get

$$\tan \frac{\alpha}{2} = \frac{\sin \alpha}{1 + \cos \alpha} \quad \blacksquare$$

Example 7. Express $3 \sin \alpha + 4 \cos \alpha$ in the form $k \sin (\alpha + \beta)$ where k is some constant and β is some number between $-\pi/2$ and $\pi/2$.

Solution: We know that

$$\sin (\alpha + \beta) = \sin \alpha \cos \beta + \sin \beta \cos \alpha$$

Hence $k \sin (\alpha + \beta) = k \cos \beta \sin \alpha + k \sin \beta \cos \alpha$ \hfill (1)

We want to find a k and a β such that

$k \sin (\alpha + \beta) = 3 \sin \alpha + 4 \cos \alpha$ \hfill (2)

Comparing equalities 1 and 2, it is sufficient to find k and β such that $k \cos \beta = 3$ and $k \sin \beta = 4$. This can easily be done in the following way:

Consider the point M with coordinates $(3, 4)$. The distance from the origin to that point is

$$\sqrt{(3 - 0)^2 + (4 - 0)^2} = \sqrt{25} = 5$$

Figure 2.

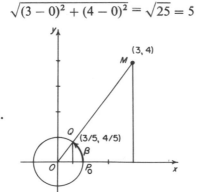

The line passing through 0 and M intersects the circle C_0 at Q. Using the similarity of right triangles (see figure 2), the coordinates of Q are easily found to be $(\frac{3}{5}, \frac{4}{5})$. Let the length of the arc $\overparen{P_0 Q}$ be β. Clearly $-\pi/2 < \beta < \pi/2$, $\cos \beta = \frac{3}{5}$, and $\sin \beta = \frac{4}{5}$. Hence, $3 = 5 \cos \beta$ and $4 = 5 \sin \beta$. It suffices to take $k = 5$ and $\beta = $ length of the arc $\overparen{P_0 Q}$ to get

$$3 \sin \alpha + 4 \cos \alpha = 5 \sin (\alpha + \beta) \quad \blacksquare$$

Exercises   1. Using the addition formulas, compute the following:

(a) $\sin \left(\dfrac{5\pi}{12} \right)$ 　　　　(b) $\cos \left(\dfrac{11\pi}{12} \right)$

(c) $\tan \left(\dfrac{7\pi}{12} \right)$ 　　　　(d) $\sin \left(\dfrac{-13\pi}{12} \right)$

2. Find the exact value of $\tan (\pi/12)$, noting that $\pi/12 = \pi/4 - \pi/6$ and using identity 6. Also find $\tan (\pi/12)$, using the fact that $\pi/12 = (1/2) \cdot (\pi/6)$ and the result of example 6 of this section. Show that the values you obtained using both methods are equal.

Express each of the following in terms of trigonometric functional values at α only.

3. $\sin \left(\dfrac{\pi}{2} + \alpha \right)$ 　　　　4. $\cos (\pi - \alpha)$

5. $\tan \left(\dfrac{\pi}{2} + \alpha \right)$ 　　　　6. $\cot \left(\dfrac{\pi}{2} + \alpha \right)$

7. $\sec \left(\alpha - \dfrac{\pi}{2} \right)$ 　　　　8. $\csc \left(\dfrac{3\pi}{2} + \alpha \right)$

9. $\cos \left(\dfrac{\pi}{3} + \alpha \right)$ 　　　　10. $\sin \left(\dfrac{\pi}{4} - \alpha \right)$

11. $\tan \left(\dfrac{2\pi}{3} - \alpha \right)$ 　　　　12. $\cot \left(\dfrac{\pi}{6} - \alpha \right)$

13. $\sec \left(\dfrac{\pi}{6} + \alpha \right)$ 　　　　14. $\csc \left(\alpha - \dfrac{11\pi}{6} \right)$

Show that the following are identities:

15. $\tan \left(\alpha + \dfrac{\pi}{4} \right) = \dfrac{1 + \tan \alpha}{1 - \tan \alpha}$

16. $\tan \left(\alpha + \dfrac{\pi}{4} \right) - \tan \left(\alpha - \dfrac{3\pi}{4} \right) = 0$

17. Prove, using the addition formulas, that the sine and tangent functions are odd and the cosine function is even. (*Hint:* $-\alpha = 0 - \alpha$.)

18. Show that the following are identities:
    (a) $(\sin \alpha + \cos \alpha)^2 = 1 + \sin 2\alpha$ (*Hint:* Note that $2\alpha = \alpha + \alpha$)
    (b) $\sin 3\alpha = 3 \sin \alpha - 4 \sin^3 \alpha$
    (c) $\cos 3\alpha = 4 \cos^3 \alpha - 3 \cos \alpha$
    (d) $\sin (\alpha + \beta) \cos \beta - \cos (\alpha + \beta) \sin \beta = \sin \alpha$

**19. A theorem from algebra states that if m/n (where m and n are integers and m/n is in its lowest terms) is a solution of $c_0 x^n + c_1 x^{n-1} + \ldots + c_n = 0$ (where $c_0, c_1, \ldots, c_n$ are integers) then m is a factor of c_n and n is a factor of c_0.
Use this theorem, together with identity b of exercise 18, to prove that $\sin (\pi/18)$ is an irrational number. (*Hint:* Note that $\sin [3 \cdot (\pi/18)] = \sin (\pi/6) = 1/2$.)

2.10. Some identities obtainable from the addition formulas Many useful identities can be very easily obtained from the addition formulas. The reader is urged to understand the derivations thoroughly enough so that he can mentally supply them. Noting that $2\alpha = \alpha + \alpha$, we get

$$\sin 2\alpha \equiv \sin (\alpha + \alpha)$$

$$\equiv \sin \alpha \cos \alpha + \cos \alpha \sin \alpha$$

and $$\sin 2\alpha \equiv 2 \sin \alpha \cos \alpha \tag{7}$$

Also, $$\cos 2\alpha \equiv \cos (\alpha + \alpha)$$

$$\equiv \cos \alpha \cos \alpha - \sin \alpha \sin \alpha$$

Therefore, $$\cos 2\alpha \equiv \cos^2 \alpha - \sin^2 \alpha \tag{8a}$$

Noting that $\cos^2 \alpha + \sin^2 \alpha \equiv 1$, and therefore, that $\cos^2 \alpha \equiv 1 - \sin^2 \alpha$, we can write identity 8a in the following way:

$$\cos 2\alpha \equiv 1 - \sin^2 \alpha - \sin^2 \alpha$$

or $$\cos 2\alpha \equiv 1 - 2 \sin^2 \alpha \tag{8b}$$

Further, noting that we also have $\sin^2 \alpha \equiv 1 - \cos^2 \alpha$, we get

$$\cos 2\alpha \equiv \cos^2 \alpha - (1 - \cos^2 \alpha)$$

$$\equiv \cos^2 \alpha - 1 + \cos^2 \alpha$$

and $$\cos 2\alpha \equiv 2 \cos^2 \alpha - 1 \tag{8c}$$

$$\tan 2\alpha \equiv \frac{\tan \alpha + \tan \alpha}{1 - \tan \alpha \tan \alpha}$$

$$\tan 2\alpha \equiv \frac{2 \tan \alpha}{1 - \tan^2 \alpha} \tag{9}$$

Identities 8b and 8c are very useful in deriving the next two identities. In identity 8b, letting $\beta = 2\alpha$, we get $\beta/2 = \alpha$ and

$$\cos \beta \equiv 1 - 2 \sin^2 \frac{\beta}{2}$$

$$2 \sin^2 \frac{\beta}{2} \equiv 1 - \cos \beta$$

$$\sin^2 \frac{\beta}{2} \equiv \frac{1 - \cos \beta}{2}$$

$$\sin \frac{\beta}{2} \equiv \pm \sqrt{\frac{1 - \cos \beta}{2}} \tag{10}$$

Performing the same replacement in identity 8c, we obtain

$$\cos \beta \equiv 2 \cos^2 \frac{\beta}{2} - 1$$

$$2 \cos^2 \frac{\beta}{2} \equiv 1 + \cos \beta$$

$$\cos^2 \frac{\beta}{2} \equiv \frac{1 + \cos \beta}{2}$$

$$\text{and } \cos \frac{\beta}{2} \equiv \pm \sqrt{\frac{1 + \cos \beta}{2}} \tag{11}$$

Other formulas can be obtained from identities 1–4. We shall illustrate these other types in the examples.

Example 1. Express $\sin \pi/3 \cos \pi/4$ as a sum of trigonometric functional values.

Solution: We note that the expression $\sin \alpha \cos \beta$ occurs in both identities 3 and 4. Hence, we add these two identities, thus getting

$$\sin (\alpha + \beta) + \sin (\alpha - \beta) \equiv 2 \sin \alpha \cos \beta \tag{12}$$

Comparing the right side of this new identity to the given expression, we are led to set $\alpha = \pi/3$ and $\beta = \pi/4$. Thus,

$$\sin \left(\frac{\pi}{3} + \frac{\pi}{4}\right) + \sin \left(\frac{\pi}{3} - \frac{\pi}{4}\right) = 2 \sin \frac{\pi}{3} \cos \frac{\pi}{4}$$

$$\text{and } \sin \frac{\pi}{3} \cos \frac{\pi}{4} = \frac{1}{2} \sin \frac{7\pi}{12} + \frac{1}{2} \sin \frac{\pi}{12} \quad \blacksquare$$

Example 2. Express $\cos \pi/3 - \cos \pi/4$ as a product of trigonometric functional values.

Solution: Subtracting identity 1 from identity 2, we obtain

$$\cos(\alpha - \beta) - \cos(\alpha + \beta) \equiv 2\sin\alpha\sin\beta \tag{13}$$

Comparing the left side of this identity with the given expression, we are led to set

$$\alpha - \beta = \frac{\pi}{3} \quad \text{and} \quad \alpha + \beta = \frac{\pi}{4}$$

Solving the foregoing system of two equations in two unknowns, we get

$$2\alpha = \frac{\pi}{3} + \frac{\pi}{4} = \frac{7\pi}{12}$$

$$\alpha = \frac{7\pi}{24}$$

and

$$2\beta = \frac{\pi}{4} - \frac{\pi}{3} = -\frac{\pi}{12}$$

$$\beta = -\frac{\pi}{24}$$

Hence, $\cos\dfrac{\pi}{3} - \cos\dfrac{\pi}{4} = 2\sin\dfrac{7\pi}{24}\cdot\sin\left(-\dfrac{\pi}{24}\right)$

$$\cos\frac{\pi}{3} - \cos\frac{\pi}{4} = -2\sin\frac{7\pi}{24}\cdot\sin\frac{\pi}{24} \quad \blacksquare$$

Example 3. Find two distinct values of x between 0 and 2π for which the equality $\sin[x - (\pi/4)] - \sin[3x - (\pi/3)] = 0$ is satisfied.

Solution: Since the right side of the given equation is zero, it is our aim to write the left side as a product and to use the fact that a product of real numbers is zero if and only if at least one of the factors is zero. Subtracting identity 4 from identity 3, we get

$$\sin(\alpha + \beta) - \sin(\alpha - \beta) = 2\cos\alpha\sin\beta \tag{14}$$

Comparing the left side of the given equation with the left side of identity 14, we are led to set

$$\alpha + \beta = x - \frac{\pi}{4}$$

$$\alpha - \beta = 3x - \frac{\pi}{3}$$

Solving for α and β in terms of x, we get

$$2\alpha = 4x - \frac{7\pi}{12}$$

$$\alpha = 2x - \frac{7\pi}{24}$$

and $2\beta = -2x + \dfrac{\pi}{12}$

$$\beta = \frac{\pi}{24} - x$$

Hence, by replacing $\alpha + \beta$ and $\alpha - \beta$ by $x - (\pi/4)$ and $3x - (\pi/3)$ respectively in identity 14, we obtain

$$\sin\left(x - \frac{\pi}{4}\right) - \sin\left(3x - \frac{\pi}{3}\right) = 2\cos\left(2x - \frac{7\pi}{24}\right)\sin\left(\frac{\pi}{24} - x\right)$$

The given equation can therefore be written in an equivalent form

$$2\cos\left(2x - \frac{7\pi}{24}\right)\sin\left(\frac{\pi}{24} - x\right) = 0$$

It suffices to have

$$\cos\left(2x - \frac{7\pi}{24}\right) = 0 \tag{a}$$

or $\sin\left(\dfrac{\pi}{24} - x\right) = 0$ (b)

Equality (a) above is certainly satisfied if

$$2x - \frac{7\pi}{24} = \frac{\pi}{2}$$

That is, if $x = \dfrac{19\pi}{48}$

and equality (b) is satisfied if

$$\frac{\pi}{24} - x = 0$$

That is, if $x = \dfrac{\pi}{24}$

Hence, two solutions of the given equation are $\pi/24$ and $19\pi/48$. ∎

Note: There is a much shorter way to solve this equation (see exercise 10 below). In our solution, however, we tried to illustrate the technique of writing a sum as a product.

Example 4. Compute $\tan(\pi/12)$ in two different ways.

Solution 1: Dividing identity 11 by identity 10, we obtain

$$\tan\frac{\beta}{2} \equiv \frac{\sin\beta/2}{\cos\beta/2} \equiv \pm\frac{\sqrt{(1-\cos\beta)/2}}{\sqrt{(1+\cos\beta)/2}}$$

and $\qquad \tan\dfrac{\beta}{2} \equiv \pm\sqrt{\dfrac{1-\cos\beta}{1+\cos\beta}}$ $\qquad\qquad$ (15)

Noting that $(\pi/12) = (\pi/6)/2$, we can use identity 15 and get

$$\tan\frac{\pi}{12} = \sqrt{\frac{1-\cos(\pi/6)}{1+\cos(\pi/6)}}$$

where we choose the positive square root, since the terminal point of the standard path $(P_0, \pi/12)$ is in the first quadrant. Thus,

$$\tan\frac{\pi}{12} = \sqrt{\frac{1-\sqrt{3}/2}{1+\sqrt{3}/2}} = \sqrt{\frac{2-\sqrt{3}}{2+\sqrt{3}}} = \sqrt{\frac{(2-\sqrt{3})(2-\sqrt{3})}{(2+\sqrt{3})(2-\sqrt{3})}}$$

$$= \sqrt{\frac{(2-\sqrt{3})^2}{4-3}}$$

$$\tan\frac{\pi}{12} = 2-\sqrt{3}$$

Solution 2: Recalling the identity $\tan(\alpha/2) \equiv \sin\alpha/(1+\cos\alpha)$ derived in the previous section (example 6), we obtain

$$\tan\frac{\pi}{12} = \frac{\sin\pi/6}{1+\cos\pi/6} = \frac{\frac{1}{2}}{1+\sqrt{3}/2} = \frac{1}{2+\sqrt{3}}$$

$$= \frac{2-\sqrt{3}}{(2+\sqrt{3})(2-\sqrt{3})} = \frac{2-\sqrt{3}}{4-3}$$

Hence, $\tan\dfrac{\pi}{12} = 2-\sqrt{3}$ ∎

Note: In the previous section (example 2), we computed $\tan(\pi/12)$ using the fact that $\pi/12 = \pi/3 - \pi/4$. We obtained

$$\tan\frac{\pi}{12} = \frac{\sqrt{3}-1}{\sqrt{3}+1}$$

The reader can verify that

$$\frac{\sqrt{3}-1}{\sqrt{3}+1} = 2 - \sqrt{3}$$

Example 5. Find the trigonometric functional values at $11\pi/12$.

Solution: We first note that $11\pi/12 = (1/2)\cdot(11\pi/6)$ and $11\pi/6$ is a special number. We shall use identities 10 and 11.

$$\sin\frac{11\pi}{12} = \sqrt{\frac{1 - \cos 11\pi/6}{2}} \quad \text{and} \quad \cos\frac{11\pi}{12} = -\sqrt{\frac{1 + \cos 11\pi/6}{2}}$$

where we took the positive square root for $\sin(11\pi/12)$ and the negative one for $\cos(11\pi/12)$, since $\pi/2 < 11\pi/12 < \pi$.

Hence $\sin\dfrac{11\pi}{12} = \sqrt{\dfrac{1 - (\sqrt{3}/2)}{2}} = \sqrt{\dfrac{2 - \sqrt{3}}{4}} = \dfrac{\sqrt{2 - \sqrt{3}}}{2}$

and $\cos\dfrac{11\pi}{12} = -\sqrt{\dfrac{1 + (\sqrt{3}/2)}{2}} = -\sqrt{\dfrac{2 + \sqrt{3}}{4}} = -\dfrac{\sqrt{2 + \sqrt{3}}}{2}$

The other four trigonometric functional values can be obtained easily from the two preceding. ∎

Example 6. Given that $\sin\alpha = \frac{1}{3}$ and that $\pi/2 < \alpha < \pi$, find $\sin 2\alpha$.

Solution: We know that $\sin 2\alpha \equiv 2\sin\alpha\cos\alpha$. We need only find the value of $\cos\alpha$.

Since $\sin^2\alpha + \cos^2\alpha \equiv 1$

we get $\left(\dfrac{1}{3}\right)^2 + \cos^2\alpha = 1$

$$\cos^2\alpha = 1 - \frac{1}{9} = \frac{8}{9}$$

$$\cos\alpha = \pm\frac{2\sqrt{2}}{3}$$

Since $\pi/2 < \alpha < \pi$, we choose $\cos\alpha = -(2\sqrt{2}/3)$ and we get

$$\sin 2\alpha = 2\cdot\frac{1}{3}\cdot\left(-\frac{2\sqrt{2}}{3}\right)$$

$$\sin 2\alpha = -\frac{4\sqrt{2}}{9}$$

Note: We should expect the value of $\sin 2\alpha$ to be negative, since $\pi/2 < \alpha < \pi$ implies $\pi < 2\alpha < 2\pi$. ∎

Exercises   1. Compute the following:

(a) $\sin\left(-\pi/8\right)$ (b) $\cos\left(7\pi/12\right)$

(c) $\tan\left(9\pi/8\right)$ (d) $\cot\left(-\pi/8\right)$

2. Given that $\sin\alpha = -\frac{2}{3}$ and $\pi < \alpha < 3\pi/2$, find $\sin 2\alpha$ and $\cos 2\alpha$.

3. Given that $\cos\alpha = -\frac{4}{5}$ and $-\pi < \alpha < -\pi/2$, find $\sin 2\alpha$ and $\cos 2\alpha$.

4. Given that $\tan\alpha = \frac{4}{3}$ and $\pi < \alpha < 3\pi/2$, find $\sin 2\alpha$, $\cos 2\alpha$ and $\tan 2\alpha$.

5. Express $\sin\left(\pi/5\right)\cos\left(\pi/3\right)$ as a sum of trigonometric functional values.

6. Express $\sin\left(\pi/3\right)\sin\left(2\pi/5\right)$ as a difference of trigonometric functional values.

7. Express $\cos\left(7\pi/12\right)\cos\left(3\pi/5\right)$ as a sum of trigonometric functional values.

8. Express the following as a product of trigonometric functional values.

(a) $\sin\left(\pi/5\right) + \sin\left(7\pi/12\right)$ (b) $\sin\left(3\pi/4\right) - \sin\left(2\pi/7\right)$

(c) $\cos\left(\pi/3\right) + \cos\left(5\pi/7\right)$ (d) $\cos\left(3\pi/10\right) - \cos\left(7\pi/4\right)$

9. Find two distinct solutions between 0 and 2π for each of the following equations (use the technique illustrated in example 3 of the preceding section).

(a) $\sin\left(x + \dfrac{\pi}{4}\right) + \sin\left(5x - \dfrac{\pi}{3}\right) = 0$

(b) $\sin\left(2x - \dfrac{\pi}{3}\right) - \sin\left(7x + \dfrac{\pi}{4}\right) = 0$

(c) $\cos\left(x - \dfrac{\pi}{10}\right) - \cos\left(\dfrac{2\pi}{3} - 3x\right) = 0$

(d) $\cos\left(3x - \dfrac{\pi}{5}\right) + \cos\left(x - \dfrac{\pi}{2}\right) = 0$

10. Give a different solution for the problem of example 3, section 2.10. (*Hint:* Use the fact that if we want $\sin\alpha = \sin\beta$, it is sufficient to have $\alpha = \beta$ or $\alpha = \pi - \beta$.)

11. Do exercise 9 using a different technique. (See exercise 10.)

12. Show that the following are identities:

(a) $2\cos\alpha\sin 3\alpha = \sin 4\alpha + \sin 2\alpha$

(b) $\sin\left(\alpha + \beta\right)\sin\left(\alpha - \beta\right) = \sin^2\alpha - \sin^2\beta$

(c) $2\sin\left(\alpha + \beta\right)\cos\left(\alpha - \beta\right) = \sin 2\alpha + \sin 2\beta$

(d) $\cos\left(\alpha + \beta\right)\cos\left(\alpha - \beta\right) = \cos^2\alpha - \sin^2\beta$

(e) $\sin\alpha = 2\sin\dfrac{\alpha}{2}\cos\dfrac{\alpha}{2}$

(f) $\sin 3\alpha = 3\sin\alpha - 4\sin^3\alpha$

(g) $\cos 3\alpha = 4\cos^3\alpha - 3\cos\alpha$

(h) $\sqrt{2}\sin\left(\alpha + \dfrac{\pi}{4}\right) = \sin\alpha + \cos\alpha$

(i) $\tan\dfrac{\alpha}{2} = \csc\alpha - \cot\alpha$

2.11. Trigonometric identities In the previous sections, we derived some basic identities. These may be used to prove more complex identities and to solve trigonometric equations. In this section, we shall discuss some techniques for proving identities.

We first recall some basic concepts from elementary algebra. In any discussion involving a free variable (x or some other symbol), we must agree on some universe for that discussion. In this text, unless otherwise specified, the universe X will always be understood to be the set of all real numbers which have the following property: If the free variable is replaced, throughout the discussion, by a member of that set, then every statement is meaningful. For example, if, in the discussion, we have divided by $x - 1$, then 1 is *not* a member of the universe since division by $1 - 1 = 0$ is meaningless.

If $L(x) = R(x)$ is an equation and X is the universe for a particular discussion, then the set $\{x \mid x \in X$ and $L(x) = R(x)\}$ is called the *solution set* of the equation. Note that the solution set of an equation depends not only on the equation, but also on the universe. For example, if the universe is the set of all real numbers, then $\{x \mid x^2 = -1\}$ is the empty set. Later, however, we shall see that, with a different universe, the set $\{x \mid x^2 = -1\}$ has two members. If an equation $L(x) = R(x)$ is given and X is the universe for this equation, then the equation $L'(x) = R'(x)$ is said to be *equivalent* to the equation $L(x) = R(x)$ if and only if

$$\{x \mid L(x) = R(x)\} = \{x \mid L'(x) = R'(x) \text{ and } x \in X\}$$

The reader is undoubtedly familiar with the process of solving elementary algebraic equations. The basic idea is taking steps so that an equivalent equation is obtained until, finally, the solution set of one of the equivalent equations has been trivially found. Then this solution set is also the solution set of the original equation.

At times, it is necessary to take steps which do not yield equations which are equivalent to the previous ones (for example, squaring both sides in order to eliminate radicals). In this case, the solution set is not necessarily identical with the solution set of the original equation. Then great caution must be used in determining the solution set of the original equation.

We shall use the following basic idea in proving identities: When we are asked to prove that $L_1(x) = R_1(x)$ is an identity, we shall proceed as follows:

1. Determine the universe X for the given equation

2. Take a sequence of steps, each time getting an equation $L_i(x) = R_i(x)$ such that, for each i, $i = 2, \ldots, n$, we have $\{x \mid L_{i-1}(x) = R_{i-1}(x) \text{ and } x \in X\} = \{x \mid L_i(x) = R_i(x) \text{ and } x \in X\}$

And we also have

$$\{x \mid L_n(x) = R_n(x) \text{ and } x \in X\} = X$$

Then we shall be able to conclude that

$$\{x \mid L_1(x) = R_1(x)\} = X$$

and therefore that $L_1(x) = R_1(x)$ is an identity.

The techniques are best illustrated with examples.

Example I. Prove that $\tan^2 x/\sec x = (1 - \cos x)(1 + \sec x)$ is an identity.

Solution: We want to show that the foregoing equality is true for all values of x for which both sides are defined. We note that

$$D_{\tan x} = D_{\sec x} = R \setminus \left\{ (2n + 1)\frac{\pi}{2} \,\middle|\, n \text{ an integer} \right\}$$

Hence, the universe X (the set of all permissible values for x) is the set of all real numbers with the exception of the odd multiples of $\pi/2$. Using the basic identities, the given equality can be written

$$\frac{(\sin x/\cos x)^2}{1/\cos x} = (1 - \cos x)\left(1 + \frac{1}{\cos x}\right)$$

or equivalently

$$\frac{\sin^2 x}{\cos^2 x} \cdot \cos x = \frac{(1 - \cos x)(1 + \cos x)}{\cos x}$$

and, simplifying, we get

$$\frac{\sin^2 x}{\cos x} = \frac{1 - \cos^2 x}{\cos x}$$

which is equivalent to

$$\frac{\sin^2 x + \cos^2 x}{\cos x} = \frac{1}{\cos x}$$

Since $\sin^2 x + \cos^2 x \equiv 1$, the last equality is true for all $x \in X$. Since the last equality is equivalent to the given one, we conclude that

$$\frac{\tan^2 x}{\sec x} = (1 - \cos x)(1 + \sec x) \text{ is an identity. } \blacksquare$$

Example 2. Prove that

$$\frac{\csc x[\sin^2 x + 2(\cos x)(1 + \cos x)]}{1 + \cos x} = \frac{(\sec x)(\sin 2x)}{2(1 - \cos x)}$$

is an identity.

Solution: We shall show that the foregoing equality is satisfied for all permissible values of x.

The universe X is the set of all real numbers with the exception of those real numbers which are multiples of $\pi/2$. (The reader should verify this fact.)

We now claim the following: (The reader should also supply the justification of each step).

$$\left\{ x \left| \frac{\csc x[\sin^2 x + 2(\cos x)(1 + \cos x)]}{1 + \cos x} = \frac{(\sec x)(\sin 2x)}{2(1 - \cos x)} \right. \right\}$$

$$= \left\{ x \left| \frac{\sin^2 x + 2(\cos x)(1 + \cos x)}{\sin x(1 + \cos x)} = \frac{2 \sin x \cos x}{2 \cos x(1 - \cos x)} \right. \right\}$$

$$= \left\{ x \left| \frac{\sin x}{1 + \cos x} + \frac{2 \cos x}{\sin x} = \frac{\sin x}{1 - \cos x} \text{ and } x \in X \right. \right\}$$

$$= \left\{ x \left| \frac{2 \cos x}{\sin x} = \frac{\sin x}{1 - \cos x} - \frac{\sin x}{1 + \cos x} \text{ and } x \in X \right. \right\}$$

$$= \left\{ x \left| \frac{2 \cos x}{\sin x} = \frac{\sin x(1 + \cos x - 1 + \cos x)}{(1 - \cos x)(1 + \cos x)} \text{ and } x \in X \right. \right\}$$

$$= \left\{ x \left| \frac{2 \cos x}{\sin x} = \frac{(\sin x)(2 \cos x)}{1 - \cos^2 x} \text{ and } x \in X \right. \right\}$$

$$= \left\{ x \left| \frac{2 \cos x}{\sin x} = \frac{(\sin x)(2 \cos x)}{\sin^2 x} \text{ and } x \in X \right. \right\}$$

$$= \left\{ x \left| \frac{2 \cos x}{\sin x} = \frac{2 \cos x}{\sin x} \text{ and } x \in X \right. \right\} = X$$

Hence, we have shown that the given equality is an identity. ∎

Example 3. Prove that

$$\tan (\pi - x) + \frac{\cos (\pi - x)}{1 + \sin x} = -\sec x$$

is an identity.

Solution: We first note that $\tan (\pi - x) \equiv -\tan x$ and $\cos (\pi - x) \equiv -\cos x$. These two identities may be obtained directly from the definitions or by using the addition formulas. The reader should determine the universe for the given equation and check that each equation which we presently obtain is equivalent to the previous one.

$$\tan(\pi - x) + \frac{\cos(\pi - x)}{1 + \sin x} = -\sec x$$

$$-\tan x + \frac{-\cos x}{1 + \sin x} = -\sec x$$

$$-\frac{\sin x}{\cos x} - \frac{\cos x}{1 + \sin x} = -\frac{1}{\cos x}$$

$$\frac{1}{\cos x} - \frac{\sin x}{\cos x} = \frac{\cos x}{1 + \sin x}$$

$$\frac{1 - \sin x}{\cos x} = \frac{\cos x}{1 + \sin x}$$

$$(1 - \sin x)(1 + \sin x) = \cos^2 x$$

$$1 - \sin^2 x = \cos^2 x$$

$$1 = \sin^2 x + \cos^2 x$$

Hence, the given equality is an identity. ∎

Example 4. Show that the equality $\tan x + \sin x = \cot x$ is not an identity.

Solution: It is sufficient to show that there is a permissible value of x for which the given equality is not satisfied. We try $\pi/4$. Recalling that $\tan(\pi/4) = 1$, $\sin(\pi/4) = 1/\sqrt{2}$ and $\cot(\pi/4) = 1$, we see that

$$\tan\frac{\pi}{4} + \sin\frac{\pi}{4} \neq \cot\frac{\pi}{4}$$

Hence, the given equality is not an identity. ∎

Note: The equality above is called a *conditional trigonometric equation*. In section 2.14, we shall discuss certain methods for finding solutions of trigonometric equations.

Exercises Prove that the given equalities are identities:

1. $\tan x + \cot x = \sec x \cdot \csc x$

2. $\dfrac{1}{1 - \cos x} + \dfrac{1}{1 + \cos x} = 2\csc^2 x$

3. $\dfrac{\sin x \cot x + \cos x}{\cot x} = 2\sin x$

4. $\sin^2 x - \cos^2 x = (\tan x - \cot x)/(\tan x + \cot x)$

5. $\sin x \cos x \sec x \csc x = 1$

6. $(\sin x + \cos x)^2 = 1 + 2 \sin x \cos x$

7. $\dfrac{\sec^2 x + \csc^2 x}{\tan^2 x} = \csc^4 x$

8. $\cos^4 x - \sin^4 x = 2\cos^2 x - 1$

9. $\dfrac{\sec^2 x - 1}{\tan^2 x} = 2 + \tan^2 x$

10. $(\sec^2 x - 1)\csc^2 x = \sec^2 x$

11. $\tan x + \cot x = \tan x \csc^2 x$

12. $\cot x + \tan x = \sec x \csc x$

13. $\tan^2 x + \cot^2 x = \dfrac{1 - 2\sin^2 x \cdot \cos^2 x}{\sin^2 x \cdot \cos^2 x}$

14. $\dfrac{\sec^2 x}{1 + \sin x} = \dfrac{\sec^2 x - \sec x \tan x}{\cos^2 x}$

15. $\dfrac{1 + \tan^2 x}{\tan^2 x} = \csc^2 x$

16. $\dfrac{1 - \cos^6 x}{\sin^2 x} = 1 + \cos^2 x + \cos^4 x$

17. $(\cos x + \cos y)^2 + (\sin x - \sin y)^2 = 2 + 2\cos(x + y)$

18. $\dfrac{\sin x}{\sec x + 1} + \dfrac{\sin x}{\sec x - 1} = 2\cot x$

19. $(\csc x - \cot x)(\sec x + 1) = \tan x$

20. $\sec^2 x - (\cos x - \tan x)^2 = \sin^2 x + 2\sin x$

21. $(1 + \cot x + \tan x)(\sin x - \cos x) = \dfrac{\sec x}{\csc^2 x} - \dfrac{\csc x}{\sec^2 x}$

22. $\dfrac{\cos^2 x - \sin(\pi - x)\sin(\pi + x)}{\csc(\pi - x)} = \sin x$

23. $\dfrac{\tan x}{1 - \cot x} + \dfrac{\cot x}{1 - \tan x} = 1 + \tan x + \cot x$

24. $\dfrac{\sec x + \tan x}{\cos x - \tan x - \sec x} = -\csc x$

25. $\csc x + \cot x = \dfrac{\sin x}{1 - \cos x}$

26. $\sin 2x \cdot \cos 3x + \cos 2x \cdot \sin 3x = \sin 5x$

Show that the following are not identities:

27. $\cot x + 1 = 0$

28. $\dfrac{2 \tan x}{1 - \tan^2 x} = \cos x$

29. $\cot x + 2 \sin x = \csc x$

30. $\tan x - 2 \sec x = 3$

2.12. The inverse trigonometric functions We recall that the functions f and g are inverses of each other if and only if $f[g(x)] = x$ for all $x \in D_g$ and $g[f(x)] = x$ for all $x \in D_f$. We proved in section 1.11 that a function f has an inverse if and only if it is a one-to-one function. It follows that any periodic function cannot have an inverse since a periodic function is not one-to-one. Sometimes, however, it is possible for a suitably chosen restriction of a periodic function to be one-to-one. Hence, such a restriction has an inverse.

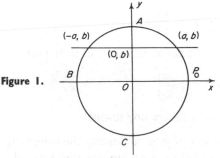

Figure 1.

Let the intersections of the circle C_0 with the x and y axes be P_0, A, B, and C (see figure 1). Then, given a real number b such that $-1 \le b \le 1$, we can find the points on the circle C_0 which have ordinate b by drawing a parallel to the x axis passing through the point $(0, b)$. The points of intersection of that line with the circle will have coordinates (a, b) and $(-a, b)$. There are at most two such points of intersection and certainly there is exactly one on the arc $\overset{\frown}{CP_0A}$.

We note now that if $-\pi/2 \le \alpha \le \pi/2$, then the terminal point of the standard path (P_0, α) must be on the arc $\overset{\frown}{CP_0A}$. The foregoing geometric discussion shows that if we define the function Sin to be the restriction of the sine function to the set $\{\alpha \mid -\pi/2 \le \alpha \le \pi/2\}$, then Sin is one-to-one. Similar arguments for the other five circular functions lead to the following definitions.

Definitions 2.12.1. The *principal sine, cosine, tangent, cotangent, secant,* and *cosecant* functions are denoted by Sin, Cos, Tan, Cot, Sec, and Csc and are defined in the following way:

Sin is the restriction of the sine function to the set

$$\left\{\alpha \,\middle|\, -\frac{\pi}{2} \le \alpha \le \frac{\pi}{2}\right\}$$

Cos is the restriction of the cosine function to the set

$$\{\alpha \,|\, 0 \le \alpha \le \pi\}$$

Tan is the restriction of the tangent function to the set

$$\left\{\alpha \,\middle|\, -\frac{\pi}{2} < \alpha < \frac{\pi}{2}\right\}$$

Cot is the restriction of the cotangent function to the set

$$\{\alpha \,|\, 0 < \alpha < \pi\}$$

Sec is the restriction of the secant function to the set

$$\left\{\alpha \,\middle|\, 0 \le \alpha < \frac{\pi}{2}\right\} \cup \left\{\alpha \,\middle|\, \pi \le \alpha < \frac{3\pi}{2}\right\}$$

Csc is the restriction of the cosecant function to the set

$$\left\{\alpha \,\middle|\, 0 < \alpha \le \frac{\pi}{2}\right\} \cup \left\{\alpha \,\middle|\, \pi < \alpha \le \frac{3\pi}{2}\right\}$$

Theorem 2.12.2. The principal circular functions are one-to-one.

Proof: The proof that Sin is one-to-one was outlined at the beginning of the section. We shall prove that Tan is one-to-one and leave the other four parts of the proof as exercises.

Note that $D_{\text{Tan}} = \{\alpha \,|\, -\pi/2 < \alpha < \pi/2\}$ and $R_{\text{Tan}} = R$, the set of all real numbers. Further, if $\alpha \in D_{\text{Tan}}$, then Tan α = tan α. Clearly then, given any $\alpha \in D_{\text{Tan}}$, there is one and only one corresponding Tan α. We need to show that if $\alpha_1 \in D_{\text{Tan}}$, $\alpha_2 \in D_{\text{Tan}}$, and $\alpha_1 \ne \alpha_2$, then Tan $\alpha_1 \ne$ Tan α_2. Since α_1 and α_2 are in the domain of Tan, we have Tan α_1 = tan α_1 and Tan α_2 = tan α_2. Hence, it is sufficient to show that $\alpha_1 \ne \alpha_2$ implies tan $\alpha_1 \ne$ tan α_2. Consider the standard paths (P_0, α_1), and (P_0, α_2) with end points (a, b) and (c, d) respectively. (See figure 2.) It is easy to show (see exercise 7 below) that

Figure 2.

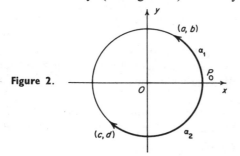

$b/a = d/c$ if and only if $a = c$ and $b = d$ or $a = -c$ and $b = -d$. Hence, $\tan \alpha_1 = \tan \alpha_2$ if and only if (a, b) and (c, d) are coordinates of the same point or coordinates of two points which are symmetric with respect to the origin. Since, however, $\alpha_1 \neq \alpha_2$, either one of the two conditions can be satisfied only if α_1 and α_2 differ by a non-zero multiple of π. But this is impossible, since both α_1 and α_2 satisfy the following inequalities.

$$-\frac{\pi}{2} < \alpha_1 < \frac{\pi}{2} \tag{1}$$

$$-\frac{\pi}{2} < \alpha_2 < \frac{\pi}{2} \tag{2}$$

Inequality 2 is equivalent to

$$-\frac{\pi}{2} < -\alpha_2 < \frac{\pi}{2} \tag{3}$$

and using (1) and (3) above, we get

$$-\pi < \alpha_1 - \alpha_2 < \pi$$

which shows that $\alpha_1 - \alpha_2$ cannot be a non-zero multiple of π. Hence, $\alpha_1 \neq \alpha_2$ implies $\operatorname{Tan} \alpha_1 \neq \operatorname{Tan} \alpha_2$ and we have proved that Tan is one-to-one. ∎

From theorem 2.12.2, we conclude that the principal circular functions have inverses. We denote these inverses by Sin^{-1}, Cos^{-1}, Tan^{-1}, Cot^{-1}, Sec^{-1}, and Csc^{-1} and call them the *inverse trigonometric functions*.

Remark: In Chapter 3, we shall learn to use the trigonometric tables. Tables are very useful when one seeks the answer to the following question: Given a value of α, what is the corresponding value of $f(\alpha)$ where f is either a trigonometric function or an inverse trigonometric function. We can often answer this question easily in the case where f is a trigonometric function and α is a special number or in the case where f is an inverse trigonometric function and α is such that $f(\alpha)$ is a special number. In all other cases, we shall, in this chapter, use the symbol $f(\alpha)$ for the value of f at α. That is, we shall not try to approximate the value of that symbol.

Example 1. Find $\operatorname{Sin}^{-1} \sqrt{3}/2$.

Solution: Let $\alpha = \operatorname{Sin}^{-1} \sqrt{3}/2$. Then we know that $-\pi/2 \leq \alpha \leq \pi/2$ and $\sin \alpha = \sqrt{3}/2$. It is clear that α is a special number (as can be seen from figure 3). Further, $\alpha = \pi/3$. Hence,

$$\sin^{-1} \frac{\sqrt{3}}{2} = \frac{\pi}{3} \quad \blacksquare$$

Figure 3.

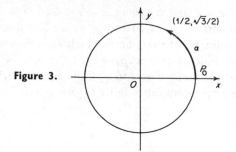

Example 2. Find all values of x which satisfy the equation $\cos x = \frac{1}{3}$.

Solution: By definition of the function Cos^{-1}, we know that $x = \mathrm{Cos}^{-1}\frac{1}{3}$ satisfies the given equation. (Note that we do not attempt here to approximate the value of $\mathrm{Cos}^{-1}\frac{1}{3}$.) We also know that $0 \le \mathrm{Cos}^{-1}\frac{1}{3} \le \pi$.

Figure 4.

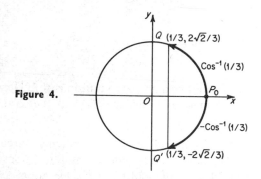

On figure 4, we illustrate the fact that the only two points on the circle C_0 which have abscissa $\frac{1}{3}$ are the points Q and Q'. These are the terminal points of the standard paths $(P_0, \mathrm{Cos}^{-1}\frac{1}{3} + 2n\pi)$ and $(P_0, -\mathrm{Cos}^{-1}\frac{1}{3} + 2n\pi)$ respectively. Hence, the solutions of the equation $\cos x = \frac{1}{3}$ are $\mathrm{Cos}^{-1}\frac{1}{3} + 2n\pi$ and $-\mathrm{Cos}^{-1}\frac{1}{3} + 2n\pi$ where $n = 0, \pm 1, \pm 2, \dots$. ∎

Remark: We note that the solution set of the equation $\cos x = \frac{1}{3}$ has infinitely many elements. It is convenient to have a special notation for such sets. We therefore adopt the following convention:

If f is a trigonometric function, the symbol arc fx will denote the set

$\{y\,|\,f(y) = x\}$,

i.e., $\arcsin x = \{y\,|\,\sin y = x\}$; $\arccos x = \{y\,|\,\cos y = x\}$; etc.

Example 3. Describe the set $\arctan \sqrt{3}$.

Solution: We know that $\alpha \in \arctan \sqrt{3}$ if and only if $\tan \alpha = \sqrt{3}$. Since we know that $\tan(\pi/3) = \sqrt{3}$, it is clear that $\pi/3 \in \arctan \sqrt{3}$. Further, it is easy to show (using the definition of the tangent function) that the only values of α which satisfy the equation $\tan \alpha = \sqrt{3}$ are $\pi/3 + n\pi$ where n is an integer.

Hence, $\arctan \sqrt{3} = \left\{ \dfrac{\pi}{3} + n\pi \mid n \text{ an integer} \right\}$ ∎

Example 4. Verify that the following statement is true

$\operatorname{Cos}^{-1} -\tfrac{4}{5} \in \arcsin \tfrac{3}{5}$

Solution: Let $\alpha = \operatorname{Cos}^{-1} -\tfrac{4}{5}$. We want to show $\alpha \in \arcsin \tfrac{3}{5}$. This is true if and only if $\sin \alpha = \tfrac{3}{5}$. We know that $\cos \alpha = -\tfrac{4}{5}$. Using the identity $\cos^2 \alpha + \sin^2 \alpha \equiv 1$, we get

$(-\tfrac{4}{5})^2 + \sin^2 \alpha = 1$

Hence, $\sin^2 \alpha = 1 - \tfrac{16}{25} = \tfrac{9}{25}$

and $\sin \alpha = \tfrac{3}{5}$

where we chose the positive square root of $\tfrac{9}{25}$, since $0 \leq \alpha \leq \pi$. We have shown that $\sin \alpha = \tfrac{3}{5}$. Hence, $\alpha \in \arcsin \tfrac{3}{5}$. ∎

Example 5. Find $\operatorname{Sin}^{-1} [\sin (5\pi/6)]$

Solution: We first note that we must have $-\pi/2 \leq \operatorname{Sin}^{-1} [\sin (5\pi/6)] \leq \pi/2$.

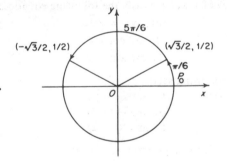

Figure 5.

We see from figure 5 that $\sin (5\pi/6) = \sin (\pi/6) = \tfrac{1}{2}$. Since $-\pi/2 \leq \pi/6 \leq \pi/2$, we have $\sin (\pi/6) = \operatorname{Sin} (\pi/6)$.

Hence, $\operatorname{Sin}^{-1} \left(\sin \dfrac{5\pi}{6} \right) = \operatorname{Sin}^{-1} \left(\sin \dfrac{\pi}{6} \right) = \operatorname{Sin}^{-1} \left(\operatorname{Sin} \dfrac{\pi}{6} \right) = \dfrac{\pi}{6}$ ∎

Remark: Example 5 shows that $\operatorname{Sin}^{-1} (\sin \alpha) \neq \alpha$ unless $\alpha \in D_{\operatorname{Sin}}$. That is to say, $\operatorname{Sin}^{-1} (\sin \alpha) \neq \alpha$ unless $-\pi/2 \leq \alpha \leq \pi/2$.

Example 6. Write the following as an algebraic expression involving only a and b.

$\cos (\operatorname{Sin}^{-1} a^2 - \operatorname{Cos}^{-1} b^2)$

Solution: Let $\operatorname{Sin}^{-1} a^2 = \alpha$ and $\operatorname{Cos}^{-1} b^2 = \beta$. Then we know that $\sin \alpha = a^2$, $\cos \beta = b^2$, $-\pi/2 \leq \alpha \leq \pi/2$ and $0 \leq \beta \leq \pi$.

We have $\cos(\operatorname{Sin}^{-1} a^2 - \operatorname{Cos}^{-1} b^2) = \cos(\alpha - \beta)$
$$= \cos\alpha\cos\beta + \sin\alpha\sin\beta$$

Since we know $\sin\alpha$ and $\cos\beta$, it is sufficient to find $\cos\alpha$ and $\sin\beta$ in terms of a and b. We have

$$\sin^2\alpha + \cos^2\alpha = 1$$

Hence, $[(a)^2]^2 + \cos^2\alpha = 1$

$$\cos^2\alpha = 1 - a^4$$

$$\cos\alpha = \sqrt{1 - a^4}$$

where we take the positive square root of $1 - a^4$, since $-\pi/2 \le \alpha \le \pi/2$ and therefore $\cos\alpha \ge 0$.

Similarly, we get

$$\sin\beta = \sqrt{1 - b^4}$$

It follows that

$$\cos(\operatorname{Sin}^{-1} a^2 - \operatorname{Cos}^{-1} b^2) = b^2\cdot\sqrt{1 - a^4} + a^2\cdot\sqrt{1 - b^4} \quad\blacksquare$$

Exercises 1. Find the following:
   (a) $\operatorname{Sin}^{-1}\tfrac{1}{2}$ (b) $\operatorname{Cos}^{-1} 1/\sqrt{2}$
   (c) $\operatorname{Tan}^{-1} 1$ (d) $\operatorname{Cot}^{-1}(-1)$
   (e) $\operatorname{Sec}^{-1} 2$ (f) $\operatorname{Csc}^{-1} 2/\sqrt{3}$

2. Find all values of x which satisfy the following equations:
   (a) $\sin x = \tfrac{1}{2}$ (b) $\cos x = \sqrt{3}/2$
   (c) $\tan x = 2$ (d) $\sqrt{3}\cot x = -1$
   (e) $\sec x = -2$ (f) $\csc x = -2/\sqrt{3}$

3. Describe the following sets:
   (a) $\arcsin(-\tfrac{1}{2})$ (b) $\arccos\sqrt{3}/2$
   (c) $\arctan 3$ (d) $\operatorname{arccot}(-5)$
   (e) $\operatorname{arcsec} 7$ (f) $\operatorname{arccsc}(-2)$

4. Verify that the following statements are true:
   (a) $\operatorname{Tan}^{-1} 1 \in \arcsin\dfrac{1}{\sqrt{2}}$

   (b) $\operatorname{Cot}^{-1}\left(-\dfrac{1}{\sqrt{3}}\right) \in \arccos\left(-\dfrac{1}{2}\right)$

   (c) $\left[\operatorname{Cot}^{-1}\left(\dfrac{2}{3}\right) + \pi\right] \in \arctan\dfrac{3}{2}$

   (d) $\left[\operatorname{Sec}^{-1}\left(-\dfrac{5}{4}\right) + \dfrac{\pi}{2}\right] \in \operatorname{arccot}\left(-\dfrac{3}{4}\right)$

   (e) $\operatorname{Sin}^{-1}\dfrac{\sqrt{3}}{2} \in \operatorname{arcsec} 2$

   (f) $\left(\pi - \operatorname{Cos}^{-1}\dfrac{5}{13}\right) \in \operatorname{arccsc}\dfrac{13}{12}$

5. Find the following:

(a) $\text{Sin}^{-1}\left(\sin\dfrac{\pi}{4}\right)$ (b) $\text{Cos}^{-1}\left(\sin\dfrac{\pi}{6}\right)$

(c) $\text{Tan}^{-1}\left(\sin\dfrac{\pi}{2}\right)$ (d) $\text{Cot}^{-1}\left(\sec\dfrac{7\pi}{6}\right)$

(e) $\text{Sec}^{-1}\left(\sec\dfrac{3\pi}{4}\right)$ (f) $\text{Csc}^{-1}\left[\sin\left(\dfrac{-\pi}{2}\right)\right]$

6. Write the following as an algebraic expression involving only a and b:
   (a) $\sin(\text{Sin}^{-1} a^2 + \text{Cos}^{-1} b^2)$
   (b) $\cos(\text{Tan}^{-1} a^2 + \text{Cot}^{-1} b^2)$
   (c) $\tan(\text{Sec}^{-1} - a^2 - \text{Csc}^{-1} - b^2)$

7. Show that if (a, b) and (c, d) are points of the circle C_0, then $b/a = d/c$ if and only if either $a = c$ and $b = d$ or $a = -c$ and $b = -d$. (*Hint:* Use the fact that the equation of C_0 is $x^2 + y^2 = 1$.)

2.13. Graphs of some elementary functions: In section 1.10, the procedure for sketching the graph of a function was outlined. We shall follow this procedure in this section to illustrate the sketching of the graphs of some of the elementary functions.

Example 1. Sketch the graph of the sine function.

Solution: Since the sine function is periodic with period 2π, it is sufficient to sketch the graph of a restriction of the sine function to an interval of length 2π. Furthermore, since the sine function is odd, we know that its graph is symmetric with respect to the origin. Hence, it is sufficient to plot the points $(x, \sin x)$ where $0 \le x \le \pi$ and x is a special number. For convenience, we tabulate some of those pairs of numbers.

x	0	$\pi/6$	$\pi/4$	$\pi/3$	$\pi/2$	$2\pi/3$	$3\pi/4$	$5\pi/6$	π
$\sin x$	0	$1/2$	$1/\sqrt{2}$	$\sqrt{3}/2$	1	$\sqrt{3}/2$	$1/\sqrt{2}$	$1/2$	0

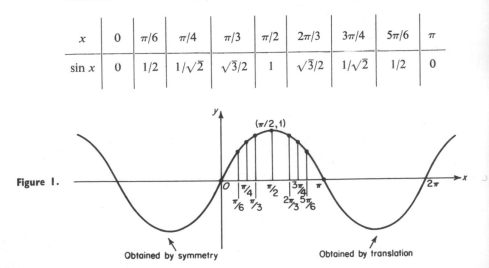

Figure 1.

Obtained by symmetry   Obtained by translation

Using the tables obtained in exercise 2, section 2.6, we can sketch the graphs of the other five trigonometric functions. The graphs of the inverse trigonometric functions are obtained by symmetry. We illustrate these graphs in figures 2–7.

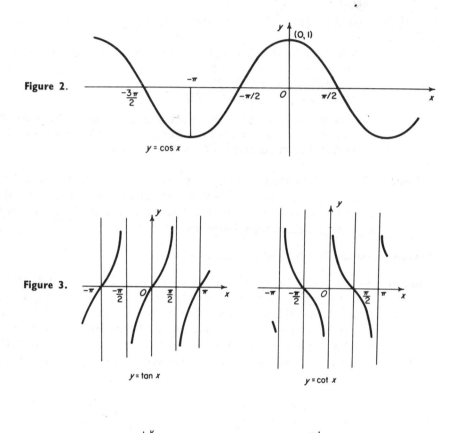

Figure 2.

$y = \cos x$

Figure 3.

$y = \tan x$

$y = \cot x$

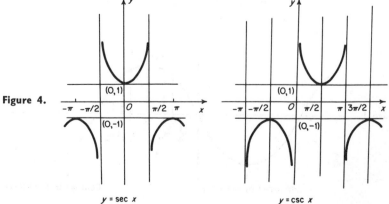

Figure 4.

$y = \sec x$

$y = \csc x$

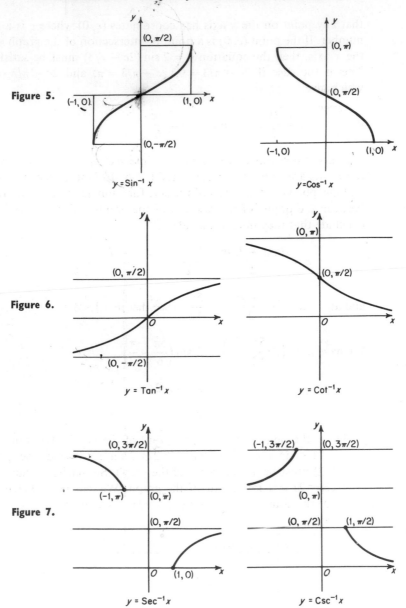

Figure 5.

$y = \text{Sin}^{-1} x$

$y = \text{Cos}^{-1} x$

Figure 6.

$y = \text{Tan}^{-1} x$

$y = \text{Cot}^{-1} x$

Figure 7.

$y = \text{Sec}^{-1} x$

$y = \text{Csc}^{-1} x$

We illustrate with examples some techniques for rapid sketching of the graphs of certain equations.

Example 2. Sketch the graph of the equation $y = 2 \sin (2x - \pi/3)$.

Solution: We know the general shape of the graph of the sine function. Hence, it is sufficient to find three consecutive points of intersection of the graph with the x axis, a "high" point and a "low" point. We first note that any point on the x axis has coordinates $(c, 0)$ where c is a real number. If the point $(c, 0)$ is a point of intersection of the graph with the x axis, then the equation $0 = 2 \sin (2c - \pi/3)$ must be satisfied. This is the case if $2c - \pi/3 = 0$, $2c - \pi/3 = \pi$, and $2c - \pi/3 = 2\pi$ which give

$$c = \frac{\pi}{6}; \qquad c = \frac{2\pi}{3}; \qquad \text{and} \qquad c = \frac{7\pi}{6}$$

Hence, three consecutive points of intersection of the graph with the x axis are $(\pi/6, 0)$, $(2\pi/3, 0)$, and $(7\pi/6, 0)$. Noting that the high and low points of the graph of the sine function are situated midway between the points of intersection of the graph with the x axis, we conclude that they must occur at

$$x = \frac{2\pi/3 + 7\pi/6}{2} = \frac{11\pi}{12}$$

and at $\qquad x = \dfrac{\pi/6 + 2\pi/3}{2} = \dfrac{5\pi}{12}$ (See theorem 1.9.4.)

We have $2 \sin \left(2 \cdot \dfrac{5\pi}{12} - \dfrac{\pi}{3} \right) = 2 \sin \left(\dfrac{5\pi}{6} - \dfrac{\pi}{3} \right)$

$$= 2 \sin \pi/2$$

$$= 2$$

Hence, the point $(5\pi/12, 2)$ is a point of the graph. We note that since $-1 \le \sin \alpha \le 1$, we have $-2 \le 2 \sin \alpha \le 2$ and the point $(5\pi/12, 2)$ must be a high point of the graph. Similarly, we find that $(11\pi/12, -2)$ is a low point of the graph. We can now sketch the graph of the equation $y = 2 \sin (2x - \pi/3)$. (See figure 8.)

Figure 8.

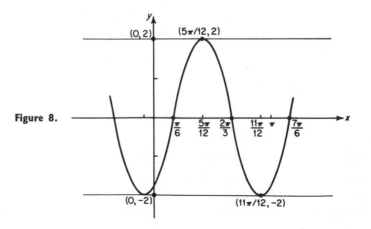

Example 3. Sketch the graph of the equation $y = x + \sin x$.

Solution: On the same set of coordinates, we sketch the graph of the equations $y = x$ and $y = \sin x$. Then, for each value of x, we add graphically the corresponding ordinates of the points (x, x) and $(x, \sin x)$. This is illustrated in figure 9.

Figure 9.

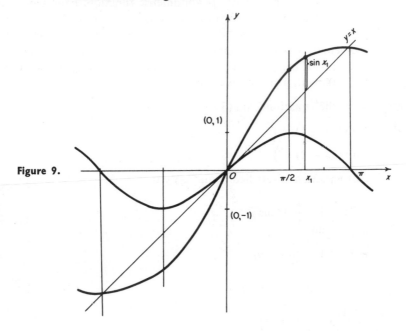

We remark that the function defined by the equation $f(x) = x + \sin x$ is the sum of two odd functions; hence, it is odd. It follows that the graph of the equation $y = x + \sin x$ must be symmetric with respect to the origin.

Exercises Sketch the graphs of the following equations:

1. $y = 2 \sin \left(3x - \dfrac{\pi}{4}\right)$ 2. $y = 3 \cos \left(\dfrac{x}{2} + \dfrac{\pi}{3}\right)$

3. $y = \dfrac{1}{2} \sin \left(5x + \dfrac{\pi}{7}\right)$ 4. $y = 4 \cos \left(\dfrac{x}{3} - \dfrac{\pi}{4}\right)$

5. $y = 2 \tan \left(3x - \dfrac{\pi}{4}\right)$ 6. $y = 3 \cot 2x$

7. $y = \dfrac{1}{2} \sec \left(3x - \dfrac{\pi}{2}\right)$ 8. $y = 2 \csc (5x - 1)$

9. $y = 2x - \sin 3x$ 10. $y = x + 3 \sin x$

11. $y = x \sin 2x$ 12. $y = x \cos 3x$

2.14. Trigonometric equations We have seen that a statement of equality involving some variable may be an identity or a conditional equation. Given a conditional equation, the process of finding the values of the variable which satisfy it is called *solving the equation.*

The simplest trigonometric equation is that of the form $F(ax + b) = c$ where F is a trigonometric function. Examples of this type were given in a previous section. One can solve a quadratic equation by factoring, thus reducing a somewhat complicated problem to two simpler ones. We shall show in this section that many solutions of trigonometric equations involve exactly the same idea. We start with a simple example:

Example 1. Solve the equation $2 \sin (3x - 1) = 1$

Solution: $2 \sin (3x - 1) = 1$

$$\sin (3x - 1) = \tfrac{1}{2}$$

This equation is satisfied if and only if

$$3x - 1 = \frac{\pi}{6} + 2n\pi \tag{1}$$

$$\text{or } 3x - 1 = \frac{5\pi}{6} + 2n\pi \tag{2}$$

From equation (1) we get

$$x = \frac{1}{3}\left(1 + \frac{\pi}{6} + 2n\pi\right)$$

and from (2) we get

$$x = \frac{1}{3}\left(1 + \frac{5\pi}{6} + 2n\pi\right) \blacksquare$$

Note: There is a neat way of writing the solution set of the equation of example 1.

We remark that $5\pi/6 = \pi - \pi/6$. Hence,

$$\frac{1}{3}\left(1 + \frac{5\pi}{6} + 2n\pi\right) = \frac{1}{3}\left(1 + \pi - \frac{\pi}{6} + 2n\pi\right) = \frac{1}{3}\left[1 - \frac{\pi}{6} + (2n + 1)\pi\right]$$

Recalling that $2n + 1$ is always an odd integer and $2n$ is always even, we see that the solutions are

$$x = \frac{1}{3}\left[1 + \frac{\pi}{6} + (\text{even integer}) \cdot \pi\right] \tag{3}$$

$$\text{and } x = \frac{1}{3}\left[1 - \frac{\pi}{6} + (\text{odd integer}) \cdot \pi\right] \tag{4}$$

If we write

$$x = \frac{1}{3}\left[1 + (-1)^k \frac{\pi}{6} + k\pi\right]$$

we get equality (3) if k is even and (4) if k is odd. Hence, the solution set of the equation

$$2 \sin (3x - 1) = 1$$

is $\left\{\frac{1}{3}\left(1 + (-1)^k \frac{\pi}{6} + k\pi\right) \middle| k \text{ an integer}\right\}$

Example 2. Solve the equation $2 \cos^2 x + 5 \sin x - 4 = 0$.

Solution: Recalling that $\cos^2 x \equiv 1 - \sin^2 x$, we get

$$2(1 - \sin^2 x) + 5 \sin x - 4 = 0$$
$$2 - 2 \sin^2 x + 5 \sin x - 4 = 0$$
$$-2 \sin^2 x + 5 \sin x - 2 = 0$$
$$2 \sin^2 x - 5 \sin x + 2 = 0$$
$$(\sin x - 2)(2 \sin x - 1) = 0$$

The last equality is satisfied if and only if

$$2 \sin x - 1 = 0 \quad \text{or} \quad \sin x - 2 = 0$$

$\sin x - 2 = 0$ is satisfied for no value of x, since $-1 \le \sin x \le 1$ for all x.

Hence, the only solutions are obtained from

$$2 \sin x - 1 = 0$$
$$\sin x = \tfrac{1}{2}$$

Hence, $x = \dfrac{\pi}{6} + 2n\pi \quad \text{or} \quad x = \dfrac{5\pi}{6} + 2n\pi$

As in the previous example, we can write the solution set of the given equation as

$$\left\{(-1)^k \frac{\pi}{6} + k\pi \middle| k \text{ an integer}\right\} \blacksquare$$

Example 3. Solve the equation $3 \sin x + 4 \cos x = 2$.

Solution: In section 2.9, example 7, we were able to write the expression $3 \sin \alpha + 4 \cos \alpha$ as $5 \sin (\alpha + \beta)$ where $\beta = \mathrm{Cos}^{-1} \tfrac{3}{5}$. Using this result, we can write the given equation in the equivalent form:

$$5 \sin (x + \beta) = 2 \cdot \quad \text{where } \beta = \mathrm{Cos}^{-1} \tfrac{3}{5}$$

Hence, $\sin (x + \beta) = \tfrac{2}{5}$

which is satisfied if and only if

$$x + \beta = \mathrm{Sin}^{-1}\, \tfrac{2}{5} + 2n\pi$$

$$\text{or } x + \beta = \pi - \mathrm{Sin}^{-1}\, \tfrac{2}{5} + 2n\pi$$

That is, if and only if

$$x + \beta = k\pi + (-1)^k \,\mathrm{Sin}^{-1}\, \tfrac{2}{5}$$

$$x = k\pi - \beta + (-1)^k \,\mathrm{Sin}^{-1}\, \tfrac{2}{5} \quad \text{where } \beta = \mathrm{Cos}^{-1}\, \tfrac{3}{5} \quad \blacksquare$$

Example 4. Solve the equation $\tan 2x = \cot x$.

Solution: For illustration, we shall give a solution which is not correct and discuss the fault in the argument.

Recalling that

$$\tan 2x \equiv \frac{2 \tan x}{1 - \tan^2 x} \quad \text{and} \quad \cot x \equiv \frac{1}{\tan x}$$

the given equation can be written in the equivalent form

$$\frac{2 \tan x}{1 - \tan^2 x} = \frac{1}{\tan x} \tag{1}$$

Multiplying both sides by $(1 - \tan^2 x) \tan x$, we get

$$2 \tan^2 x = 1 - \tan^2 x \tag{2}$$

$$3 \tan^2 x = 1 \tag{3}$$

$$\tan^2 x = \tfrac{1}{3} \tag{4}$$

$$\tan x = \frac{\pm 1}{\sqrt{3}} \tag{5}$$

The solutions of the last equation are easily seen to be $x = \pi/6 + k\pi$ and $x = -\pi/6 + k\pi$. Of course, these are also solutions of the equation $\tan 2x = \cot x$. We note, however, that $\cot \pi/2 = 0$ and $\tan (2 \cdot \pi/2) = \tan \pi = 0$. Hence, $x = \pi/2$ is also a solution of the equation $\tan 2x = \cot x$. Since $\pi/2 \neq \pm\pi/6 + k\pi$ for any integer k, we conclude that the equation $\tan 2x = \cot x$ and $\tan x = 1/\sqrt{3}$ are not equivalent. The fault in our solution lies in the fact that we multiplied both sides of equation (1) by $(1 - \tan^2 x) \tan x$. But for $x = \pi/2$, $\tan x$ is not defined. It should always be remembered that multiplication by an undefined quantity is as serious an error as division by zero.

We now give a correct solution. The given equation is written in the following equivalent form:

$$\frac{\sin 2x}{\cos 2x} = \frac{\cos x}{\sin x} \tag{1}$$

which is equivalent to

$$\frac{\sin x \sin 2x - \cos x \cos 2x}{\sin x \cdot \cos 2x} = 0 \qquad (2)$$

Equation (2) is satisfied if and only if

$$\sin x \sin 2x - \cos x \cos 2x = 0 \qquad (3)$$

which is equivalent to

$$\cos x \cos 2x - \sin x \sin 2x = 0 \qquad (4)$$

and to $\qquad \cos (x + 2x) = 0 \qquad (5)$

The solutions of equation (5) are obtained in the following way:

$$3x = \pm \frac{\pi}{2} + 2n\pi$$

$$x = \pm \frac{\pi}{6} + \frac{2n\pi}{3}$$

Since equation (5) is equivalent to $\tan 2x = \cot x$, the required solution set is

$$\left\{ \pm \frac{\pi}{6} + \frac{2n\pi}{3} \,\middle|\, n \text{ an integer} \right\} \; \blacksquare$$

Of course, trigonometric equations can involve inverse functions. A method for solving such equations is illustrated by the following example:

Example 5. Solve the equation $\mathrm{Cos}^{-1} x - \mathrm{Cos}^{-1} 2x = \pi/3$.

Solution: Let $\alpha = \mathrm{Cos}^{-1} x$ and $\beta = \mathrm{Cos}^{-1} 2x$. Then the original equation can be written in the form

$$\alpha - \beta = \frac{\pi}{3}$$

Hence, $\cos (\alpha - \beta) = \cos \dfrac{\pi}{3} = \dfrac{1}{2}$

It follows that

$$\cos \alpha \cos \beta + \sin \alpha \sin \beta = \frac{1}{2}$$

Clearly $\cos \alpha = x$, $\cos \beta = 2x$. Further, we find that

$$\sin \alpha = \sqrt{1 - x^2} \quad \text{and} \quad \sin \beta = \sqrt{1 - 4x^2}$$

It follows that

$$2x^2 + \sqrt{1 - x^2} \cdot \sqrt{1 - 4x^2} = \frac{1}{2}$$

$$2\sqrt{(1 - x^2)(1 - 4x^2)} = (1 - 4x^2)$$

Squaring both sides, we get

$$4(1 - 5x^2 + 4x^4) = 1 - 8x^2 + 16x^4$$

$$4 - 20x^2 + 16x^4 = 1 - 8x^2 + 16x^4$$

$$12x^2 - 3 = 0$$

$$x^2 = \tfrac{1}{4}$$

$$x = \pm\tfrac{1}{2}$$

One or both of these solutions may be extraneous. Hence, we must check whether they satisfy the original equation.

$$\text{Cos}^{-1}\left(\frac{1}{2}\right) - \text{Cos}^{-1}\left(2\cdot\frac{1}{2}\right) = \text{Cos}^{-1}\left(\frac{1}{2}\right) - \text{Cos}^{-1}(1)$$

$$= \frac{\pi}{3} - 0$$

$$= \frac{\pi}{3}$$

Hence, 1/2 is a solution.

$$\text{Also } \text{Cos}^{-1}\left(-\frac{1}{2}\right) - \text{Cos}^{-1}(-1) = \frac{2\pi}{3} - \pi$$

$$= -\frac{\pi}{3} \neq \frac{\pi}{3}$$

Therefore, $-\tfrac{1}{2}$ is an extraneous root and must be rejected. The only solution of the given equation is $\tfrac{1}{2}$. ∎

Example 6. Solve the equation $\sin x = x/2$.

Solution: Since we have no simple device to solve this equation, we shall approximate its solution graphically.

Figure 1.

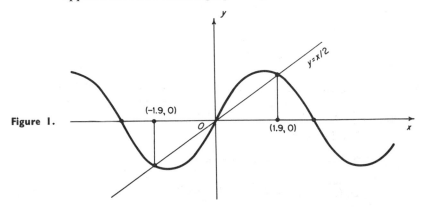

On the same coordinate system, we sketch the graphs of the equations $y = \sin x$ and $y = x/2$. These graphs intersect at three points. We note that two of these points are symmetric with respect to the origin. (See figure 1.) Suppose that the coordinates of these two points of intersection are (x_1, y_1) and $(-x_1, -y_1)$. Then, these coordinates must satisfy both equations. It follows that

$$y_1 = \sin x_1 \quad \text{and} \quad y_1 = \frac{x_1}{2}$$

Therefore, $\sin x_1 = \dfrac{x_1}{2}$

and x_1 is a solution of the given equation. Similarly, we see that $-x_1$ is a solution. From the graph, we find that the solutions are approximately 1.9, -1.9, and 0 (since the origin was the third point of intersection). ∎

Exercises Solve the equations:

1. $\cos^2 x = \frac{1}{2}$

2. $4\cos^2 x - 3 = 0$

3. $\tan x = 3$

4. $\sin 6x = \sin 3x$ (*Hint:* Solve for $3x$ first.)

5. $\cos^2 x + \sin x = 0$

6. $\sin 2x + \sin x = 0$

7. $4\sin^2 x + 4\cos 2x = 1$

8. $\sin^2 x + 2\sin x - 2 = 0$

9. $\sin^2 x + \sin x + 3 = 0$

10. $3\sec^2 x + \tan x - 5 = 0$

11. $3\cos x - \sin x = 1$

12. $\sec x + 3\cos x = 1$

13. $\cos 2x - 3\sin x + 1 = 0$

14. $2\sin^2 x - 2\cos x + 2\sin x = 1$

15. $\sin 3x + 10\sin x = 6$

16. $\cos x + \cos \dfrac{x}{2} = 0$

17. $2\sin 3x - 5(\csc 3x) - 3 = 0$

18. $\cos \left(\dfrac{\pi}{2} - x\right) = \frac{1}{2}$

19. $\sin\left(x + \dfrac{\pi}{3}\right) = \cos\left(x + \dfrac{\pi}{3}\right)$

20. $5 \sin x + 12 \cos x = 13$

21. $\cos x - 3 \sin x = 1$

22. $3 \cos x + 4 \sin x = 5$

23. $\text{Tan}^{-1} x + \text{Sin}^{-1} x = 0$

24. $\text{Sin}^{-1} x - \text{Cos}^{-1} x = \dfrac{\pi}{6}$

25. $\text{Tan}^{-1} 2x + \text{Tan}^{-1} 3x = \dfrac{3\pi}{4}$

26. $2\,\text{Sin}^{-1} x + \text{Cos}^{-1} x = \pi$

27. $\tan x + 2x = 0$

28. $x \tan x = 1$

29. $x^2 = \cos x$

2.15. The exponential function In section 1.7, example 12, we observed that the function g defined by $g : x \to ax$ has the property $g(x_1 + x_2) = g(x_1) + g(x_2)$. We raised the question whether there is a function f with the property $f(x_1 + x_2) = f(x_1) \cdot f(x_2)$.

Let us try to construct a function with this property and with domain N, the set of positive integers.

First suppose that $f(1) = a$ with $a > 0$.
Then we must have

$$f(2) = f(1 + 1) = f(1) \cdot f(1) = a \cdot a = a^2$$
$$f(3) = f(2 + 1) = f(2) \cdot f(1) = a^2 \cdot a = a^3$$

and by induction, we see that we must have

$$f(n) = a^n$$

The reader will recognize that the symbol a^n was defined in basic algebra. We review here some of the fundamental facts about exponents which were presented in algebra.

Definitions 2.15.1. If n is a positive integer, then

$$a^n = \underbrace{a \cdot a \ldots a}_{n \text{ factors}}$$

$$a^0 = 1 \qquad \text{if } a \neq 0$$

$$a^{-n} = \frac{1}{a^n} \qquad \text{if } a \neq 0$$

$$a^{1/n} = \sqrt[n]{a} \quad \text{if } a > 0$$

$$a^{m/n} = \sqrt[n]{a^m} = (\sqrt[n]{a})^m \quad \text{if } a > 0$$

Using definitions 2.15.1, it can be shown that if a and b are any positive real numbers and r and s are any rational numbers, then the following laws of exponents hold.

$$a^r \cdot a^s = a^{r+s} \tag{1}$$

$$\frac{a^r}{a^s} = a^{r-s} \tag{2}$$

$$(ab)^r = a^r \cdot b^r \tag{3}$$

$$\left(\frac{a}{b}\right)^r = \frac{a^r}{b^r} \tag{4}$$

$$(a^r)^s = a^{rs} \tag{5}$$

$$a^r > 0 \tag{6}$$

If $a \neq 1$, then $a^r = a^s$ if and only if $r = s$ $\tag{7}$

If $a > 1$, then $a^r > a^s$ if and only if $r > s$ $\tag{8}$

If $a < 1$, then $a^r > a^s$ if and only if $r < s$ $\tag{9}$

The proofs of these basic laws can be found in most algebra texts and will be omitted here. In this section, we give a precise definition of a^x where x is any real number. Of course, it is desirable to define a^x in such a way that the laws of exponents will hold. Suppose that we want to give a meaning to $2^{\sqrt{2}}$ in such a way that law 8 is satisfied. We note that $1.4 < \sqrt{2} < 1.5$. Hence, whatever value we assign to $2^{\sqrt{2}}$, we must have

$$2^{1.4} < 2^{\sqrt{2}} < 2^{1.5}$$

Further, noticing that

$$1.4 < 1.41 < 1.414 < \ldots < \sqrt{2} < \ldots < 1.415 < 1.42 < 1.5$$

we must have

$$2^{1.4} < 2^{1.41} < 2^{1.414} < \ldots < 2^{\sqrt{2}} < \ldots < 2^{1.415} < 2^{1.42} < 2^{1.5}$$

Considering the foregoing remarks, we conclude that if r is a rational number less than $\sqrt{2}$, we must have $2^r < 2^{\sqrt{2}}$. Hence, $2^{\sqrt{2}}$ is an upper bound of the set $\{2^r \mid r$ is rational and $r < \sqrt{2}\}$. Now if r' is any rational number greater than $\sqrt{2}$, then $2^{\sqrt{2}} < 2^{r'}$, and $2^{r'}$ is also an upper bound of the set $\{2^r \mid r$ is rational and $r < \sqrt{2}\}$. It therefore seems natural to define $2^{\sqrt{2}}$ to be the least upper bound of that set. Keeping in mind the preceding intuitive discussion, we state the following definitions.

Definition 2.15.2.
1. If $a > 1$ and x is any real number, then
$$a^x = \text{l.u.b.} \{a^r \mid r \text{ is rational and } r < x\}$$
2. $1^x = 1$ for any x
3. If $0 < a < 1$, then $1/a > 1$ and we define a^x to be the number

$$\frac{1}{(1/a)^x}$$

Remark: If s is a rational number and $a > 1$, then a^s (as defined in algebra) is the least upper bound of the set $\{a^r \mid r \text{ is rational and } r < s\}$. A similar remark holds when $0 < a < 1$. Hence, definitions 2.15.1 and 2.15.2 are equivalent when the exponent x is a rational number.

We can now define a function with domain the set of real numbers in the following way:

Definition 2.15.3. If $a > 0$, the function E_a is defined by the equation $E_a(x) = a^x$ and is called the *exponential function with base a*.

*Theorem 2.15.4. If $a > 1$, E_a is an increasing function; i.e., $x_1 < x_2$ implies $E_a(x_1) < E_a(x_2)$.

On the other hand, if $a < 1$, E_a is a decreasing function; i.e., $x_1 < x_2$ implies $E_a(x_1) > E_a(x_2)$.

Proof: Suppose $a > 1$. Let x_1 and x_2 be any two real numbers such that $x_1 < x_2$. Then

$$a^{x_1} = \text{l.u.b. } S \text{ where } S = \{a^r \mid r \text{ is rational and } r < x_1\}$$

and $a^{x_2} = \text{l.u.b. } T$ where $T = \{a^s \mid s \text{ is rational and } s < x_2\}$

We know that between any two real numbers, there is some rational number. Hence, there exists a rational number t_1 such that $x_1 < t_1 < x_2$.

Hence, if $r < x_1$, we have $r < t_1$ and $a^r < a^{t_1}$. It follows that a^{t_1} is an upper bound of the set S. Since a^{x_1} is its least upper bound, we must have

$$a^{x_1} \le a^{t_1}$$

There exists another rational number t_2 such that $t_1 < t_2 < x_2$. Hence, $a^{t_1} < a^{t_2}$. But a^{x_2} is an upper bound of the set T and $a^{t_2} \in T$. It follows that $a^{t_2} \le a^{x_2}$.

We have shown that

$$a^{x_1} \le a^{t_1} < a^{t_2} \le a^{x_2}$$

Hence, $a^{x_1} < a^{x_2}$

If $0 < a < 1$, $1/a > 1$, and $E_{1/a}$ is an increasing function. But

$$E_a(x) = a^x = \frac{1}{(1/a)^x} = \frac{1}{E_{1/a}(x)}$$

Therefore, $x_1 < x_2$ implies $E_{1/a}(x_1) < E_{1/a}(x_2)$ which in turn implies

$$\frac{1}{E_{1/a}(x_1)} > \frac{1}{E_{1/a}(x_2)}$$

that is, $E_a(x_1) > E_a(x_2)$. We have shown that E_a is decreasing when $0 < a < 1$. ∎

Corollary 2.15.5. If $a \neq 1$ and $a > 0$, the function E_a is one-to-one.

Proof: Suppose $a > 1$ and $x_1 \neq x_2$. Then $x_1 < x_2$ or $x_1 > x_2$. By the previous theorem, $x_1 < x_2$ implies $E_a(x_1) < E_a(x_2)$ and $x_2 < x_1$ implies $E_a(x_2) < E_a(x_1)$. In either case, we have $E_a(x_1) \neq E_a(x_2)$.

A similar argument can be given for the case $0 < a < 1$.

Hence, we have shown that the function E_a is one-to-one. ∎

By theorem 1.11.3, it follows that E_a has an inverse. We shall study this inverse in section 2.17.

In the next section, a proof that the laws of exponents hold for all real exponents will be given. We assume this fact here and conclude the section with some examples.

Example 1. Sketch the graph of E_2.

Solution: Since $2 > 1$, E_2 is an increasing function and its graph is rising. We consider the following table of values.

x	-3	-2	-1	0	1	2	3
2^x	$\frac{1}{8}$	$\frac{1}{4}$	$\frac{1}{2}$	1	2	4	8

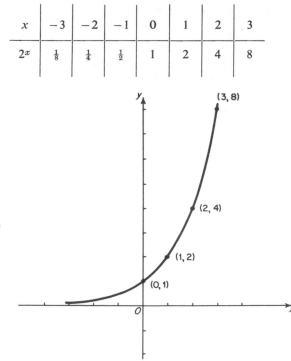

Figure 1.

The graph is sketched in figure 1 by first plotting the points $(-3, \frac{1}{8})$, $(-2, \frac{1}{4})$, $(-1, \frac{1}{2})$, $(0, 1)$, $(1, 2)$, $(2, 4)$, and $(3, 8)$ and by drawing a smooth curve passing through those points.

Remark: Since $a^0 = 1$ for any $a \neq 0$, the graph of any one of the functions E_a must pass through the point $(0, 1)$.

Example 2. Use the laws of exponents to show that if $0 < a < b$, then $x > 0$ implies $a^x < b^x$.

Solution: A natural way of starting this problem is to say $a < b$ implies $1 < b/a$ from which it follows that $1 = 1^x < (b/a)^x = b^x/a^x$. If, however, we claim that $1 < b/a$ implies $1^x < (b/a)^x$, we are using the very fact that we have to prove! Therefore, the argument must be modified. We first want to show that $1 < c$ and $x > 0$ implies $1 < c^x$. Note that $1 < 2$. Since $x > 0$, it follows that $x < 2x$. Further, since $1 < c$, we have $c^x < c^{2x}$. Since $c^{-x} > 0$, we get

$$c^x \cdot c^{-x} < c^{2x} \cdot c^{-x}$$

$$c^{x-x} < c^{2x-x}$$

$$1 < c^x$$

The step $1 < b/a$ and $x > 0$ implies $1 < (b/a)^x$ has now been justified and the proof is complete. ∎

Example 3. Find x if $4^x = 8$.

Solution: We note that $4 = 2^2$ and $8 = 2^3$. Hence, $4^x = 8$ is equivalent to $(2^2)^x = 2^3$ and to $2^{2x} = 2^3$. It follows that $2x = 3$ and $x = \frac{3}{2}$. ∎

Exercises Sketch the graphs of the following functions:

1. E_3 2. E_4

3. $E_{1/2}$ 4. $E_{1/3}$

5. $E_{\sqrt{2}}$ 6. E_1

Find the values of x which satisfy the following:

7. $27^x = 9$

8. $2^x 3^{2x} = \frac{1}{18}$

9. $3^x/4^{2x} = \frac{16}{3}$

10. $4^{x-1} = 8^{2x}$

11. $(2^{x-3})^{x+3} = \dfrac{1}{2^{5x+3}}$

12. Use the laws of exponents to show that if $0 < a < b$, then $x < 0$ implies $b^x < a^x$.

13. Prove the laws of exponents for the case where the exponents are positive integers.

*14. Prove the laws of exponents for the case where the exponents are integers.

**15. Prove the laws of exponents for the case where the exponents are rational numbers.

2.16. **Proof of the laws of exponents We shall now proceed to prove some of the laws of exponents for the case where the exponents are arbitrary real numbers. We shall assume that the laws have been proved for rational exponents.

Theorem 2.16.1. If $a > 0$, then $a^x \cdot a^y = a^{x+y}$.

Proof: First suppose $a > 1$.

Let $S = \{a^r \mid r$ is rational and $r < x\}$

$T = \{a^s \mid s$ is rational and $s < y\}$

$U = \{a^t \mid t$ is rational and $t < x + y\}$

Then, $a^x = $ l.u.b. S; $a^y = $ l.u.b. T,   and $a^{x+y} = $ l.u.b. U

Clearly, $a^x \cdot a^y = $ (l.u.b. S)(l.u.b. T)

$$= \text{l.u.b. } (S \cdot T)$$

But $S \cdot T = \{a^r \cdot a^s \mid r$ and s are rational, $r < x$ and $s < y\}$

$$= \{a^{r+s} \mid r \text{ and } s \text{ are rational, } r < x \text{ and } s < y\}$$

The proof will be complete if we can show that l.u.b. $S \cdot T = $ l.u.b. U. This can be done by using theorem 1.6.1.

Suppose $a^{r+s} \in S \cdot T$. Then $r < x$, $s < y$, and therefore, $r + s < x + y$. It follows that $a^{r+s} \in U$.

On the other hand, suppose $a^t \in U$. Then $t < x + y$. Suppose that it could be shown there exist rational numbers t_1 and t_2 such that $t_1 < x$, $t_2 < y$, and $t < t_1 + t_2$. Then we would have

$$a^t < a^{t_1 + t_2} \quad \text{and} \quad a^{t_1 + t_2} \in S \cdot T.$$

This would show that the hypothesis of theorem 1.6.1 is satisfied and we could conclude that l.u.b. $U = $ l.u.b. $S \cdot T$. It remains to show that such rational numbers t_1 and t_2 can be found.

The basic idea is to find $t_1 < x$ and $t_2 < y$ such that t_1 and t_2 are close enough to x and y respectively so that $t < t_1 + t_2$.

We first recall that if a and b are real numbers with $a < b$, then $a < (a + b)/2 < b$. (Section 1.2, exercise 22.)

Now we know that $t < x + y$.

Hence $\qquad\qquad t - x < y$

and $\qquad\qquad\qquad t - x < \dfrac{t - x + y}{2} < y$

There exists a rational number t_1 such that

$$t - x < \frac{t - x + y}{2} < t_1 < y \tag{1}$$

Similarly, we have

$$t - y < x$$

$$t - y < \frac{t - y + x}{2} < x$$

and there exists a rational number t_2 such that

$$t - y < \frac{t - y + x}{2} < t_2 < x \tag{2}$$

Adding inequalities (1) and (2), we get

$$\frac{t - x + y}{2} + \frac{t - y + x}{2} < t_1 + t_2 < x + y.$$

From which it follows that $t < t_1 + t_2 < x + y$. The proof of theorem 2.16.1 is complete in the case $a > 1$.

If $a = 1$, the proof is obvious. If $0 < a < 1$, we have

$$a^x \cdot a^y = \frac{1}{(1/a)^x} \cdot \frac{1}{(1/a)^y} = \frac{1}{(1/a)^x \cdot (1/a)^y} = \frac{1}{(1/a)^{x+y}} = a^{x+y} \quad \blacksquare$$

Theorem 2.16.2. If a and b are positive, then $(ab)^x = a^x \cdot b^x$.

Proof: *Case 1:* $a > 1$ and $b > 1$. Let

$$S = \{a^r \mid r \text{ is rational and } r < x\}$$

$$T = \{b^r \mid r \text{ is rational and } r < x\}$$

$$U = \{(ab)^r \mid r \text{ is rational and } r < x\}$$

Then $a^x = \text{l.u.b. } S$; $\qquad b^x = \text{l.u.b. } T$ and $(ab)^x = \text{l.u.b. } U$.
We want to show l.u.b. $U = (\text{l.u.b. } S)(\text{l.u.b. } T)$.
Since $(\text{l.u.b. } S)(\text{l.u.b. } T) = \text{l.u.b. } (S \cdot T)$, we need show only that l.u.b. $U = \text{l.u.b. } (S \cdot T)$.

Again we shall make use of theorem 1.6.1. Suppose $u \in U$. Then there exists a rational number $r < x$ such that $u = (ab)^r$. Since r is rational $(ab)^r = a^r \cdot b^r$. Hence, $u \in S \cdot T$. Suppose now that $v \in S \cdot T$.

Then there exist rational numbers r_1 and r_2 less than x such that $v = a^{r_1} \cdot b^{r_2}$. Without loss of generality, we can assume that $r_1 \leq r_2$.

Since $a > 1$, we have

$$a^{r_1} \leq a^{r_2}$$

and since $b^{r_2} > 0$, we get

$$a^{r_1}b^{r_2} \leq a^{r_2}b^{r_2} = (ab)^{r_2} = w$$

It follows that $v \leq w$ and $w \in U$.

We have now shown that given $v \in S \cdot T$, we can find $w \in U$ such that $v \leq w$ and given a $u \in U$, we also have $u \in S \cdot T$. Hence the hypothesis of theorem 1.6.1 is satisfied and we conclude that l.u.b. $U = $ l.u.b. $S \cdot T$.

Hence, $(ab)^x = a^x \cdot b^x$.

Case 2: $0 < a < 1$ and $0 < b < 1$.

Then $0 < ab < 1$ and, by definition, we have

$$(ab)^x = \frac{1}{(1/ab)^x}$$

But $1/a > 1$ and $1/b > 1$. Hence from case 1, we obtain

$$\left(\frac{1}{ab}\right)^x = \left[\frac{1}{a} \cdot \frac{1}{b}\right]^x = \left(\frac{1}{a}\right)^x \cdot \left(\frac{1}{b}\right)^x$$

It follows that

$$(ab)^x = \frac{1}{(1/ab)^x} = \frac{1}{(1/a)^x \cdot (1/b)^x} = \frac{1}{(1/a)^x} \cdot \frac{1}{(1/b)^x} = a^x \cdot b^x$$

Case 3: $0 < a < 1$ and $b > 1$.

In this case, $1/a > 1$. Hence, $1/a$ and b are both greater than 1. We must consider two subcases.

(a) If $1 < 1/a \leq b$. Then $ab \geq 1$.

Since both ab and $1/a$ are greater than or equal to 1, we can write

$$b^x = \left(ab \cdot \frac{1}{a}\right)^x = (ab)^x \left(\frac{1}{a}\right)^x$$

It follows that

$$(ab)^x = b^x \cdot \frac{1}{(1/a)^x} = b^x \cdot a^x = a^x \cdot b^x$$

(b) If $1 < b < 1/a$, we write

$$\left(\frac{1}{a}\right)^x = \left[\left(\frac{1}{ab}\right)(b)\right]^x = \left(\frac{1}{ab}\right)^x \cdot b^x$$

(since both $1/ab$ and b are greater than 1). Hence,

$$\frac{1}{(1/ab)^x} = \frac{1}{(1/a)^x} \cdot b^x$$

Since ab and a are both less than 1, the last equality can be written

$$(ab)^x = a^x \cdot b^x$$

Case 4: $0 < b < 1$ and $a > 1$. This is the same as case 3 with the role of a and b interchanged. ∎

Theorem 2.16.3. If $a > 0$ and x and y are any real numbers, then $(a^x)^y = a^{xy}$.

Proof: *Case 1:* y is an integer.

If $y = 1$, $(a^x)^y = (a^x)^1 = a^x = a^{xy}$

Suppose that the theorem has been verified for every positive integer y up to $y = k$.

Now $(a^x)^{k+1}\quad = (a^x)^k \cdot a^x \quad$ by theorem 2.16.1

$$= a^{xk} \cdot a^x \quad \text{by the induction hypothesis}$$

$$= a^{xk+x} \quad \text{by theorem 2.16.1}$$

Hence, $(a^x)^{k+1} = a^{x(k+1)}$

It follows that $(a^x)^y = a^{xy}$ is true if y is any positive integer. The case where $y < 0$ follows from the definition $a^{-n} = 1/a^n$.

Case 2: y is a rational number. Then $y = m/n$ where m and n are integers. Since the laws of exponents hold for rational numbers, we get

$$(a^x)^{m/n} = (a^x)^{m \cdot 1/n} = [(a^x)^m]^{1/n}$$

But, by case 1 $\quad (a^x)^m = a^{xm}$

Hence, $\qquad (a^x)^{m/n} = (a^{xm})^{1/n} = (a^{xm/n \cdot n})^{1/n}$

$$= [(a^{xm/n})^n]^{1/n} \quad \text{(by case 1)}$$

$$= (a^{xm/n})^{n \cdot 1/n}$$

$$= a^{xm/n}$$

Case 3: $a > 1$, $x > 0$, and y arbitrary.

Let $\qquad S = \{(a^x)^r \mid r \text{ is rational and } r < y\}$

and $\qquad T = \{a^s \mid s \text{ is rational and } s < xy\}$

Then $(a^x)^y = \text{l.u.b. } S \quad$ and $\quad a^{xy} = \text{l.u.b. } T$

We want to show l.u.b. $S = $ l.u.b. T.

Since, when r is rational, we have $(a^x)^r = a^{xr}$, we can write

$S = \{a^{xr} \mid r \text{ is rational and } r < y\}$. Let $u \in S$. Then there is a rational number $r < y$ such that $u = a^{xr}$. Since $x > 0$, $r < y$ implies $rx < xy$. There is a rational number t such that $rx < t < xy$. Then $a^{xr} < a^t$. Let $w = a^t$. Since t is rational and $t < xy$, we have $w \in T$ and $u < w$.

On the other hand, let $u \in T$. Then there is a rational number $t < xy$ such that $u = a^t$. Since $x > 0$, $t < xy$ implies $t/x < y$. Hence, there is a rational number r such that $t/x < r < y$. It follows that $t < xr$. Hence, $a^t < a^{xr}$. Let $w = a^{xr}$. Since r is rational and $r < y$, $w \in S$. Furthermore, $u < w$. It follows that the hypothesis of theorem 1.6.1 is satisfied and we conclude l.u.b. $S = $ l.u.b. T. That is to say, $(a^x)^y = a^{xy}$.

Case 4: $0 \leqslant a < 1$, $x > 0$, and y arbitrary.

First note that $1 = c \cdot 1/c$ for any $c \neq 0$

Hence,
$$1^y = \left(c \cdot \frac{1}{c}\right)^y = c^y \cdot \left(\frac{1}{c}\right)^y$$

By definition, $1^y = 1$. Hence, $\left(\dfrac{1}{c}\right)^y = \dfrac{1}{c^y}$

Now we can write
$$(a^x)^y = \left[\frac{1}{(1/a)^x}\right]^y = \frac{1}{[(1/a)^x]^y} = \frac{1}{(1/a)^{xy}} = a^{xy}$$

Case 5: $0 < a$, $x < 0$, and y arbitrary.

First we note that by theorem 2.15.1, we have
$$a^x \cdot a^{-x} = a^{x+(-x)} = a^{x-x} = a^0 = 1$$

Hence, $a^x = \dfrac{1}{a^{-x}}$

Now, if $x < 0$, then $0 < -x$. Hence,
$$(a^x)^y = \left[\frac{1}{a^{-x}}\right]^y = \frac{1}{(a^{-x})^y} = \frac{1}{a^{-xy}} = a^{xy} \quad \blacksquare$$

We shall omit the proofs of the other laws of exponents. We must remark that, although it is natural to define a^x by starting with a^n where n is an integer and generalizing the definition to a^r where r is rational and to a^x where x is any real number, this method leads to quite complicated proofs for the laws of exponents. We shall briefly discuss a different approach at the end of Chapter 2.

2.17. The logarithm function In section 2.15, we showed that if $a > 0$ and $a \neq 1$, the exponential function with base a is a one-to-one function. (See corollary 2.15.5.) Hence, it has an inverse. We shall now study some of the properties of this inverse.

The graph of the function E_2 defined by $E_2(x) = 2^x$ (figure 1, section 2.15) suggests that the domain of that function is the set of all real numbers and its range is the set of all positive real numbers. We shall omit the proof that the range of any exponential function with base $a \neq 1$ is the set of positive real numbers. This can be most efficiently done by using some techniques of the calculus which students will learn later. For the present, we give the following definition:

Definition 2.17.1. Given any real number $a > 0$, not equal to 1, the inverse of the exponential function E_a is called the *logarithm function to the base a* and is denoted by $\log_a$.

Remarks:
1. The domain of the logarithm function is the set of all positive real numbers.
2. The range of the logarithm function is the set of all real numbers.
3. $E_a[\log_a (x)] = x$ for every $x \in D_{\log_a}$, and
   $\log_a [E_a(x)] = x$ for every $x \in D_{E_a}$.
4. The graphs of E_a and $\log_a$ are symmetric to each other with respect to the graph of the equation $y = x$.

The logarithm function has some very useful properties. Some of them can be used for computation. Indeed, the discovery of logarithms was prompted by the desire of scientists to simplify some very complicated computations connected with their work. In the age of electronic computing machines, logarithms have lost much of their usefulness as a computing device, but the logarithm function is one that every young (and old) scientist must be familiar with. Its basic properties are the content of the next theorem.

Theorem 2.17.2. If $a > 0$ and $a \neq 1$, then for any positive real numbers x and y, we have

1. $\log_a (xy) = \log_a (x) + \log_a (y)$
2. $\log_a \left(\dfrac{x}{y}\right) = \log_a (x) - \log_a (y)$
3. $\log_a (x^p) = p \cdot \log_a (x)$ for any real number p
4. $\log_a (1) = 0$
5. $\log_a (a) = 1$

Proof: 1. Let $\log_a (x) = u$ and $\log_a (y) = v$.

Then, $E_a[\log_a (x)] = E_a(u)$ and $E_a[\log_a(y)] = E_a(v)$.

That is, $x = E_a(u)$ and $y = E_a(v)$

which can be written as

$$x = a^u \quad \text{and} \quad y = a^v$$

Hence, $xy = a^u \cdot a^v$

$$= a^{u+v}$$

$$= E_a(u + v)$$

It follows that

$$\log_a (xy) = \log_a [E_a(u + v)]$$

$$= u + v$$

Hence, $\log_a (xy) = \log_a (x) + \log_a (y)$

2. The proof is similar to that of part 1 and is left as an exercise.

3. Let $\log_a (x) = u$

Then $\quad E_a[\log_a (x)] = E_a(u)$

$$x = E_a(u)$$

$$= a^u$$

Hence, $\quad\quad x^p = (a^u)^p$

$$= a^{up} = E_a(up)$$

Therefore, $\log_a (x^p) = \log_a [E_a(up)] = up = pu$

$$= p \cdot \log_a (x)$$

4. For any $a \neq 0$, $a^0 = 1$. Hence, for any $a \neq 0$ and $a \neq 1$, we also have

$$E_a(0) = 1$$

It follows that

$\log_a (1) = \log_a [E_a(0)]$

$\log_a (1) = 0$

5. The proof is left as an exercise. ∎

Theorem 2.17.3. The logarithm function is one-to-one.

Proof: Since E_a and $\log_a$ are inverses of each other and since a function has an inverse if and only if it is one-to-one, then $\log_a$ is one-to-one. ∎

Theorem 2.17.4. Given any two positive numbers a and b each different from 1, it is true that

$$\log_a(b) \cdot \log_b (a) = 1$$

Proof: Let $\log_a (b) = x$ and $\log_b (a) = y$

Then $a^x = b$ and $b^y = a$

From $a^x = b$, we get

$$b^y = (a^x)^y = a^{xy}$$

But $b^y = a.$

Hence, $a = a^1 = a^{xy}$

It follows that

$$1 = xy$$

That is, $\log_a (b) \cdot \log_b (a) = 1$ ∎

Example 1. Prove the "chain rule of logarithms."

$$\log_a (b) \cdot \log_b (c) \cdot \log_c (a) = 1$$

Solution: Let $\log_a (b) = x,$ $\log_b (c) = y,$ and $\log_c (a) = z$

Then $a^x = b$ $\quad\quad$ (1)

$\quad\quad b^y = c$ $\quad\quad$ (2)

$\quad\quad c^z = a$ $\quad\quad$ (3)

From (1), we get

$b^y = (a^x)^y = a^{xy}$ $\quad\quad$ (4)

Comparing (2) and (4), we obtain

$c = a^{xy}$ $\quad\quad$ (5)

From (5), we get

$c^z = (a^{xy})^z = a^{xyz}$ $\quad\quad$ (6)

Comparing (3) and (6), we conclude

$a = a^1 = a^{xyz}$

Hence, $xyz = 1$

That is, $\log_a (b) \cdot \log_b (c) \cdot \log_c (a) = 1$ ∎

Example 2. Write the following in an equivalent exponential form:

(a) $\log_2 (8) = 3$ $\quad\quad$ (b) $\log_5 \left(\frac{1}{25}\right) = -2$

Solution: (a) $\log_2 (8) = 3$

Hence, $E_2[\log_2 (8)] = E_2(3)$

$$8 = 2^3$$

(b) $\log_5 \left(\frac{1}{25}\right) = -2$

Therefore $E_5[\log_5 \left(\frac{1}{25}\right)] = E_5(-2)$

$$\tfrac{1}{25} = 5^{-2}$$ ∎

Remark: In the proofs of the theorems and in the solutions of the examples, we have used the fact that the functions E_a and $\log_a$ are inverses of each other. It is now obvious that $\log_a (b) = x$ if and only if $a^x = b$, provided that $a > 0$ and $a \neq 1$.

Example 3. Find x if

$$\text{(a) } \log_{10} 1000 = x \qquad \text{(b) } \log_3 x = 2 \qquad \text{(c) } \log_x \tfrac{1}{8} = -3$$

Solution: (a) $\log_{10} 1000 = x$ is equivalent to $10^x = 1000$
But $1000 = 10^3$. Hence, $10^x = 10^3$ and $x = 3$.
(b) $\log_3 x = 2$ is equivalent to $3^2 = x$
Hence, $x = 9$
(c) $\log_x \tfrac{1}{8} = -3$ is equivalent to $x^{-3} = \tfrac{1}{8}$
But $\tfrac{1}{8} = (\tfrac{1}{2})^3 = 2^{-3}$
Hence, $x^{-3} = 2^{-3}$ and $x = 2$. ∎

Example 4. Given that $\log_2 (3) = a$ and $\log_2 (5) = b$, find an expression in terms of a and b for

$$\text{(a) } \log_2 (15) \qquad \text{(b) } \log_2 (135) \qquad \text{(c) } \log_2 (8/3)$$

Solution: (a) Note that $15 = (3)(5)$

$$\text{Hence, } \log_2 (15) = \log_2 [(3)(5)]$$

$$= \log_2 (3) + \log_2 (5)$$

$$= a + b$$

(b) Note that $135 = (27)(5) = (3^3)(5)$

$$\text{Hence, } \qquad \log_2 (135) = \log_2 [(3^3)(5)]$$

$$= \log_2 (3^3) + \log_2 (5)$$

$$= 3 \log_2 (3) + \log_2 (5)$$

$$= 3a + b$$

(c) We note that $8/3 = 2^3/3$

$$\text{Hence, } \log_2 (8/3) = \log_2 (2^3) - \log_2 (3)$$

$$= 3 \log_2 (2) - \log_2 (3)$$

But in general $\log_a (a) = 1$

$$\text{Hence} \qquad \log_2 (8/3) = (3)(1) - a$$

$$\text{and} \qquad \log_2 (8/3) = 3 - a \quad ∎$$

Exercises

1. Prove part 2 of theorem 2.17.2.
2. If a, b, c, and d are all positive numbers different from 1, prove that
$\log_a (b) \cdot \log_b (c) \cdot \log_c (d) \cdot \log_d (a) = 1$.

3. Write the following in an equivalent exponential form.
   (a) $\log_3 81 = 4$ (b) $\log_{81} 3 = \frac{1}{4}$
   (c) $\log_4 \frac{1}{2} = -\frac{1}{2}$ (d) $\log_{10} \cdot 01 = -2$
   (e) $\log_{10} 1 = 0$

4. Write the following in an equivalent logarithm form.
   (a) $2^4 = 16$ (b) $2^{-3} = .125$
   (c) $3^5 = 243$ (d) $10^{-1} = .1$
   (e) $(\frac{1}{2})^{-1} = 2$

5. Find x if
   (a) $\log_2 32 = x$ (b) $\log_x 4 = \frac{1}{2}$
   (c) $\log_{13} x = 0$ (d) $\log_x 8 = 1$
   (e) $\log_{10} x = -3$ (f) $\log_4 2 = x$
   (g) $\log_x \frac{4}{9} = -2$ (h) $\log_8 x = \frac{1}{3}$

6. Given that $\log_{10}(2) = a$ and $\log_{10}(3) = b$, find an expression in terms of a and b for the following:
   (a) $\log_{10}(6)$ (b) $\log_{10}(36)$
   (c) $\log_{10}(\frac{9}{8})$ (d) $\log_{10}(\sqrt{3})$
   (e) $\log_{10}(5)$ (f) $\log_{10}(.25)$

**2.18. The area function Suppose that the graph of some function is a curve C without breaks and lying above the x axis. A function may be defined in the following way: Let B be a fixed point with coordinates $(a, 0)$. For each value $x \geq a$, let $A(x)$ denote the area bounded by the curve C, the x axis and the perpendiculars to the x axis through the points $(a, 0)$ and $(x, 0)$. We know (intuitively) that for each value of $x \geq a$, there is one and only one corresponding value of $A(x)$. Hence, we have a set of ordered pairs $\{(x, A(x) \mid x \geq a\}$ which is a function. Its domain is the set $\{x \mid x \geq a\}$. (See figure 1.) In this section, we shall give a formal definition for such an area. We begin with some trivial examples.

Figure 1.
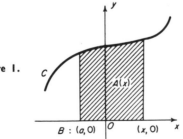

Example 1. Let the curve C be the graph of the equation $y = 2x$, and let the point B be the origin. Find the area function.

Solution: In this case, the area is that of a triangle whose base is x and height $2x$.

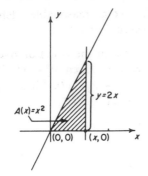

Figure 2.

Hence, (see figure 2) it can be easily calculated

$$A(x) = \tfrac{1}{2} \cdot x \cdot 2x$$

$$= x^2 \quad \blacksquare$$

Example 2. Let the curve C be the graph of the constant function f defined by $f(x) = 2$ and let the point B be the point $(2, 0)$. Find the area function.

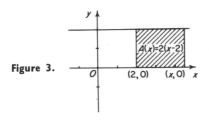

Figure 3.

Solution: For each $x > 2$, the area is that of a rectangle with base $(x - 2)$ and height 2. (See figure 3.) If $x = 2$, the area is 0. Hence, the area function is given by the equation

$$A(x) = 2(x - 2), \; x \geq 2 \quad \blacksquare$$

   In the case where the curve C is not a straight line, defining the area is a complicated matter. It can be done by using the axiom of completeness, as we shall illustrate in example 3. First, we need to introduce some new terms. If a and b are real numbers with $a < b$, the set $\{x \mid a \leq x \leq b\}$ is called a *closed interval* and is denoted by $[a, b]$. The ordered set $(x_0, x_1, x_2, \ldots, x_n)$ where $a = x_0 < x_1 < x_2 < \ldots < x_n = b$ is called a *partition* of $[a, b]$. For any i such that $1 \leq i \leq n$, the interval $[x_{i-1}, x_i]$ is called the i-th *subinterval* determined by the partition $(x_0, x_1, x_2, \ldots, x_n)$. If the partition is such that $x_1 - x_0 = x_2 - x_1 = x_3 - x_2 = \ldots = x_n - x_{n-1}$, then it is said to be *regular*. We are now ready to use the following example to illustrate how the area under a curve can be defined.

Example 3. Let the curve C be the graph of the equation $y = x^2$. Let the point B

be the origin. For each $x > 0$, give a "reasonable" definition for the area $A(x)$. Formulate $A(x)$ in terms of x.

Solution: First we shall show that the graph of the equation over the positive x axis is rising; i.e., if $0 < x_1 < x_2$, then $x_1^2 < x_2^2$. We need only remark that $x_1 < x_2$ implies $(x_2 - x_1) > 0$. Since x_1 and x_2 are positive, so is $(x_2 + x_1)$, and we get

$$(x_2 - x_1)(x_2 + x_1) > 0(x_2 + x_1)$$

That is, $$x_2^2 - x_1^2 > 0$$

Hence, $$x_2^2 > x_1^2$$

Let x be any positive number. Suppose we divide the closed interval $[0, x]$ into n equal subintervals. Then the length of each subinterval will be x/n. Hence, the regular partition which we obtain is the set $(0, x/n, 2 \cdot x/n, 3 \cdot x/n, 4 \cdot x/n, \ldots, n \cdot x/n)$. Since the graph of the

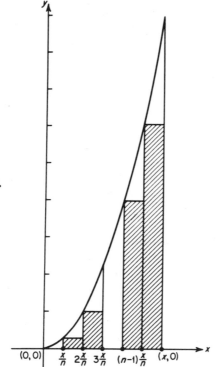

Figure 4.

equation $y = x^2$ is rising, for any of the intervals $[i \cdot x/n, (i + 1) \cdot x/n]$, the rectangle whose base is that interval and whose height is $(i \cdot x/n)^2$ is contained in the area we are seeking. (See figure 4.) If we call this rectangle R_i, we see that its area is $x/n \cdot (i \cdot x/n)^2 = x^3/n^3 \cdot i^2$. There are n such rectangles. Their union is called a *regular rectangular polygon* and is contained in the area we are seeking. The area of the rectangular polygon is

$$A_n = \frac{x^3}{n^3} \cdot 0^2 + \frac{x^3}{n^3} \cdot 1^2 + \frac{x^3}{n^3} \cdot 2^2$$

$$+ \frac{x^3}{n^3} \cdot 3^2 + \ldots + \frac{x^3}{n^3} \cdot (n-1)^2 = \frac{x^3}{n^3}(1^2 + 2^2 + \ldots + (n-1)^2)$$

And if we use the formula from algebra (section 1.3, see example 1),

$$1^2 + 2^2 + 3^2 + \ldots + k^2 = \frac{k(k+1)(2k+1)}{6}$$

we get

$$A_n = \frac{x^3}{n^3} \cdot \frac{(n-1)(n)(2n-1)}{6}$$

$$= \frac{x^3}{6}\left(1 - \frac{1}{n}\right)\left(2 - \frac{1}{n}\right)$$

We now make the following remarks:

1. The positive integer n is arbitrary.
2. For each value of the integer n, if we construct a regular rectangular polygon as just described, it is inscribed (contained) in the area we are considering.
3. Hence, we may assume that $A(x)$ is greater than, or equal to, any of the area of inscribed rectangular polygons obtained as described above. Hence, $A(x)$ is an upper bound of the set of all areas A_n of regular inscribed rectangular polygons.
4. The area of the rectangle whose base is $[0, x]$ and the height of which is x^2, that is, $x \cdot x^2 = x^3$, is certainly greater than any of the A_n; hence, it is an upper bound of the set $\{A_n \mid n \text{ a positive integer}\}$. Therefore, that set has a l.u.b. It is intuitively clear that this least upper bound is what we call the *area* $A(x)$.

We note that $0 < 1 - \dfrac{1}{n} < 1$ if $n > 2$

$$0 < 2 - \frac{1}{n} < 2$$

Hence, $A_n = \dfrac{x^3}{6}\left(1 - \dfrac{1}{n}\right)\left(2 - \dfrac{1}{n}\right) < \dfrac{x^3}{6} \cdot 2 = \dfrac{x^3}{3}$

It is clear that $x^3/3$ is the l.u.b. of the set $\{A_n \mid n \text{ an integer}\}$. Hence $A(x) = x^3/3$. ∎

In general, if we want to define $A(x)$ of figure 1, we proceed as follows. Consider the set of all possible regular partitions of the closed interval $[a, x]$. With each regular partition, there is associated an area of the largest inscribed regular polygon formed by taking the union of all inscribed rectangles whose bases are the subintervals determined by the partition. The least upper bound of the set of all such areas of the rectangular polygons is by definition $A(x)$.

Example 4. Let the curve C be the graph of the equation $y = k/x$ where $k > 0$. Let the point B be the point $(1, 0)$. Show that for any a and b both greater than 1, we have $A(ab) = A(a) + A(b)$.

We introduce the following notation. If α and β are real numbers with $\alpha < \beta$ and if C is a curve above the interval $[\alpha, \beta]$, then the area bounded by the curve C, the x axis, and the perpendiculars to the x axis through the points $(\alpha, 0)$ and $(\beta, 0)$ is denoted by A_α^β. (See figure 5.)

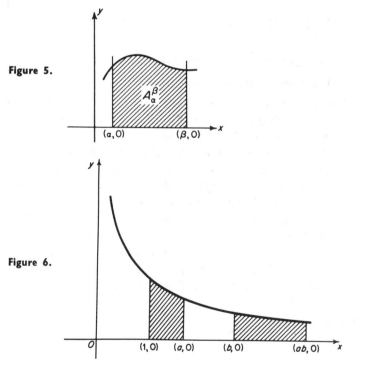

Figure 5.

Figure 6.

We want to show that $A(ab) = A(a) + A(b)$ (see figure 6); i.e., we need to show that

$$A_1^{ab} = A_1^a + A_1^b$$

But $A_1^{ab} = A_1^a + A_a^b + A_b^{ab}$ (assuming $a < b$)

and $A_1^b = A_1^a + A_a^b$.

(Note that we have not proved that area is additive. This can be done using the same techniques as in the proof of theorem 2.2.4.) We shall leave the proof of the fact as an exercise. Hence, we need prove only that

$$A_1^a + A_a^b + A_b^{ab} = A_1^a + A_1^a + A_a^b$$

The foregoing equality will certainly be satisfied if it is true that $A_b^{ab} = A_1^a$. But, $A_1^a = $ l.u.b. S where S is the set of all areas of all regular inscribed rectangular polygons in the region under the curve C and above the interval $[1, a]$. Also $A_b^{ab} = $ l.u.b. T where T is the set of areas of all regular inscribed rectangular polygons in the region under the curve C and above the interval $[b, ab]$. The proof will be complete if we can show that $S = T$.

Figure 7.

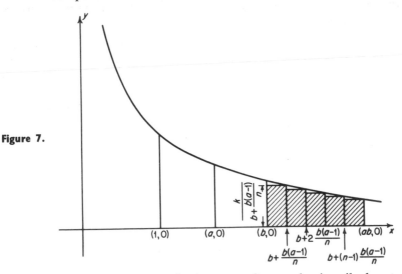

Let $u \in T$. Then u is the area of a regular inscribed rectangular polygon in the region under the curve C and above the interval $[b, ab]$. Hence there is a positive integer n such that u is the area of the rectangular polygon obtained by taking the union of the inscribed rectangles whose bases are the subintervals $[b, b + b(a - 1)/n]$, $[b + b(a - 1/n, b' + 2 \cdot b(a - 1)/n], \ldots, [b + (n - 1) \cdot b(a - 1)/n, b + n \cdot b(a - 1)/n]$. (See figure 7.) Hence,

$$u = \frac{b(a - 1)}{n} \cdot \frac{k}{b + [b(a - 1)/n]} + \frac{b(a - 1)}{n} \cdot \frac{k}{b + [2b(a - 1)/n]} + \cdots$$

$$+ \frac{b(a - 1)}{n} \cdot \frac{k}{b + [nb(a - 1)/n]} = \frac{a - 1}{n} \cdot \frac{k}{1 + [(a - 1)/n]}$$

$$+ \frac{a - 1}{n} \cdot \frac{k}{1 + [2(a - 1)/n]} + \cdots + \frac{a - 1}{n} \cdot \frac{k}{1 + [n(a - 1)/n]}$$

But this expression gives the area of an inscribed rectangular polygon in the region under C and above the interval $[1, a]$. Hence, we also have $u \in S$. The argument is reversible, which shows that $S = T$ and the proof is complete. ∎

We note that the property of this area function $A(ab) = A(a) + A(b)$ is the same as one of the properties of the logarithm functions. Indeed, it can be shown that these two functions are equal. This idea yields a different approach to the exponential function. We can first define the logarithm function as an area function, as we did in example 4. Then the exponential function is introduced as the inverse of the logarithm function.

Exercises 1. Prove that area is additive. (*Hint:* Follow the same pattern as in the proof of theorem 2.2.4.)

2. Let the curve C be the graph of the equation $y = x^3$. Let the point B be the origin. For each $x > 0$, formulate the area $A(x)$ in terms of x. (*Hint:* See section 2.18, example 3, and use the result of section 1.3, exercise 7.)

Chapter 3

Applications of Elementary Functions

Application of the elementary functions to such problems as simplification of computations (using the logarithms), size of populations (using the exponential function), and physical problems which reduce to solving triangles are given in this chapter. Although computation with logarithms is losing its importance with the use of improved electronic computing devices, we begin our study of the applications of the elementary functions with this topic.

3.1. Calculations with logarithms We have seen in section 2.17 that any positive number other than "one" can be used as a base for a logarithm function. It is most convenient for computation to use 10 as a base. Henry Briggs (1560–1631) discovered the logarithms to that base; hence, the function $\log_{10}$ is sometimes called the *Briggs logarithm function*. We shall also call it the *common logarithm function* and, in our notation, the base will not be written if it is 10; i.e., $\log = \log_{10}$.

We first remark that any positive real number x can be written as $(y)(10^n)$ where n is some integer and $1 \le y < 10$. For example, $256.1 = (2.561)(10^2)$ and $.0013 = (1.3)(10^{-3})$.

Hence, if $x = (y)(10^n)$, then $\log(x) = \log[(y)(10^n)]$

$$= \log(y) + \log(10^n) \quad \text{(by theorem 2.17.2)}$$
$$= \log(y) + n\log(10) \quad \text{(by theorem 2.17.2)}$$
$$= \log(y) + n \quad \text{(since } \log 10 = \log_{10} 10 = 1)$$

Log (y) is called the *mantissa* of the logarithm of x, and n is called its *characteristic*.

Remarks:
1. Since $1 \le y < 10$, $\log(1) = 0$, $\log(10) = 1$, and the logarithm function to the base 10 is an increasing function, we must have $0 \le \log(y) < 1$. Hence, the mantissa of the logarithm of a number is always of the form $0.d_1 d_2 d_3 d_4 \ldots$ where each d_i is one of the digits $0, 1, 2, \ldots, 9$. The 0 and decimal point are usually not shown in the tables of logarithms.

2. The characteristic of a logarithm does not depend on the actual digits in the number and depends only on the powers of 10 between which the number lies.

3. The characteristic of the logarithm of a number will always be found by inspection. Its mantissa, or rather an approximation of its mantissa, will usually be found from tables. We give a few examples to illustrate this practice.

Example 1. Find an approximation for $\log(.002351)$.

Solution: First we note that

$$.002351 = (2.351)(10^{-3})$$

Hence, $\log(.002351) = \log(2.351) - 3$

To find an approximation for $\log(2.351)$, we refer to the table of logarithms under 235 and to the right under 1 to find the number .37125.

Hence, $\log(.002351) \doteq .37125 - 3*$

$$= -2.62875 \ \blacksquare$$

---

* $\doteq$ indicates an approximation.

Remark: It is not convenient to write the logarithm of a number in the form given in the last step of the previous example. That is, the logarithm should be given in a form from which the characteristic and mantissa can both be read easily. It is not evident from

$$\log(.002351) = -2.62875$$ that the mantissa is .37125.

Hence, we usually write

$$\log(.002351) \doteq .37125 - 3 \quad \text{or} \quad \log(.002351) \doteq 7.37125 - 10$$

(using the fact that $-3 = 7 - 10$ or, in general,

$$\log(.002351) \doteq N.37125 - P$$

(where N and P are positive integers conveniently chosen so that $N - P = -3$). For example, if, in a particular problem, we need to divide $\log(.002351)$ by 7, we would choose N and P so that P is divisible by 7.

Example 2. Find an approximation of x if $\log(x) = 8.37328 - 10$.

Solution: Obviously, the characteristic of the logarithm is -2 and the mantissa is .37328. Referring to the tables, we find 37328 in the row to the right of 236 and in the column under 2. Hence, $.37328 = \log(2.362)$. Since the characteristic of the logarithm of x is -2, we have

$$x = (2.362)(10^{-2}) = .02362$$

It is sometimes useful to use linear interpolation in the case where the tables are not given to enough places for the problem at hand.

Example 3. Find an approximation to $\log(3.2168)$.

Solution: From the tables, we find that

$$\log(3.216) = .50732 \quad \text{and} \quad \log(3.217) = .50745$$

Since $3.2160 < 3.2168 < 3.2170$ and since the logarithm function is an increasing function, we must have

$$\log(3.2160) < \log(3.2168) < \log(3.2170)$$

Hence, $.50732 < \log(3.2168) < .50745$

To get an *approximation* for $\log(3.2168)$, we *assume* that the graph of the logarithm function between the points (3.216, .50732) and (3.217, .50745) is a straight line. We illustrate the procedure with figure 1 which is obviously not to scale. From the two similar right triangles, we obtain

$$\frac{x}{13} = \frac{8}{10}$$

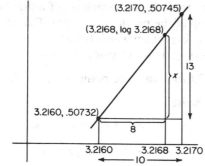

Figure 1.

Hence, $x = \frac{104}{10} = 10.4$

Therefore,

$$\log (3.2168) \doteq .50732 + .000104 = .507424 \quad \blacksquare$$

Example 4. Using logarithms, compute an approximation of

$$\frac{(2.51)^5(\sqrt[3]{.012})}{(31.2)^2(51.06)^3}$$

Solution: Let $x = (2.51)^5(\sqrt[3]{.012})$, $y = (31.2)^2(51.06)^3$, and $z = x/y$.
From the properties of the logarithm function, we know that
$\log (z) = \log (x) - \log (y)$ where $\log (x) = 5 \log (2.51) + \frac{1}{3} \log (.012)$
and $\log (y) = 2 \log (31.2) + 3 \log (51.06)$. We set up the necessary
calculations below and then make a few remarks about them.

$$\log (2.51) \doteq 0.39967 \tag{1}$$

$$5 \log (2.51) \doteq 1.99835 \tag{2}$$

$$\log (.012) \doteq 1.07918 - 3 \tag{3}$$

$$\frac{1}{3} \log (.012) \doteq .35973 - 1 \tag{4}$$

$$\log (x) \quad = 1.35808 = 8.35808 - 7 \tag{5}$$

$$\log (31.2) \doteq 1.49415 \tag{6}$$

$$2 \log (31.2) = 2.98830 \tag{7}$$

$$\log (51.06) \doteq 1.70808 \tag{8}$$

$$3 \log (51.06) \doteq 5.12424 \tag{9}$$

$$\log (y) \quad \doteq 8.11254 \tag{10}$$

$$\log (z) = \log (x) - \log (y) \doteq 0.24554 - 7 \tag{11}$$

$$z = (1.7601)(10^{-7}) \tag{12}$$

$$= .00000017601$$

Remarks: The characteristic of log (.012) is -2. We wrote it as $1-3$ on line (3) because we had to divide log (.012) by 3. Log $(x) = 1.35808$ On line (5), however, we wrote it as $8.35808 - 7$. The reason for doing so is that log $(y) = 8.11254$ and we had to subtract log (y) from log (x). Since, in this case, log $(y) >$ log (x), log $(x) -$ log $(y) < 0$. Since the mantissa of the logarithm of a number is always non-negative, writing

$$\log (z) = \log (x) - \log (y) \doteq 1.35808 - 8.11254 = -6.75446$$

would not be convenient for reading off the characteristic and mantissa of log (z).

Hence, we added a large enough integer N (in this case 7) to log (x) so that $N +$ log $(x) >$ log (y) and then subtracted N in order to obtain the correct value of log (z).

Finally, having log $(z) \doteq .24554 - 7$, we must use interpolation to find z. We indicate the details below.

$$
\begin{array}{ccc}
\log (n) & & n \\
.24551 & & 1.7600 \\
.24554 & & z' \\
.24576 & & 1.7610
\end{array}
$$

$$25 \left\{ \; 3 \left\{ \begin{array}{c} .24551 \\ .24554 \end{array} \right\} d \right\} 10$$

From the foregoing table, we set up the proportion $d/10 = \frac{3}{25}$. Hence, $d = 30/25 \doteq 1$. Hence, $z' = 1.7600 + .0001 = 1.7601$. ∎

Exercises   Find an approximation of each of the following:

1. log (2.561)   2. log (31.41)

3. log (.0023)   4. log (.25613)

Find an approximation for x if

5. log $(x) = 3.1571$ 6. log $(x) = 2.1062 - 8$

7. log $(x) = 1.00123 - 10$ 8. log $(x) = 6.00124$

Calculate approximations for the following, using logarithms:

9. $(21.56)^4$ 10. $\sqrt[4]{.00512}$

11. $(3.001)^4 \cdot \sqrt[5]{.016}$ 12. $\dfrac{(21.3)^2}{(.0051)^3}$

13. $\dfrac{(213.1)^4 \sqrt[5]{21.56}}{(2.31)^3}$ 14. $\dfrac{(.00125)^2 \sqrt{21.57}}{(5.002)^5 \sqrt[3]{.0076}}$

3.2. Trigonometric angles So far, we have assumed that the student is familiar with the notion of angle from his course in basic geometry. We have talked, without compunction, about perpendicular lines, right triangles, 30° angles, etc. In this section, we shall generalize the notion of the geometric angle to that of a trigonometric angle.

In plane geometry, an angle is usually described as the configuration of two rays (half lines) with a common end point. In trigonometry, this configuration is thought of as the *image* of some angle. The angle itself consists of its image together with a rotation carrying one ray into the other. The ray which is being rotated is called the *initial side* of the angle; the other is called the *terminal side*; their common end point is called the *vertex* of the angle. Clockwise and counterclockwise rotations are by convention rotations in the *negative and positive direction* respectively. We must introduce some units for measuring the magnitude of an angle (i.e., the amount of rotation). The most natural one is one complete *revolution* of the initial side. Although revolutions are the most natural units for measuring angles, the systems most commonly used are the *sexagesimal system*, in which the degree is the basic unit, and the *radian system*, in which the fundamental unit is the radian. In calculus and more advanced courses, the radian system is considered so fundamental that, if a unit of measure of an angle is not specified, then it is always assumed to be the radian. We shall presently define these two units.

Definitions 3.2.1.   A *degree* is a rotation of a half line, about its end point, equal to 1/360 complete revolution.

A *minute* is a rotation equal to 1/60 degree, and a *second* is equal to 1/60 minute. Degrees, minutes and seconds are usually denoted by the superscripts °, ′, ″.

A *radian* is a rotation of a half line, about its end point, with the property that 2π radians is equal to a complete revolution.

There is a close connection between the idea of trigonometric angle and that of a directed path described in section 2.3. An angle is completely described if we know its vertex, its initial side, and the amount of its rotation. Hence, we adopt the notation $(Oz, m$ (units)) to describe the angle whose vertex is O, initial side Oz and amount of rotation m (units).

The angle $(Oz, -90°)$ is represented in figure 1.

Figure 1.

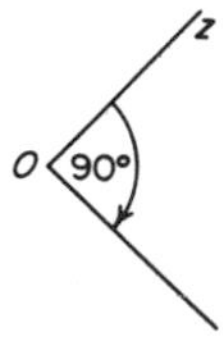

Suppose that an angle $(Oz, m$ (units)) is given. Consider a circle with center O (the vertex of the angle) and radius R. (See figure 2.) The initial side Oz intersects the circle at the point P. As the initial side rotates an amount m units to be carried onto the terminal side,

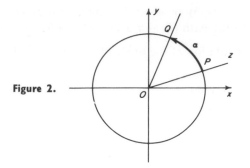

Figure 2.

the point Q on the initial side, which is at a distance R from the vertex, travels a distance α on the circle. Hence, a directed path (P, α) is uniquely determined by the angle $(Oz, m \text{ (units)})$. Conversely, suppose that we are given a circle of radius R and a directed path (P, α). We recall that P is a fixed point on the circle and a point Q starting at P moves a directed distance α on the circle. This path uniquely determines a trigonometric angle in the following way. The center O of the circle is the vertex of the angle, the half line Oz starting at O and passing through P is its initial side, and the half line starting at O and passing through the terminal point of the path is its terminal side. The amount of rotation is, of course, determined by α. Clearly, since for one complete revolution the distance traveled by Q is $2\pi R$, when this distance is α, the amount of rotation is $\alpha/2\pi R$. Hence, the angle corresponding to the path (P, α) is $(Oz, \alpha/2\pi R \text{ rev})$.

Example I. Given the circle with center the point $(0, 2)$ and with radius 2, and given that the point P has coordinates $(-2, 2)$ find the angle corresponding to the path $(P, -\pi/3)$.

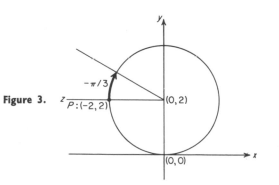

Figure 3.

Solution: Let the center of the circle be the point O, (see figure 3), and the half line starting at O and passing through P be Oz. The circumference of the circle is $(2\pi)(2) = 4\pi$. Hence, if a ray Oz is rotated about O, the point Q at a distance 2 from O on the ray travels $-\pi/3$. Hence, the amount of rotation is $-(\pi/3)/4\pi = -1/12$ revolution. Hence, the angle corresponding to the path $(P, -\pi/3)$ is $(Oz, -1/12 \text{ rev})$. ∎

Example 2. Express the amount of rotation of the angle of example 1 in degrees and radians.

Solution: We know that $360° = 1$ revolution. If we let $x = -1/12$ revolution, we get the following proportion:

$$\frac{x}{360} = \frac{-1/12}{1}$$

Hence, $x = (360)\dfrac{-1}{12}$

$$= -30$$

Hence, the angle of example 1 is $(Oz, -30°)$. We also know that 2π radians $= 1$ revolution. If we let x radians $= -1/12$ revolution, we get

$$\frac{x}{2\pi} = \frac{-1/12}{1}$$

Hence, $x = (2\pi)\dfrac{-1}{12}$

$$= \frac{-\pi}{6}$$

Therefore, the angle of example 1 can also be expressed as $(Oz, -\pi/6)$. ∎

Note: If the unit of measure is not specified, it is always understood to be the radian.

If the vertex of an angle is the origin of a rectangular coordinate system and if its initial side coincides with the positive x axis, then the angle is said to be in *standard position*.

Suppose now that we consider the circle C_0 (the circle with center the origin and with radius 1). Then, given an angle $(Oz, m \text{ (units)})$ in standard position, it determines uniquely a standard path (P_0, α). Recalling that the definitions of the circular functions were given via a standard path, we can now define trigonometric functions whose domains are sets of measures of angles. For example, we can give a meaning to $\sin (30°)$, $\cos (3/4 \text{ rev})$, $\tan (2 \text{ radians}) = \tan (2)$. Logically, these functions are different from those defined in Chapter 2, since they have different domains. Nevertheless, we shall use the same names and symbols. This should cause no difficulty since the intended meaning will always be clear from the context. We are now ready to give the following definition:

Definition 3.2.2. Let f be a trigonometric function (as defined in Chapter 2) and let m(units) be a measure of angle. Then the value of $f[m$(units)$]$ is equal to the value of $f(\alpha)$ where (P_0, α) is the standard path determined by the angle in standard position, $(Ox, m$(units)$)$.

Example 3. If it is defined, find the value of $\sin(30°)$, $\cos(-150°)$, $\tan(5/4\text{ rev})$, $\cot(3\pi/4)$.

Figure 4.

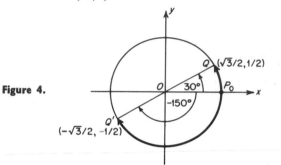

Solution: Consider the angle $(Ox, 30°)$ in standard position. (See figure 4.) since $30° = (1/12) \cdot 360°$, the length of the arc $\widehat{P_0Q}$ intercepted by the sides of the angle is $2\pi \cdot 1/12 = \pi/6$. Hence, the standard path corresponding to the angle $(Ox, 30°)$ is $(P_0, \pi/6)$. Hence,

$$\sin(30°) = \sin(\pi/6) = 1/2.$$

From figure 4, we see that the standard path corresponding to the angle $(Ox, -150°)$ is $(P_0, -5\pi/6)$. Hence,

$$\cos(-150°) = \cos(-5\pi/6) = -\sqrt{3/2}.$$

If we consider the angle $(Ox, 5/4\text{ rev})$ in standard position (see figure 5), the standard path corresponding to it is $(P_0, 5\pi/2)$ with terminal point $(0, 1)$. Hence, $\tan(5/4\text{ rev}) = \tan(5\pi/2) = 1/0$ is not defined. Finally, from figure 5, we see that the standard path corresponding

Figure 5.

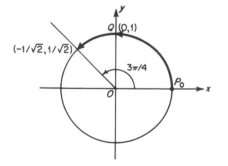

to the angle $(Ox, 3\pi/4)$ is $(P_0, 3\pi/4)$. The terminal point of $(P_0, 3\pi/4)$ is $(-1/\sqrt{2}, 1/\sqrt{2})$. Hence, $\cot(3\pi/4\text{ radians}) = \cot(3\pi/4) = (-1/\sqrt{2})/1/\sqrt{2} = -1$. ∎

Note: In the last part of example 3, notice that the standard path corresponding to the angle (Ox, m radians) is (P_0, m). This is true in general, and we state this fact in the form of a theorem.

Theorem 3.2.3. The standard path corresponding to the angle (Ox, m radians), in standard position, is always (P_0, m).

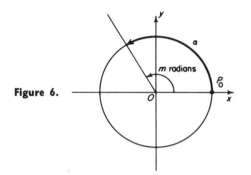

Figure 6.

Proof: Let the angle (Ox, m radians) be given. Then the amount of rotation that the initial side must undergo to coincide with the terminal side is m radians. Let Q be a point on the initial side of the angle at a unit distance from the vertex. If the initial side rotates a complete revolution, or 2π radians, the point Q travels a distance 2π. Let α be the distance traveled by the point Q when the initial side rotates m radians. These quantities are proportional. Hence, $\alpha/2\pi = m/2\pi$ and $\alpha = m$. ∎

Example 4. Find sec ($45°$).

Solution:
$$360° = 2\pi \text{ radians}$$

Let
$$45° = x \text{ radians}$$

Hence,
$$\frac{x}{2\pi} = \frac{45}{360}$$

$$x = \frac{(2\pi)(45)}{360}$$

$$= \frac{\pi}{4}$$

Therefore, $45° = \dfrac{\pi}{4}$ radian

It follows that sec ($45°$) = sec ($\pi/4$ radians) = sec ($\pi/4$) = $\sqrt{2}$. ∎

There is a convenient way to express the trigonometric function of an angle without referring to the corresponding standard path. This way is very often used in defining the trigonometric functions in terms of angle. We shall describe it in the form of the following theorem:

Theorem 3.2.4. Let $(Ox, m$ units) be an angle in standard position. Let (a, b) be a point on the terminal side of that angle and at distance $r > O$ from the origin. Then the values of the trigonometric functions at m units are given by the following expressions:

$$\sin (m \text{ units}) = \frac{b}{r} \qquad\qquad \csc (m \text{ units}) = \frac{r}{b} \text{ if } b \neq 0$$

$$\cos (m \text{ units}) = \frac{a}{r} \qquad\qquad \sec (m \text{ units}) = \frac{r}{a} \text{ if } a \neq 0$$

$$\tan (m \text{ units}) = \frac{b}{a} \text{ if } a \neq 0 \qquad \cot (m \text{ units}) = \frac{a}{b} \text{ if } b \neq 0$$

Proof: Consider the angle $(Ox, m$ units) in standard position. Let the intersection of the terminal side of that angle with the circle C_0 be the point (a', b'). If (P_0, α) is the standard path determined by the angle $(Ox, m$ units), then (a', b') is the terminal point of that path. (See figure 7.) Hence, $\sin \alpha = b'$; $\cos \alpha = a'$; $\tan \alpha = b'/a'$; $\cot \alpha = a'/b'$; $\sec \alpha = 1/a'$; $\csc \alpha = 1/b'$.

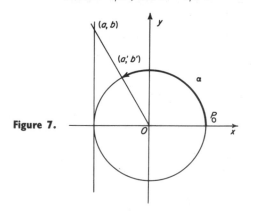

Figure 7.

By the similarity of the right triangles, we have $|b|/r = |b'|/1$. Since the points (a, b) and (a', b') are in the same quadrant (or on the same half of either axis), b and b' have like signs and we can write

$$\frac{b}{r} = b'$$

But $\qquad b' = \sin \alpha$

and $\qquad \sin \alpha = \sin (m \text{ units})$

Hence, $\sin (m \text{ units}) = \dfrac{b}{r}$

The other five expressions are derived similarly, and the proofs will be omitted. ∎

Example 5. The terminal side of an angle $(Ox, A$ units) passes through the point $(-3, 4)$. Find the values of the six trigonometric functions at A units.

Solution: Using the distance formula, we can find the distance r from the origin to the point $(-3, 4)$.

$$r = \sqrt{(-3-0)^2 + (4-0)^2} = \sqrt{9+16} = \sqrt{25}$$
$$= 5$$

Hence, by theorem 3.2.4, we get

$$\sin (A \text{ units}) = \tfrac{4}{5} \qquad \csc (A \text{ units}) = \tfrac{5}{4}$$
$$\cos (A \text{ units}) = -\tfrac{3}{5} \qquad \sec (A \text{ units}) = -\tfrac{5}{3}$$
$$\tan (A \text{ units}) = -\tfrac{4}{3} \qquad \cot (A \text{ units}) = -\tfrac{3}{4} \ \ ∎$$

Note: It can easily be shown that all the identities proved in Chapter 2 for the circular functions hold for trigonometric functions of angles.

Corollary 3.2.5. Let $(Ox, m$ units) be an angle in standard position and let (x, y) be a point on the terminal side of that angle. If the distance from the origin to that point is $r > 0$, then

$$x = r \cos (m \text{ units}) \quad \text{and} \quad y = r \sin (m \text{ units})$$

Proof: By theorem 3.2.4, we have

$$\cos (m \text{ units}) = \frac{x}{r} \quad \text{and} \quad \sin (m \text{ units}) = \frac{y}{r}$$

The required expressions follow directly. ∎

Exercises 1. Given the circle with center $(1, 1)$ and radius $\sqrt{2}$ and given that point P has coordinates $(2, 0)$, find the angles corresponding to the following paths:

(a) $(P, \sqrt{2}\pi)$ (b) $(P, \pi/3)$
(c) $(P, -\pi)$ (d) $(P, -3\pi/7)$

Give your answers in revolutions, radians, and degrees.

2. Give the following in degrees and in radians:

(a) 2/3 rev   (b) $-5/6$ rev
(c) $3/4\pi$ rev   (d) -62π rev

3. Give the following in degrees and in revolutions:

(a) 5π radian   (b) $-3\pi/4$ radian
(c) -23 radian   (d) $1/\pi$ radian

4. Give the following in radians and in revolutions:

(a) $23°$ (b) $51°30'$
(b) $-372°$ (d) $-3,172°21'$

3.3. Solution of right triangles An interesting application of the trigonometric functions of angles is the solving of triangles. A triangle has three sides and three angles. It is often possible to measure three of these quantities and, from the results of these measurements, to calculate the other three. This calculation is referred to as *solving the triangle*. We begin, in this section, with solutions of right triangles.

We adopt the convention that the three angle measures at the vertices of a triangle ABC are $\alpha°$, $\beta°$, and $\gamma°$, respectively, and their corresponding sides are a, b, c units of length. We can now easily prove the following theorem.

Theorem 3.3.1. Let ABC be a right triangle with $\alpha = 90$.

$$\text{Then, } \sin(\gamma°) = \frac{c}{a} = \frac{\text{length of the side opposite the vertex } C}{\text{length of hypotenuse}}$$

$$\cos(\gamma°) = \frac{b}{a} = \frac{\text{length of the side adjacent to the vertex } C}{\text{length of hypotenuse}}$$

$$\tan(\gamma°) = \frac{c}{b} = \frac{\text{length of the side opposite the vertex } C}{\text{length of the side adjacent to the vertex } C}$$

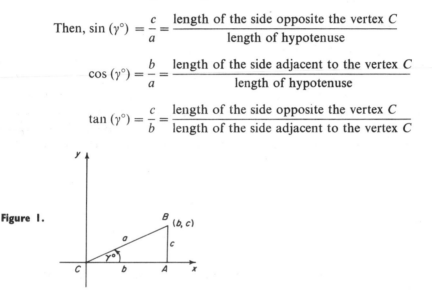

Figure 1.

Proof: Set the right triangle in a rectangular coordinate system as in figure 1. Since $\alpha + \beta + \gamma = 180$, $\alpha = 90$, and $\beta > 0$, we must have $0 < \gamma < 90$, and the point B is in the first quadrant. Its coordinates are obviously (b, c) and its distance from the origin is a. Since the angle $(Cx, \gamma°)$ is in standard position, by theorem 3.2.4, we get $\sin(\gamma°) = c/a$, $\cos(\gamma°) = b/a$, and $\tan(\gamma°) = c/b$. ∎

Tables in the back of the book give the values (or approximate values) of the trigonometric functions of measures of angles. Since we have the relations

$$\sin(\alpha°) = \cos(90° - \alpha°)$$

$$\cos(\alpha°) = \sin(90° - \alpha°)$$

$$\tan(\alpha°) = \cot(90° - \alpha°)$$

tables can be given for $0 \leq \alpha \leq 90$ in a compact way because each entry does double duty as, for example, cos (25°) = sin (65°). We use the following device. If $0 \leq \alpha \leq 45$, then we read the values of α in the left column and choose the proper column for the function by referring to the top row which lists the six functions. On the other hand, if $45 < \alpha \leq 90$, then we read the value of α in the right column and choose the proper column for the function by referring to the bottom row. The reader will notice that the column which has "sin" at the top has "cos" at the bottom; and if the angle measure $\alpha°$ is on the left, on the same row and to the far right, the angle measure $90° - \alpha°$ is given.* A few examples will illustrate the use of the tables.

Example 1. Find sin 31°24′.

Solution: Since 31°24′ < 45°, we refer to the left column of the tables and go down to the row where the angle measures 31°20′ and 31°30′ are given. We then find the proper column by referring to the top row where the functions are indicated. We find the column of the sine function and, in this column, choose the numbers which are on the same rows as 31°20′ and 31°30′. We find that sin 31°20′ = .5200 and sin 31°30′ = .5225. We shall use linear interpolation to find sin 31°24′.

Angle Measure   Sine

Tabular difference 10′ $\left\{ \begin{matrix} 31°20′ \\ 31°24′ \\ 31°30′ \end{matrix} \right.$ $\left. 4′\, d \right\{ \begin{matrix} .5200 \\ \text{sin } 31°24′ \\ .5225 \end{matrix} \right\}$ Tabular difference .0025

From the preceding tabulation, we set the proportion

$$\frac{d}{.0025} = \frac{4}{10}$$

Hence, $d = (.0025)\frac{4}{10} = .0010$

Therefore, sin 31°24′ = .5200 + .0010 = .5210 ∎

Example 2. Find tan $(-591°10′)$.

Solution: Since the tangent function is odd, we have

tan $(-591°10′) = -\tan 591°10′$

But

$$591°10′ = 540° + 51°10′$$
$$= (3)(180°) + 51°10′$$

* See theorem 2.7.3 page 98.

Since, if n is an integer, $\tan(n\pi + \alpha) = \tan\alpha$, we also have

$$\tan(n \cdot 180° + \alpha°) = \tan\alpha°$$

Hence,

$$-\tan(591°10') = -\tan(3.180° + 51°10') = -\tan(51°10')$$

Because $51°10' > 45°$, we refer to the right column of the tables to find $51°10'$ and we read the value of $\tan(51°10')$ in the column which is labeled "tan" at the bottom. We find that $\tan(51°10') = 1.242$.

Hence, $\tan(-591°10') = -1.242$ ∎

Example 3. A man drives his car at an average speed of 50 miles per hour along a straight road which runs $35°$ north of east. How far east of his starting point is he after 3 hr of driving?

Figure 2.

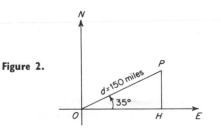

Solution: The idea of the problem is illustrated in figure 2. The distance which the man actually drove is $(50 \text{ mph})(3 \text{ hr}) = 150$ miles. After 3 hr driving, his distance east of his starting point is $|OH|$. By theorem 3.3.1, we have $\cos 35° = |OH|/150$. From the table, we get $\cos 35° \doteq .8192$. Hence, $|OH| \doteq (150)(.8192) \doteq 122.88$ miles.

Exercises 1. Find the values of the following (use the tables if necessary):

    (a) $\sin(-51°)$ (b) $\cos(5\pi/6)$
    (c) $\tan(-395°)$ (d) $\cot(\frac{2}{3}$ rev.)
    (e) $\sec(7\pi/3)$ (f) $\csc(-275°)$

2. An angle $(Ox, A°)$ is in standard position. Find the values of the six trigonometric functions at $A°$ if the point P is on the terminal side of the angle and the coordinates of P are

    (a) $(-1, 3)$ (b) $(2, 5)$
    (c) $(-3, -2)$ (d) $(5, -11)$

3. Find the following, using linear interpolation and the tables:

    (a) $\sin(-51°22'35'')$ (b) $\cos(253°21'37'')$
    (c) $\tan(-27°21')$ (d) $\cot(523°48')$
    (e) $\sec(-357°2')$ (f) $\csc(275°5'25'')$

4. What angle does the diagonal of a cube make with each of the edges of the cube?

5. In figure 3, ABC is a right triangle with $|AB| = 2{,}000$ ft. The angles of elevation of the top of the inaccessible tower as viewed from A and B are, respectively, $4°20'$ and $10°10'$. Find the height of the tower.

Figure 3.

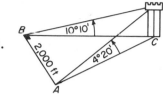

6. A right circular cone of vertex angle 2α degrees is inscribed in a sphere of radius a. Find an expression for the volume of the cone in terms of a and the trigonometric functions at α degrees.

7. A line passes through the points $(3, 5)$ and $(5, 12)$. Find the angle it makes with the x axis.

3.4. The law of cosines In the previous section, we derived some relationships between the angles and sides of a right triangle. There are important relationships between the angles and the sides of any triangle. One of these is the so-called law of cosines.

Theorem 3.4.1. Let ABC be an arbitrary triangle. Suppose that its sides have lengths a, b, and c units and the measures of the corresponding angles are α, β, and γ units. Then the following relation holds:

$$a^2 = b^2 + c^2 - 2bc \cdot \cos(\alpha \text{ units})$$

Figure 1.

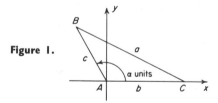

Proof: Place the triangle as in figure 1 where the angle $(Ax, \alpha$ units$)$ is in standard position. By corollary 3.2.5, the coordinates of the point B are $[c \cdot \cos(\alpha \text{ units}), c \cdot \sin(\alpha \text{ units})]$. It is clear that the coordinates of the point C are $(b, 0)$. Using the distance formula to express the distance between the points B and C, we get

$$|BC| = \sqrt{[b - c \cdot \cos(\alpha \text{ units})]^2 + [0 - c \cdot \sin(\alpha \text{ units})]^2}$$

Squaring both sides, we obtain

$$|BC|^2 = [b - c \cdot \cos(\alpha \text{ units})]^2 + [c \cdot \sin(\alpha \text{ units})]^2$$
$$= b^2 - 2bc \cdot \cos(\alpha \text{ units}) + c^2[\cos^2(\alpha \text{ units}) + \sin^2(\alpha \text{ units})]$$
$$= b^2 + c^2 - 2bc \cdot \cos(\alpha \text{ units})$$

But $|BC| = a$

Hence, $a^2 = b^2 + c^2 - 2bc \cdot \cos$ (α units)

Similarly, we get

$b^2 = a^2 + c^2 - 2ac \cdot \cos$ (β units)

$c^2 = a^2 + b^2 - 2ab \cdot \cos$ (γ units)

In particular, if γ units $= 90°$, then $\cos$ (γ units) $= \cos 90° = 0$, and we obtain, as a special case, the Pythagorean theorem:

$c^2 = a^2 + b^2$

Note The reader should not think of the last remark as a proof of the Pythagorean theorem. We recall that, in proving the law of cosines, we used the distance formula. But, in proving the distance formula, we used the Pythagorean theorem. Hence, the law of cosines cannot be used in proving the Pythagorean theorem.

We now illustrate how the law of cosines can be used.

Example 1. In the triangle ABC, it is given that $a = 6$, $b = 4$, and $c = 5$. Find α, β, and γ.

Solution: Using the law of cosines, we get

$6^2 = 4^2 + 5^2 - (2)(4)(5) \cos (\alpha°)$

$4^2 = 6^2 + 5^2 - (2)(6)(5) \cos (\beta°)$

and

$5^2 = 6^2 + 4^2 - (2)(6)(4) \cos (\gamma°)$

from which we obtain:

$\cos (\alpha°) = .125$; $\cos (\beta°) = .750$; $\cos (\gamma°) = .5625$.

Using the tables, we get

$\alpha° = 82°49'$; $\beta° = 41°25'$; $\gamma° = 55°46'$

Check: $82°49' + 41°25' + 55°46' = 178°120' = 178° + 2° = 180°$ ∎

We must note that usually, in a problem of this type, the sum of the measures of angles which are obtained is only approximately 180°. That is to be expected, since each of the three results is itself an approximation.

Example 2. Two men leave in their cars from the same point and at the same time. One of them travels at an average speed of 40 mph on a straight road which runs 10° south of east. The other travels at an average speed of 45 mph on another straight road which runs 25° north of east. How far apart are they after 2 hr of driving?

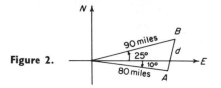

Figure 2.

Solution: The essentials of the problem are illustrated in figure 2. After 2 hr of driving, the men have traveled 80 and 90 miles respectively. Let d miles be the distance which separates them. From the law of cosines, we get $d^2 = 80^2 + 90^2 - (2)(80)(90) \cdot \cos(35°)$

$$d^2 = 6,400 + 8,100 - (11,400)(.8192)$$

$$= 5,161.12$$

$$d \doteq \sqrt{5,161.12}$$

$$= 71.84$$

Hence, the two men are approximately 71.84 miles apart after 2 hr of driving. ∎

Exercises 1. Given $b = 4$, $c = 5$, $\alpha° = 36°$, find a.

2. Given $a = 2$, $b = 5$, $c = 6$, find α.

3. Given $a = 11$, $b = 13$, $c = 15$, find β.

4. Two men leave in their cars from the same point and at the same time. One of them travels at an average speed of 35 mph on a straight road which runs 10° east of north. The other travels at an average speed of 40 mph on a straight road which runs 15° north of east. How far apart are they after 3 hr?

Figure 3.

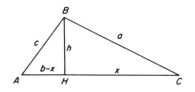

5. For the special triangle of figure 3, derive the law of cosines by stating that the values of h^2 obtained from the right triangles AHB and BHC are equal.

6. Show that in any triangle it is true that

$$\frac{\cos(\alpha°)}{a} + \frac{\cos(\beta°)}{b} + \frac{\cos(\gamma°)}{c} = \frac{a^2 + b^2 + c^2}{2abc}$$

3.5. The law of sines   A second interesting relationship between the sides and angles of an arbitrary triangle is the law of sines. This law is useful in solving triangles when two angles are given, together with the side opposite one of them, and in the case where two sides and the angle opposite one of them are given.

Theorem 3.5.1. Let ABC be an arbitrary triangle. If the magnitudes of the three angles are $\alpha°$, $\beta°$, and $\gamma°$, and the sizes of the sides are a, b, and c units, then the following relations hold:

$$\frac{a}{\sin(\alpha°)} = \frac{b}{\sin(\beta°)} = \frac{c}{\sin(\gamma°)}$$

Figure 1.

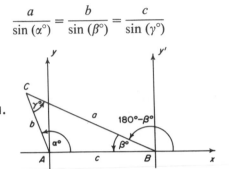

Proof: Set the triangle as in figure 1. We see that with respect to the xy coordinate system, the angle $(Ax, \alpha°)$ is in standard position. Hence, by corollary 3.2.5, the coordinates of the point C are $[b \cos(\alpha°),\ b \sin(\alpha°)]$. On the other hand, with respect to the xy' coordinate system, the angle $(Bx, 180° - \beta°)$ is in standard position. Hence, by corollary 3.2.5, the coordinates of the point C are $[(a \cdot \cos(180° - \beta°),\ a \cdot \sin(180° - \beta°))]$. Since the x axis is the same for both coordinate systems, the ordinate of the point C must be the same in both cases. Hence, we obtain

$$b \cdot \sin(\alpha°) = a \cdot \sin(180° - \beta°)$$

But

$$\sin(180° - \beta°) = \sin(\beta°) \qquad (1)$$

Therefore,

$$b \sin(\alpha°) = a \sin(\beta°)$$

Since $0 < \alpha < 180$ and $0 < \beta < 180$, we know that $\sin(\alpha°) \cdot \sin(\beta°) \neq 0$. Hence, we can divide both sides of equality (1) above by $\sin(\alpha°) \cdot \sin(\beta°)$ and obtain

$$\frac{b}{\sin(\beta°)} = \frac{a}{\sin(\alpha°)} \qquad (2)$$

By placing the side CA on the x axis and using the same argument, we obtain

$$\frac{c}{\sin(\gamma°)} = \frac{a}{\sin(\alpha°)} \qquad (3)$$

We can combine equalities (2) and (3) above and get

$$\frac{a}{\sin (\alpha^\circ)} = \frac{b}{\sin (\beta^\circ)} = \frac{c}{\sin (\gamma^\circ)} \quad \blacksquare$$

Example 1. Given that $\alpha^\circ = 30^\circ$, $\beta^\circ = 50^\circ$, and $a = 60$, find the remaining angle and two sides.

Solution: Since $\alpha + \beta + \gamma = 180$, we must have

$$\gamma = 180 - (30 + 50)$$

$$= 100$$

Hence, the magnitude of the third angle is 100°.

Also, $\dfrac{b}{\sin (\beta^\circ)} = \dfrac{a}{\sin (\alpha^\circ)}$

Therefore, $\dfrac{b}{\sin 50^\circ} = \dfrac{60}{\sin (30^\circ)}$

and $b = \dfrac{60 \sin 50^\circ}{\sin 30^\circ}$

$$= \frac{60(.7660)}{.5000}$$

$$= \frac{(60)(.7660)(2)}{1}$$

$$= 91.92$$

Furthermore, $\dfrac{c}{\sin (\gamma^\circ)} = \dfrac{a}{\sin (\alpha^\circ)}$

$$c = \frac{a \cdot \sin (\gamma^\circ)}{\sin (\alpha^\circ)}$$

$$= \frac{60 \sin 100^\circ}{\sin 30^\circ}$$

$$= \frac{60 \sin 80^\circ}{\sin 30^\circ} = \frac{60(.9848)}{.5000}$$

$$= \frac{(60)(.9848)(2)}{1}$$

$$= 118.176 \quad \blacksquare$$

Remark: Logarithms can be used when the computations are more complicated.

Often, some information about the number of triangles satisfying certain conditions can best be obtained geometrically. We illustrate this fact with the following example:

Example 2. Suppose that two sides of a triangle are given, together with the size of the angle opposite one of them. Construct the triangle with a ruler and compass.

Solution: Suppose that a, b, and $\alpha°$ are given with $0 < \alpha < 90$. We can easily construct an angle $(Ax, \alpha°)$. (See figure 2.)

Figure 2.

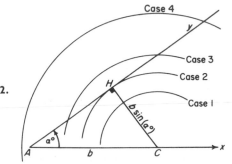

Let the terminal side of this angle be Ay. The vertex C of the triangle is to be on Ax such that $|AC| = b$. Since b is given, we can easily find the point C. The point B must be on the half line Ay (distinct from A) such that $|CB| = a$. Hence, the point B is also on the circle with center C and radius a. The intersection of that circle with the half line Ay will give the point B. Clearly, such a circle will not always intersect the half line Ay. Let CH be the perpendicular to Ay from the point C. Clearly, $|CH| = b \sin (\alpha°)$. We see geometrically that

1. If $a < |CH|$, the circle does not intersect the half line Ay, and there is no solution.

2. If $a = |CH|$, the circle is tangent to the half line Ay and there is one solution, namely, a right triangle.

3. If $|CH| < a < b$, the circle intersects the half line Ay at two distinct points and there are two solutions.

4. If $|CH| < a$ and $b < a$, the circle intersects the half line at only one point, and there is one solution.

Cases with $\alpha = 90$ and $90 < \alpha < 180$ can easily be considered by the reader. ∎

Example 3. Is it possible to have a triangle ABC with $a = 5$, $b = 9$, and $\alpha° = 30°$? If so, find the other three dimensions.

Solution: We first think of the problem geometrically. Can we construct such a triangle? The steps are exactly those of example 2 and we illustrate

Figure 3.

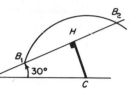

them in figure 3. Here $|CH|/9 = \sin 30° = \frac{1}{2}$. Hence, $|CH| = (9)(\frac{1}{2}) = 4.5$. Since $4.5 < 5 < 9$, there will be two solutions. We now proceed to find the other three dimensions. By the law of sines, we have

$$\frac{a}{\sin (\alpha°)} = \frac{b}{\sin (\beta°)}$$

Hence, $\dfrac{5}{\sin 30°} = \dfrac{9}{\sin \beta°}$

and $\quad \sin (\beta°) = \dfrac{(9 \sin 30°)}{5} = \dfrac{(9)(\frac{1}{2})}{5} = .9$

It follows that

$$\beta° = 64°9' \tag{1}$$

But, we know that, in general, $\sin (180° - \beta°) = \sin (\beta°)$. Therefore, $\sin (180° - 64°9') = \sin (64°9') = .9$ also. It follows that

$$180° - 64°9' = 115°51' \tag{2}$$

is another possible value for $\beta°$. In case (1), we have $\alpha° = 30°$, $\beta° = 64°9'$.

Hence, $\gamma° = 180° - (30° + 64°9')$

$$= 180° - 94°9'$$

$$= 85°51'$$

Again, using the law of sines, we get

$$\frac{5}{\sin 30°} = \frac{c}{\sin (\gamma°)}$$

from which we obtain

$$c = \frac{5}{\sin 30°} \cdot \sin (85°51') = \frac{5}{1/2} \cdot (.9974)$$

$$= 9.974$$

Hence, the triangle has the following dimensions:

$a = 5 \qquad \alpha° = 30°$

$b = 9 \qquad \beta° = 64°9'$

$c = 9.974 \quad \gamma° = 85°51'$

In case (2), we have $\alpha° = 30°$, $\beta° = 115°51'$.

Hence, $\gamma° = 180° - (30° + 115°51')$

$$= 34°9'$$

It follows that

$$\frac{5}{1/2} = \frac{c}{\sin 34°9'} = \frac{c}{.5614} \quad \text{and} \quad c = 5.614$$

Therefore, in the second case, the triangle has the following dimensions:

$a = 5$ $\alpha° = 30°$

$b = 9$ $\beta° = 115°51'$

$c = 5.614$ $\gamma° = 34°9'$ ∎

Exercises In each of the following, three dimensions of a triangle are given. Find, if possible, the remaining three dimensions.

1. $\alpha° = 40°$, $\beta° = 55°$, and $a = 6$

2. $\alpha° = 55°$, $\beta° = 32°$, and $b = 12$

3. $\alpha° = 72°24'$, $\gamma° = 49°32'$, and $b = 142$

4. $\alpha° = 54°26'$, $a = 11.3$, and $c = 12.9$

5. $\gamma° = 125°$, $b = 130$, and $c = 110$

6. $\alpha° = 30°$, $\beta° = 52°$, and $a = 73$

7. $\alpha° = 33°$, $a = 6$, and $b = 10$

8. $\alpha° = 27°25'$, $a = 8$, and $b = 6$

9. $\alpha° = 42°10'$, $a = 6.2$, and $b = 8.1$

10. $\alpha° = 102°17'$, $\gamma° = 32°34'$, and $b = 15$

11. Prove, starting with the law of sines, that for any triangle
$$\frac{a - b}{a + b} = \frac{\sin (\alpha°) - \sin (\beta°)}{\sin (\alpha°) + \sin (\beta°)}$$

12. Prove that for any triangle
$$\frac{a - b}{a + b} = \frac{\tan [(\alpha° - \beta°)/2]}{\tan [(\alpha° + \beta°)/2]}$$
(*Hint:* Start with the result of exercise 11 and write $\sin (\alpha°) - \sin (\beta°)$ and $\sin (\alpha°) + \sin (\beta°)$ as products.)

13. Show that in any triangle $\dfrac{bc \sin (\alpha°)}{a} = \dfrac{a \sin (\beta°) \cdot \sin (\gamma°)}{\sin (\alpha°)}$

14. Derive the law of sines from the law of cosines. (*Hint:* Get expressions for cos $(\alpha°)$, cos $(\beta°)$, and cos $(\gamma°)$. Then, using a well-known identity, compute sin^2 $(\alpha°)/a^2$, sin^2 $(\beta°)/b^2$, and sin^2 $(\gamma°)/c^2$.)

15. An artillery position is at a point A and a target at a point T. The battery commander is at an observation point O, 300 yd from A. He calculates the angle between OA and OT to be $52°$ and that between OA and AT to be $102°$. Find how far the target is from the gun.

3.6. Vectors Certain quantities used in the physical sciences and in engineering involve only magnitude. Examples of such quantities are length, area, and mass. They are called *scalar quantities*. There are also quantities which involve both magnitude and direction. These are called *vector quantities*. Force, velocity, and acceleration are examples of vector quantities. These can be represented mathematically using the concept of vectors in a coordinate plane. We shall presently introduce this concept. The proofs of all the theorems stated in this section are straightforward, using elementary geometry, and will be left as exercises.

Definitions 3.6.1. Given a coordinate plane P and two distinct points A and B in P, the directed line segment with *initial point A* and *terminal point B* is called the *geometric vector $\overrightarrow{AB}$*.

The *length* of the geometric vector $\overrightarrow{AB}$ is denoted by $|\overrightarrow{AB}|$ and is the length of the segment AB. The direction of $\overrightarrow{AB}$ is described as follows. Suppose that the coordinates of the point A are (a, b). In the plane P, draw a new system of coordinates so that the points with coordinates (a, b), $(a + 1, b)$, and $(a, b + 1)$ will have, in the new system, coordinates $(0, 0)$, $(1, 0)$, and $(0, 1)$ respectively. (See figure 1.) Call the new axes the x' and y' axes and consider the angle (Ax', m) whose terminal side contains the segment AB and with $0 \leq m < 2\pi$. Then the *direction* of $\overrightarrow{AB}$ is m radians.

Figure 1.

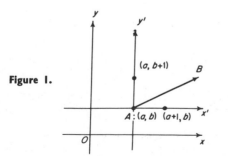

Remarks: 1. The measure of the angle (Ax', m) was given in radians. In the applications, it may be given in degrees or revolutions.

2. We agree that a single point A is a geometric vector which we call a *zero vector* and denote by $\overrightarrow{AA}$. The length of a zero vector is 0 and it has no specified direction.

Definition 3.6.2. Two geometric vectors $\overrightarrow{AB}$ and $\overrightarrow{CD}$ in a plane P are *equivalent* if and only if exactly one of the following three conditions is true:

1. $A = B$ and $C = D$ (i.e., both vectors are zero vectors).

2. A, B, C, and D are not on the same line and the quadrilateral $ABDC$ is a parallelogram.

3. A, B, C, and D are collinear and there exist two points E and F in the plane P such that both quadrilaterals $ABFE$ and $CDFE$ are parallelograms. (See figures 2a and 2b.)

Figure 2.

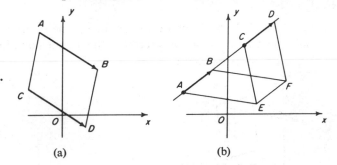

(a)   (b)

Remark: It is easy to show that two non-zero geometric vectors are equivalent if and only if they have the same length and the same direction.

Notation: If $\overrightarrow{AB}$ and $\overrightarrow{CD}$ are equivalent, we write $\overrightarrow{AB} \simeq \overrightarrow{CD}$.

Theorem 3.6.3. If P is a coordinate plane, the following three properties always hold:

1. Reflexivity: $\overrightarrow{AB} \simeq \overrightarrow{AB}$ for all geometric vectors $\overrightarrow{AB}$ in P.

2. Symmetry: If $\overrightarrow{AB} \simeq \overrightarrow{CD}$, then $\overrightarrow{CD} \simeq \overrightarrow{AB}$.

3. Transitivity: If $\overrightarrow{AB} \simeq \overrightarrow{CD}$ and $\overrightarrow{CD} \simeq \overrightarrow{EF}$, then $\overrightarrow{AB} \simeq \overrightarrow{EF}$.

Proof: Exercise 1.

It is convenient to define multiplication of a geometric vector by a real number (scalar) and also addition and subtraction of geometric vectors.

Definition 3.6.4. If $\overrightarrow{AB}$ is a non-zero geometric vector and C is a point such that A is the midpoint of the line segment BC, then and only then the geometric vector $\overrightarrow{AC}$ is denoted by $-\overrightarrow{AB}$.

Definition 3.6.5. If $\overrightarrow{AB}$ is a non-zero geometric vector and x is a real number, then $x \cdot \overrightarrow{AB}$ and $\overrightarrow{AB} \cdot x$ both denote the geometric vector $\overrightarrow{AC}$ where the point C is determined as follows:

1. If $x > 0$, then A, B, and C are on the same ray and $|\overrightarrow{AC}| = x \cdot |\overrightarrow{AB}|$.

2. If $x = 0$, then $C = A$ and $x \cdot \overrightarrow{AB}$ is a zero vector.

3. If $x < 0$, then $-x > 0$ so that $(-x)(-\overrightarrow{AB})$ is defined by definition 3.6.4 and the first part of definition 3.6.5. We let $x \cdot \overrightarrow{AB} = (-x)(-\overrightarrow{AB})$.

For any real number x, we define $x \cdot \overrightarrow{AA} = \overrightarrow{AA}$. We obtain immediately from the definitions the following theorem:

Theorem 3.6.6. If $\overrightarrow{AB} \simeq \overrightarrow{CD}$ and x is a real number, then $x \cdot \overrightarrow{AB} \simeq x \cdot \overrightarrow{CD}$.

Proof: Exercise 2.

Definition 3.6.7. If $\overrightarrow{AB}$ and $\overrightarrow{CD}$ are geometric vectors in a plane P, the *sum* $\overrightarrow{AB} + \overrightarrow{CD}$ is the geometric vector AE where E is the unique point in P for which $\overrightarrow{BE} \simeq \overrightarrow{CD}$. (See figure 3.)

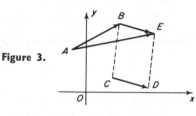

Figure 3.

Note: $\overrightarrow{AB} + \overrightarrow{CD}$ and $\overrightarrow{CD} + \overrightarrow{AB}$ are not necessarily the same geometric vector, but they will always be equivalent.

Definition 3.6.8. If $\overrightarrow{AB}$ and $\overrightarrow{CD}$ are geometric vectors in a plane P, the difference $\overrightarrow{AB} - \overrightarrow{CD}$ is the geometric vector $\overrightarrow{AB} + (-\overrightarrow{CD})$.

Theorem 3.6.9. If $\overrightarrow{AB} \simeq \overrightarrow{A'B'}$ and $\overrightarrow{CD} \simeq \overrightarrow{C'D'}$, then $\overrightarrow{AB} + \overrightarrow{CD} \simeq \overrightarrow{A'B'} + \overrightarrow{C'D'}$.

Proof: Exercise 3.

Now let $\overrightarrow{AB}$ be a geometric vector in a coordinate plane. If we project the points A and B on the x and y axes, we get the points A_x, A_y, B_x and B_y. (See figure 4.) We note that $\overrightarrow{A_xB_x}$ and $\overrightarrow{A_yB_y}$ are

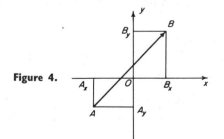

Figure 4.

themselves geometric vectors. They are often called the x and y components of $\overrightarrow{AB}$. In this text, we shall not follow this procedure. The two terms just mentioned will be given a different (but related) meaning as indicated in the following:

Definition 3.6.10. If $\overrightarrow{AB}$ is a geometric vector in a coordinate plane P and if the co-ordinates of A and B are (a_x, a_y) and (b_x, b_y) respectively, then $b_x - a_x$ is called the x *component* and $b_y - a_y$ the y *component* of $\overrightarrow{AB}$.

If it is not important to specify the initial and terminal point of a geometric vector, we often use a single letter to denote that vector. We can now state the following:

Theorem 3.6.11. If $\overrightarrow{v_1}$ and $\overrightarrow{v_2}$ are geometric vectors in a coordinate plane P, then $\overrightarrow{v_1} \simeq \overrightarrow{v_2}$ if and only if the x and y components of $\overrightarrow{v_1}$ are equal respectively to the x and y components of $\overrightarrow{v_2}$.

Proof: Exercise 4.

In many applications, it becomes necessary to represent a physical quantity mathematically. If this quantity has only "magnitude" and "direction," then we must choose for its mathematical representation some entity for which "magnitude" and "direction" have been defined. We have seen that a geometric vector can be used to represent magnitude and direction. But there are infinitely many geometric vectors with the same length and the same direction, each having a distinct initial point. If initial and terminal points are of no importance insofar as the "vector quantity" is concerned, we have one of two alternatives in choosing a mathematical model for that vector quantity. Either we choose a fixed point (usually the origin of the coordinate system) and we agree that all geometric vectors will have that point as their common initial point, or we agree that a vector quantity will be represented by a set of geometric vectors such that all members of that set will have the same length and the same direction which are determined by the magnitude and direction of the vector quantity.

In view of the foregoing remarks, we give the following definition.

Definition 3.6.12. Given a coordinate plane P, let $\vec{v}$ be the geometric vector with initial point the origin and terminal point (a, b). Then the symbol $(a, b)_v$ denotes the set of vectors defined by the following equation:

$$(a, b)_v = \{\vec{u} \,|\, \vec{u} \text{ is a geometric vector in } P \text{ and } \vec{u} \simeq \vec{v}\}$$

The set $(a, b)_v$ is called an *equivalence class* of geometric vectors. We shall call $\vec{v}$ the *representative* of that class.

Remark: By theorem 3.6.11, any element of $(a, b)_v$ must be a geometric vector whose x component is a and whose y component is b.

There are four more useful theorems which we wish to state.

Theorem 3.6.13. If $\vec{v_1} \in (a, b)_v$ and $\vec{v_2} \in (c, d)_v$, then $\vec{v_1} + \vec{v_2} \in (a + c, b + d)_v$.

Proof: Exercise 5.

Theorem 3.6.14. If $\vec{v} \in (a, b)_v$ and x is any real number, then $x \cdot \vec{v} \in (xa, xb)_v$.

Proof: Exercise 6.

Theorem 3.6.15. If $\overrightarrow{AB}$ is a geometric vector in a coordinate plane P and if a, b and m units are respectively the x component, y component, and direction of $\overrightarrow{AB}$, then

$$a = |\overrightarrow{AB}| \cos (m \text{ units}) \quad \text{and} \quad b = |\overrightarrow{AB}| \sin (m \text{ units})$$

Proof: Exercise 7.

Theorem 3.6.16. If $\vec{v_1}$ and $\vec{v_2}$ are two non-zero geometric vectors in a plane P which do not lie either on the same line or on parallel lines, then for any geometric vector $\vec{v}$ in P, there exist two real numbers x_1 and x_2 such that

$$\vec{v} \simeq x_1\vec{v_1} + x_2\vec{v_2}$$

Proof: Exercise 8.

Definition 3.6.17. The set $\{\vec{v_1}, \vec{v_2}\}$ described in theorem 3.6.16 is said to be a *base* for the set of all vectors in the plane P.

We shall conclude this section with some examples.

Example 1. Find the length and direction of the geometric vector $\overrightarrow{AB}$ if the coordinates of A and B are $(2, 5)$ and $(1, 5 + \sqrt{3})$ respectively.

Solution: $|\overrightarrow{AB}| = |AB|$

$$= \sqrt{(1 - 2)^2 + (5 + \sqrt{3} - 5)^2}$$

$$= \sqrt{1 + 3}$$

$$= 2$$

The x component of $\overrightarrow{AB}$ is -1 (since $1 - 2 = -1$) and its y component is $\sqrt{3}$ (since $5 + \sqrt{3} - 5 = \sqrt{3}$).

Hence, if m radians is the direction of $\overrightarrow{AB}$, we have, by theorem 3.6.15, the following:

$$-1 = 2 \cos (m) \quad \text{and} \quad \sqrt{3} = 2 \sin (m) \tag{1}$$

It follows that

$$\tan (m) = \frac{\sin (m)}{\cos (m)} = \frac{2 \sin (m)}{2 \cos (m)} = \frac{\sqrt{3}}{-1} = -\sqrt{3}$$

Hence, $m \in \tan^{-1}(-\sqrt{3})$ \tag{2}

Further, by definition, we have

$$0 \le m < 2\pi \tag{3}$$

The only value of m which satisfies conditions (1), (2), and (3) is $2\pi/3$. Therefore, the direction of $\overrightarrow{AB}$ is $2\pi/3$ radian. ∎

Example 2. Find $\overrightarrow{AB} + \overrightarrow{CD}$ both geometrically and analytically if $(-1, 3)$, $(2, 4)$, $(-2, 0)$, and $(2, -4)$ are the coordinates of A, B, C, and D respectively.

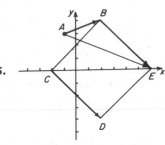

Figure 5.

(a) *Geometric solution:* With a ruler and compass, we construct the parallelogram $BCDE$ (see figure 5). Then $\overrightarrow{BE} \simeq \overrightarrow{CD}$ and the geometric vector $\overrightarrow{AE}$ is the sum $\overrightarrow{AB} + \overrightarrow{CD}$.

(b) *Analytic solution:* The x and y components of $\overrightarrow{AB}$ and $\overrightarrow{CD}$ are obtained as follows:

$$2 - (-1) = 3$$
$$4 - 3 = 1$$
$$2 - (-2) = 4$$
$$-4 - 0 = -4$$

Hence, 3 is the x component of $\overrightarrow{AB}$; 1 is its y component, whereas 4 and -4 are respectively the x and y components of $\overrightarrow{CD}$.

By theorem 3.6.13, we have $\overrightarrow{AB} + \overrightarrow{CD} \in (3 + 4, 1 + (-4))_v$.

That is, $\overrightarrow{AB} + \overrightarrow{CD} \in (7, -3)_v$

By definition, the initial point of $\overrightarrow{AB} + \overrightarrow{CD}$ is the point A with coordinates $(-1, 3)$. Suppose that the coordinate of the terminal point of $\overrightarrow{AB} + \overrightarrow{CD}$ are (x, y). Since the x and y components of $\overrightarrow{AB} + \overrightarrow{CD}$ are 7 and -3, we must have

$$x - (-1) = 7 \quad \text{and} \quad y - 3 = -3$$

From which we get

$$x = 6 \quad \text{and} \quad y = 0$$

Therefore, the point $(6, 0)$ is the terminal point of $\overrightarrow{AB} + \overrightarrow{CD}$. ∎

Example 3. If S_1 and S_2 are sets of geometric vectors in a coordinate plane P, we define $S_1 + S_2 = \{\overrightarrow{v_1} + \overrightarrow{v_2} \mid \overrightarrow{v_1} \in S_1 \text{ and } \overrightarrow{v_2} \in S_2\}$. Show that

$$(a, b)_v + (c, d)_v = (a + c, b + d)_v$$

Solution: Let $w \in (a, b)_v + (c, d)_v$. Then, by definition, there exist geometric vectors $\overrightarrow{v_1}$ and $\overrightarrow{v_2}$ such that $\overrightarrow{v_1} \in (a, b)_v$, $\overrightarrow{v_2} \in (c, d)_v$ and $\overrightarrow{w} = \overrightarrow{v_1} + \overrightarrow{v_2}$. By theorem 3.6.13, we know that $\overrightarrow{v_1} + \overrightarrow{v_2} \in (a + c, b + d)_v$. Hence, $w \in (a + c, b + d)_v$. We have shown that

$$(a, b)_v + (c, d)_v \subset (a + c, b + d)_v$$

Conversely, suppose that $w \in (a + c, b + d)_v$. Let the initial point of $\overrightarrow{w}$ be (x_1, y_1). Let $\overrightarrow{v_1}$ be the geometric vector with initial point (x_1, y_1) and with terminal point $(x_1 + a, y_1 + b)$. Also let $\overrightarrow{v_2}$ be the geometric vector with initial and terminal points (x_1, y_1) and $(x_1 + c, y_1 + d)$. The x and y components of $\overrightarrow{v_1}$ are a and b respectively. Hence, $\overrightarrow{v_1} \in (a, b)_v$. Similarly, we show that $\overrightarrow{v_2} \in (c, d)_v$. We can easily verify that $w = \overrightarrow{v_1} + \overrightarrow{v_2}$. Hence,

$$w \in (a, b)_v + (c, d)_v \quad \text{and} \quad (a + c, b + d)_v \subset (a, b)_v + (c, d)_v$$

It follows that

$$(a, b)_v + (c, d)_v = (a + c, b + d)_v \ \blacksquare$$

Exercises

1. Prove theorem 3.6.3.

2. Prove theorem 3.6.6.

3. Prove theorem 3.6.9.

4. Prove theorem 3.6.11.

5. Prove theorem 3.6.13.

6. Prove theorem 3.6.14.

7. Prove theorem 3.6.15.

8. Prove theorem 3.6.16.

9. Describe some "relations" between elements of certain sets which you have studied in basic algebra and geometry and which satisfy the three properties described in theorem 3.6.3.

10. Find the length and direction of the geometric vector $\overrightarrow{AB}$ in each of the following cases. (You may have to approximate the direction using tables.) The coordinates of A and B are
    (a) $(-1, 5)$ and $(3, 5)$ respectively,
    (b) $(5, 3)$ and $(2, -6)$ respectively,
    (c) $(4, 2)$ and $(-1, -3)$ respectively.

11. Find $\overrightarrow{AB} + \overrightarrow{CD}$ both geometrically and analytically. In each case, the coordinates of A, B, C, and D are given in that order.
    (a) $(1, 2)$, $(3, -1)$, $(-2, 5)$, and $(3, 7)$
    (b) $(0, 1)$, $(2, -3)$, $(5, 1)$, and $(-1, -2)$
    (c) $(3, 3)$, $(3, 3)$, $(5, 1)$, and $(-2, 3)$

*12. Show by giving an example that it is possible for S_1 and S_2 to be sets of geometric vectors in the plane P with $S_1 + S_2 \neq S_2 + S_1$.

*13. Show that addition of geometric vectors is associative.

3.7. Applications of vectors to physics

In the previous section, we remarked that a vector quantity can be represented either by a set of equivalent vectors or by a single element of that set. In this text, unless otherwise specified, we shall represent a vector quantity by a geometric vector with initial point the origin of a coordinate system. If $\vec{v}$ is such a geometric vector, it is uniquely determined by its terminal point (a, b). For this reason, we shall denote it by $\overrightarrow{(a, b)}$. Note that the x and y components of $\overrightarrow{(a, b)}$ are a and b respectively. Its length is $\sqrt{a^2 + b^2}$ and its direction is the smallest non-negative measure of the angle in standard position whose terminal side passes through the point (a, b).

We also note that

$$\overrightarrow{(a, b)} + \overrightarrow{(c, d)} = \overrightarrow{(a + c, b + d)}$$

and $x\overrightarrow{(a, b)} = \overrightarrow{(xa, xb)}$ for all real numbers x

Two of the vector quantities which are often represented by vectors are velocity and force. We shall illustrate the techniques with examples.

In physics, the word *speed* is used in referring to rate of change of distance whereas *velocity* indicates not only the speed but also the direction of motion. In the examples, we shall represent a velocity by a vector $\overrightarrow{(a, b)}$ whose length represents the speed (to some scale) of a moving object and whose direction is determined by the direction of motion.

Example I. A jet is flying in a direction $30°$ west of north at an air speed of 600 miles per hour. It encounters a 60-mph wind blowing in a direction $45°$ north of east. What are the course and speed of the jet with respect to the ground?

Solution: We represent the air velocity of the jet and the velocity of the wind by the vectors $\overrightarrow{(a, b)}$ and $\overrightarrow{(c, d)}$ respectively as indicated in figure 1. We let $|\overrightarrow{(a, b)}| = 600$, $|\overrightarrow{(c, d)}| = 60$ and from the diagram we see that the direction of $\overrightarrow{(a, b)}$ is $120°$ and that of $\overrightarrow{(c, d)}$ is $45°$.

Figure 1.

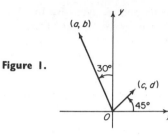

Hence, $a = 600 \cdot \cos 120° = 600(-\tfrac{1}{2}) = -300$

$$b = 600 \cdot \sin 120° = 600(\tfrac{\sqrt{3}}{2}) = 300\sqrt{3}$$

$$c = 60 \cdot \cos 45° = (60)(\tfrac{\sqrt{2}}{2}) = 30\sqrt{2}$$

$$d = 60 \cdot \sin 45° = (60)(\tfrac{\sqrt{2}}{2}) = 30\sqrt{2}$$

It is a principle of physics that the vector which represents the velocity of the jet with respect to the ground is the sum of the two vectors which represent the air velocity of the jet and the wind velocity. If $\overrightarrow{(x, y)}$ denotes the vector which represents the velocity of the jet with respect to the ground, we must have

$$\overrightarrow{(x, y)} = \overrightarrow{(-300, 300\sqrt{3})} + \overrightarrow{(30\sqrt{2}, 30\sqrt{2})}$$
$$= \overrightarrow{(-300 + 30\sqrt{2}, 300\sqrt{3} + 30\sqrt{2})}$$

Hence, the speed with respect to ground is

$$|\overrightarrow{(x, y)}| = \sqrt{(-300 + 30\sqrt{2})^2 + (300\sqrt{3} + 30\sqrt{2})^2}$$
$$= 30\sqrt{(\sqrt{2} - 10)^2 + (10\sqrt{3} + \sqrt{2})^2}$$
$$= 30\sqrt{2 - 20\sqrt{2} + 100 + 300 + 20\sqrt{6} + 2}$$
$$= 30\sqrt{404 + 20\sqrt{2}(\sqrt{3} - 1)}$$
$$\doteq 30\sqrt{424.7}$$
$$\doteq (30)(20.608)$$
$$\doteq 618.24$$

Hence, the speed of the jet with respect to the ground is approximately 618.24 mph.

If the direction of the vector $\overrightarrow{(x, y)}$ is m degrees, it is clear that

$$\tan(m°) = \frac{y}{x} = \frac{300\sqrt{3} + 30\sqrt{2}}{-300 + 30\sqrt{2}}$$

Hence, $\tan(m°) = \dfrac{10\sqrt{3} + \sqrt{2}}{\sqrt{2} - 10} = \dfrac{(10\sqrt{3} + \sqrt{2})(\sqrt{2} + 10)}{-98}$

$$\doteq -2.182$$

Using the tables, we see that the direction is approximately 114°34′. Hence, the direction of the jet with respect to the ground is approximately 24°34′ west of north. ∎

We state the following from physics.

Definition 3.7.1. A body is said to be in *equilibrium* if it is at rest or if it is moving at a constant speed on a straight line.

We now list three basic principles which we shall need for the examples.

1. A force is a vector quantity. It can be represented by a geometric vector whose length is determined by the magnitude of the force (to some scale) and whose direction is determined by the direction of the force.

2. Any set of forces which act upon a single body has the same effect as some single force acting on that body. This single force is called the *resultant* of the given set of forces. Furthermore, if all the forces act in a single plane and are represented by geometric vectors in one coordinate plane, then the sum of these vectors is the vector which represents the resultant of the forces.

3. If a body is in equilibrium, then the resultant of the set of forces acting upon it must be zero.

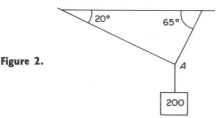

Figure 2.

Example 2. A 200-lb weight is suspended as shown in figure 2. Find the tension in each rope.

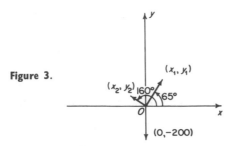

Figure 3.

Solution: There are three forces acting at the point A, two whose magnitude is unknown. If we represent these two forces by the vectors $\overrightarrow{(x_1, y_1)}$

and $\overrightarrow{(x_2, y_2)}$ as shown in figure 3, the direction of $\overrightarrow{(x_1, y_1)}$ is 65° and that of (x_2, y_2) is 160°. The known force has a magnitude of 200 lb and direction 270°. Hence, we represent it by the vector $\overrightarrow{(0, -200)}$. The system is obviously in equilibrium. Hence, the resultant must be zero. It follows that the sum of the three vectors must be a zero vector. That is, the sum of the x components and the sum of the y components must *both* be zero. Let T_1 and T_2 be the lengths of the vectors $\overrightarrow{(x_1, y_1)}$ and $\overrightarrow{(x_2, y_2)}$. Then

$$x_1 = T_1 \cos 65°; \qquad y_1 = T_1 \sin 65°; \qquad x_2 = T_2 \cos 160°;$$

$$\text{and} \qquad y_2 = T_2 \sin 160°$$

We therefore can write

$$T_1 \cos 65° + T_2 \cos 160° + 0 = 0 \tag{1}$$

$$T_1 \sin 65° + T_2 \sin 160° + (-200) = 0 \tag{2}$$

From which we get

$$T_2(\sin 160° \cos 65° - \cos 160° \sin 65°) = 200 \cos 65°$$

$$\text{and} \qquad T_2 \sin (160° - 65°) = 200 \cos 65°$$

$$T_2 = \frac{200 \cos 65°}{\sin 95°}$$

Therefore, $\qquad\qquad\qquad T_2 \doteq 84.8$

Solving for T_1, we get

$$T_1 = \frac{-T_2 \cos 160°}{\cos 65°}$$

$$= \frac{(-T_2)(-\cos 20°)}{\cos 65°}$$

$$\text{and } T_1 = \frac{200 \cos 65°}{\sin 95°} \cdot \frac{\cos 20°}{\cos 65°} = \frac{200 \cos 20°}{\sin 95°}$$

$$T_1 \doteq 188.6$$

Hence, the tension in the rope which makes an angle of 65° with the support is approximately 188.6 lb and the tension in the other rope is approximately 84.8 lb. ∎

Exercises 1. A jet is flying in a direction 35° south of east at an air speed of 500 mph. It encounters a 40-mph wind blowing in a direction 46° south of west. What are the course and speed of the jet with respect to the ground?

2. A bullet is fired from an airplane. What are the magnitude and direction of the actual velocity of the bullet given that the plane flies horizontally at a speed of 450 mph and that the bullet is fired up at an angle of 30° from the direction of the airplane with a muzzle velocity of 3000 feet per second?

3. A man who can swim at the rate of 1 mph in still water heads directly across a river flowing at 1.2 mph. If the river is 1000 ft wide, how far downstream from the point directly across from his starting point will he land?

4. The destination of a plane is 1000 miles north of its starting point. The air speed of the plane is 350 mph. If a 35-mph cross wind from the east is blowing, in what apparent direction should the plane be headed in order to reach its destination? How long will the trip take?

Figure 4.

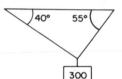

5. A 300-lb weight is suspended as shown in figure 4. Find the tension in each rope.

Figure 5.

6. A 200-lb weight is supported as shown in figure 5. Find the tension in the rope AB and in the strut CB if the length of the strut is 10 ft and the distance between A and C is 5 ft.

Figure 6.

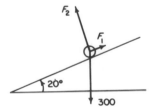

7. A barrel whose weight is 300 lb is held in place on an inclined plane as shown in figure 6. Find the magnitude of the force F_1 parallel to the plane and of the force F_2 perpendicular to it.

3.8. Miscellaneous applications In this section, we present some applications of the elementary functions. We shall not attempt to develop the background necessary to justify the techniques which are used. Results from calculus and differential equations will be stated without proof whenever they are needed.

When a natural substance or a population increases or decreases in size as a result of some action which affects each part equally, it is reasonable to assume that the rate of change of its size at any instant is proportional to the size itself at that instant. Using techniques of calculus, it can be shown that if such an assumption is made and $P(t)$ denotes the size of the substance or population at instant t,

then $P(t) = P_0 a^t$

where P_0 is the size of the substance at instant $t = 0$ and a is some positive constant which depends on the given conditions. We illustrate the usefulness of this result with an example.

Example 1. A certain town had 50,000 people in 1952 and 62,000 people in 1962. What is the expected size of the population of that town in 1972 if its growth follows the assumption made above?

Solution: We let $P_0 = 50,000$. Ten years later (when $t = 10$), the population was 62,000. Hence, we have

$$62,000 = 50,000\, a^{10}$$

Therefore, $a^{10} = 1.24$

Hence, $a = (1.24)^{1/10}$

Since $P(t) = 50,000\, a^t$

We have $P(t) = 50,000(1.24)^{t/10}$

And, in 1972, $t = 20$, from which we get

$$P(20) = 50,000(1.24)^{20/10}$$

$$= 50,000(1.24)^2$$

$$= 76,880$$

We now illustrate how the logarithm function can be used to advantage in some investment problems.

Suppose that a certain sum S is invested at an investment rate r per conversion period. Then it is easy to show that at the end of n conversion periods, the compounded amount will be

$$A = S(1 + r)^n$$

We illustrate the usefulness of this formula with the following example:

Example 2. Find the compounded amount at the end of 10 years if an original sum of \$2,000 is invested at 4 per cent a year and if the interest is compounded semiannually.

Solution: The interest rate per conversion period is 2 per cent or .02, and at the end of 10 years, there are 20 such conversion periods. Hence,

$$A = 2,000(1 + .02)^{20}$$

$$= 2,000(1.02)^{20}$$

Therefore, $\log A = \log 2000 + 20 \log 1.02$

$$= 3.30103 + 20(.00860)$$

$$= 3.30103 + 0.1720$$

$$= 3.47303$$

From which we get

$$A = 2,971.9$$

Hence, the compounded amount at the end of ten years is $2,971.90. ∎

In calculus, it is often necessary to simplify certain algebraic expressions. A change of variable using a trigonometric substitution is often very useful, as we illustrate in the following example:

Example 3. Transform the expression $(\sqrt{9 - x^2} + x)/(\sqrt{9 - x^2})$ to a trigonometric form free of radicals by means of a suitable substitution.

Solution: Starting with the identity

$$\cos^2 \alpha + \sin^2 \alpha \equiv 1,$$

we get $9 \cos^2 \alpha + 9 \sin^2 \alpha \equiv 9$

and $\qquad\qquad 9 \cos^2 \alpha \equiv 9 - 9 \sin^2 \alpha$

$$9 \cos^2 \alpha \equiv 9 - (3 \sin \alpha)^2$$

Comparing the right side of the above identity with the radical $\sqrt{9 - x^2}$, we let

$$x = 3 \sin \alpha$$

Then the foregoing expression becomes

$$\frac{\sqrt{9 \cos^2 \alpha} + 3 \sin \alpha}{\sqrt{9 \cos^2 \alpha}}$$

or, simplifying, we get

$$\frac{|\cos \alpha| + \sin \alpha}{|\cos \alpha|}$$

Recalling that we made the substitution $x = 3 \sin \alpha$, if we restrict α so that $\alpha = \text{Sin}^{-1} x/3$, then $-\pi/2 \leq \alpha \leq \pi/2$ and $\cos \alpha \geq 0$. It follows that $|\cos \alpha| = \cos \alpha$ and the expression can now be written as

$$\frac{\cos \alpha + \sin \alpha}{\cos \alpha} \quad \text{or} \quad 1 + \tan \alpha \quad \left(\text{where } \alpha = \text{Sin}^{-1} \frac{x}{3}\right) \quad \blacksquare$$

We pointed out earlier (section 1.13) that certain physical phenomena are periodic. Since the trigonometric functions are periodic, they are very useful in describing such phenomena mathematically. Mechanical systems involving springs or pendulum, electricity, sound and light waves are often described in terms of oscillation or vibrations which are usually periodic in character.

In courses on differential equations, it is usually shown that if the bob of a pendulum is pulled aside from its position of rest and released, then its motion can be described by the equation

$$\theta = \alpha \cos \sqrt{\frac{g}{l}} \cdot t$$

where θ is the measure in radians of the angle OPB at instant t, α, g, and l are appropriate constants. (See figure 1.)

Figure 1.

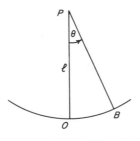

A motion which is described by an equation such as

$$d = a \sin (bt + c)$$

or $\quad d = a \cos (bt + c)$

is said to be a *simple harmonic motion*. The number a represents the maximum displacement from the central point of the motion and is called the *amplitude*. The time required for one complete cycle is called the *period* and it can easily be shown that the period is $2\pi/b$. The *frequency* is defined to be the number of complete cycles per unit of time and, since there is one cycle per period, the frequency is $b/2\pi$. We refer the reader to section 2.13, example 2, in which the graph of the equation $y = 2 \sin (2x - \pi/3)$ was sketched. This equation can be considered as an equation describing a simple harmonic motion, if x represents time and y the displacement along some line. The period is clearly π, the frequency $1/\pi$, and the amplitude 2.

Often the vibration of a spring is retarded by damping forces, such as friction and air resistance. Using techniques of differential equations, it can be shown that in such cases the motion is described by an equation of the form

$$s = e^{-at}(c_1 \cos bt + c_2 \sin bt)$$

where $a > 0$, and a, b, c_1, c_2 are constants which depend on the conditions of the motion which the equation describes. The number e is an irrational number, approximately equal to 2.71828. It is often called the *natural base* of logarithms.

In the foregoing equation, e^{-at} is called a *damping factor*. We note that since $a > 0$, e^{-at} will decrease as t increases.

Example 4. Graph the equation $s = e^{-t/2}(\cos 3t - \sqrt{3} \sin 3t)$.

Solution: We may write the just given equation in a different form as follows:

$$s = 2e^{-t/2}\left(\frac{1}{2} \cos 3t - \frac{\sqrt{3}}{2} \sin 3t\right)$$

$$= 2e^{-t/2}\left(\sin \frac{\pi}{6} \cos 3t - \cos \frac{\pi}{6} \sin 3t\right)$$

$$= 2e^{-t/2} \sin \left(\frac{\pi}{6} - 3t\right)$$

We then sketch the graphs of the equations

$$s = 2 \sin \left(\frac{\pi}{6} - 3t\right) \quad \text{and} \quad s = e^{-t/2}$$

on the same coordinate system and we obtain a sketch of the graph of the equation

$$s = 2e^{-t/2} \sin \left(\frac{\pi}{6} - 3t\right)$$

by multiplying corresponding ordinates. (See figure 2.)

Figure 2.

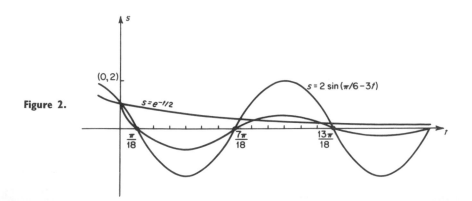

Exercises
1. A certain town had 45,000 people in 1940 and 72,000 people in 1955. What is the expected population of that town in 1965? Calculate what the size of the population must have been in 1935.

2. If, in a certain culture of bacteria, the number present at a certain instant was 2,000, and if the number present 10 hr later was 15,000, find an expression for the number of bacteria at the end of 17 hr.

3. Find the compounded amount at the end of 15 years if an original sum of $15,000 is invested at a rate of 5 per cent a year and if the interest is compounded (a) annually, (b) semiannually.

4. A man has a certain sum of money to invest. A bank will pay 4.05 per cent interest compounded annually. Another will pay 4 per cent interest compounded semiannually. Which is the better investment?

5. A man has a certain principal he wants to invest. If the interest on his investment is compounded semiannually at a rate of 5 per cent a year, how long should he keep his investment in order to double his principal?

6. Transform the expression $\sqrt{9 + x^2} + x$ to a trigonometric form free of radicals by means of a suitable substitution. (*Hint:* Start with the identity $1 + \tan^2 \alpha \equiv \sec^2 \alpha$.)

7. Transform the expression $\sqrt{x^2 + 4x} - 3x$ to a trigonometric form free of radicals by means of a suitably chosen substitution. (*Hint:* Note that $x^2 + 4x = (x + 2)^2 - 4$ and use the fact that $\sec^2 \alpha - 1 \equiv \tan^2 \alpha$.)

8. The following are equations which represent motions of a particle. Give the amplitude, period, and frequency in each case.
   (a) $s = 2 \sin 3t$ (b) $s = \frac{1}{2} \cos (2t - 1)$
   (c) $s = 3 \cos (5t - \pi)$ (d) $s = 7(\sin 2t + \cos 2t)$

9. Sketch the graphs of the equations given in exercise 8.

10. Sketch the graph of the equation
    $$s = e^{-t/3}(\cos 4t + \sin 4t)$$

Appendix A: Polar Coordinates

A.1. Introduction In section 1.9, we described the cartesian coordinate system. We now present a different way of associating points of a plane with certain ordered pairs. Although this association is often quite useful, it is not one-to-one. We shall illustrate this fact below.

Let P be a cartesian coordinate plane with origin O. Let A be any point in P, $(A \neq O)$.

There are infinitely many coterminal angles in standard position which have the point A on their terminal side. Let $(Ox, m$ units) be any one of them and let $r = |OA|$. Then the ordered pair $(r, m$ units) is called a pair of *polar coordinates* of the point A. The point O is called the *pole* and the ray Ox is called the *polar axis*. (See figure 1.)

Figure 1.

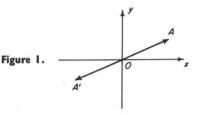

For example, the point A has polar coordinates $(2, 30°)$, $(2, 390°)$, $(2, -330°)$, etc. We agree that if $\overrightarrow{OA'} = -\overrightarrow{OA}$ and if $(Ox, m$ units) is any angle in standard position which has A' on its terminal side, then $(-r, m$ units) is also called a *pair of coordinates* of the point A. For example, in figure 1, the point A also has coordinates $(-2, 210°)$, $(-2, 570°)$, $(-2, -150°)$, etc. We also agree that the pole has coordinates, $(0, k$ units) where k units can be the measure of any angle.

We have described a way to assign for each point in the plane an ordered pair of polar coordinates, but this assignment gives us many such pairs. In general, if (r, θ), is a pair of polar coordinates of a point, then $(r, \theta + 2n\pi)$ and $(-r, \theta + (2n + 1)\pi)$ are also its polar coordinates. (Recall that if the measure of angle is not given, it is assumed to be the radian.)

Conversely, suppose we are given an ordered pair $(r, m$ units). We want to assign to it a point in the plane. Consider a cartesian coordinate system. If $r = 0$, then the pole (origin) corresponds to the ordered pair.

If $r > 0$, consider the angle $(Ox, m$ units) in standard position. Let A be the unique point on its terminal side such that $|OA| = r$. Then A corresponds to $(r, m$ units). If $r < 0$, consider the angle $(Ox, m$ units) in standard position. Let A' be on its terminal side such that $|OA'| = |r|$ and let $\overrightarrow{OA} = -\overrightarrow{OA'}$. Then the point A is assigned to the pair $(r, m$ units).

The following theorem gives the relation between cartesian and polar coordinates of a point.

Theorem A.I.I. If a rectangular and a polar coordinate system are placed in the same plane such that the positive x axis is the polar axis and the origin is the pole, and if a point A has coordinates (x, y) and $(r, m$ units$)$ in the respective systems, then

$$x = r \cos (m \text{ units}), \qquad y = r \sin (m \text{ units})$$

Proof: If the point A is the origin (pole), the two relations obviously hold since $x = y = r = 0$.

If $r > 0$, the result follows from corollary 3.2.5.

Suppose now that $r < 0$ and, for convenience, let the angle measure be given in degrees. If $(r, m°)$ are polar coordinates of the point A, so are $(-r, m° + 180°)$ where $-r > 0$. Hence,

$$x = -r \cos (m° + 180°)$$
$$= -r[\cos (m°) \cos (180°) - \sin (m°) \sin (180°)]$$
$$= (-r)(-\cos (m°))$$
$$= r \cos (m°)$$

and $y = (-r)[\sin (m° + 180°)]$
$$= -r[\sin (m°) \cos (180°) + \cos (m°) \sin (180°)]$$
$$= (-r)(-\sin (m°))$$
$$= r \sin (m°) \quad \blacksquare$$

Also note that $x^2 + y^2 = r^2(\cos^2 (m \text{ units}) + \sin^2 (m \text{ units})) = r^2 \cdot 1 = r^2$.

Example 1. Find an equation in polar coordinates for the curve whose equation in cartesian coordinates is

$$x^2 - y^2 = 1$$

Solution: Using the radian measure for angles, we get

$$(r \cos \theta)^2 - (r \sin \theta)^2 = 1$$
$$r^2(\cos^2 \theta - \sin^2 \theta) = 1$$
$$r^2 \cos 2\theta = 1 \quad \blacksquare$$

Example 2. Find an equation in cartesian coordinates for the curve whose equation in polar coordinates is

$$r = 2 \sin \theta$$

Solution: For convenience, we multiply both sides by r and get

$$r^2 = 2r \sin \theta$$

from which we get

$$x^2 + y^2 = 2y \quad \blacksquare$$

A.2. Graphs of polar equations The graph of an equation $f(r, \theta) = 0$ is the set of all points whose polar coordinates, *in some form*, satisfy the equation. The reader may easily verify the following statements about the symmetry of polar graphs.

Let G be the graph of an equation $f(r, \theta) = 0$. Then

1. If the equation is unaltered when θ is replaced by $-\theta$, G is symmetric with respect to the line which contains the polar axis.

2. If the equation is unaltered when θ is replaced by $\pi - \theta$, G is symmetric with respect to the line perpendicular to the polar axis at the pole.

3. If the equation is unaltered when r is replaced by $-r$, G is symmetric with respect to the pole.

Example 1. Sketch the graph of the equation $r = a(1 + \cos \theta)$ where a is a positive constant.

Solution: First we check for symmetry. Replacing θ by $-\theta$, we obtain

$$r = a(1 + \cos(-\theta)) = a(1 + \cos \theta)$$

Hence, the equation is unaltered when θ is replaced by $-\theta$, and its graph must be symmetric with respect to the line which contains the polar axis.

Hence, we need to consider only values of θ between 0 and π. Let us consider several convenient values of θ and calculate the corresponding values of r. The results are tabulated below. (Note that some values given for r are approximations.)

θ	0	$\pi/6$	$\pi/4$	$\pi/3$	$\pi/2$	$2\pi/3$	$3\pi/4$	$5\pi/6$	π
r	$2a$	$1.866a$	$1.707a$	$1.5a$	a	$.5a$	$.293a$	$.134a$	0

We now plot the points with polar coordinates $(2a, 0)$, $(1.866a, \pi/6)$, $(1.707a, \pi/4)$, etc., and sketch an approximation of half of the graph of the equation by drawing a smooth curve passing through the points which we have plotted. We get the other half of the graph by making use of its symmetry. (See figure 1.) The curve which we obtained is often called *cardoid* because it has the shape of a heart.

Figure 1.

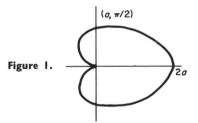

$(a, \pi/2)$

$2a$

A.3. Intersections of polar curves If $f(x, y) = 0$ and $g(x, y) = 0$ are equations of two curves in a cartesian coordinate system and we want to find the points of intersection of the two curves, we usually proceed as follows:

If (a, b) is a point of intersection, it is on both curves. Hence, both statements $f(a, b) = 0$ and $g(a, b) = 0$ must be true. Therefore, to get (a, b), we need only solve the system of two equations in two unknowns.

$$f(x, y) = 0$$

$$g(x, y) = 0$$

But if $\Phi(r, \theta) = 0$ and $\psi(r, \theta) = 0$ are equations of polar curves and we want to find the points of intersection of the two curves, we need to be somewhat more careful. We illustrate this fact with the following example.

Example I. Find the points of intersection of the two polar curves whose equations are

$$r^2 = 4 \sin \theta \quad \text{and} \quad r = 1 - \sin \theta$$

Solution: Let us first use the same technique as in the case of the cartesian coordinate system and solve the system

$$r^2 = 4 \sin \theta \tag{1}$$

$$r = 1 - \sin \theta \tag{2}$$

By substitution, we get

$$r^2 = 4(1 - r)$$

and solving the above quadratic equation, we get

$$r = -2(1 \pm \sqrt{2})$$

Replacing r by $-2(1 + \sqrt{2})$ in equation (2), we get

$$-2 - 2\sqrt{2} = 1 - \sin \theta$$

and $\quad \sin \theta = 1 + 2 + 2\sqrt{2}$

which is satisfied for no value of θ, since necessarily

$$-1 \le \sin \theta \le 1.$$

Now replacing r by $-2(1 - \sqrt{2})$ in equation (2), we get

$$-2 + 2\sqrt{2} = 1 - \sin \theta$$

$$\sin \theta = 1 + 2 - 2\sqrt{2} \doteq 0.172$$

from which we get $\theta \doteq .17278 \quad \text{or} \quad \theta \doteq \pi - .17278$

Hence, we conclude that $(-2 + 2\sqrt{2}, .17278)$ and $(-2 + 2\sqrt{2}, \pi - .17278)$ are (approximate) coordinates of the intersection. We shall show that there are two more points of intersection.

We note that the coordinates $(2, 3\pi/2)$ satisfy the equation $r = 1 - \sin\theta$. They do not, however, satisfy the equation $r^2 = 4\sin\theta$. But, if we let A be the point whose coordinates are $(2, 3\pi/2)$, then $(-2, \pi/2)$ are also coordinates of the point A. Noting that $(-2, \pi/2)$ satisfy the equation $r^2 = 4\sin\theta$, we conclude that the point A is also a point of intersection of the two polar curves.

Further, we note that the coordinates $(0, 0)$ satisfy the first equation and $(0, \pi/2)$ satisfy the second. Hence, both curves pass through the pole, and we conclude that the pole is another point of intersection of the two curves. To check whether there are other points of intersection, we argue as follows:

Suppose B is a point of intersection of the two curves. Then, its coordinates, _in some form_, must satisfy the first equation $r^2 = 4\sin\theta$. Let (r_1, θ_1) be a form of the coordinates of B which satisfy that equation. Then, all forms of the coordinates of B are expressed by $(r_1, \theta_1 + 2n\pi)$ and $(-r_1, \theta_1 + (2n + 1)\pi)$ (where n is an integer). Since B is also on the second curve, one of the two forms above must satisfy the second equation. Hence, we must have either

$$r_1^2 = 4\sin\theta_1$$
$$r_1 = 1 - \sin(\theta_1 + 2n\pi)$$

or $\quad r_1^2 = 4\sin\theta_1$
$$-r_1 = 1 - \sin(\theta_1 + (2n + 1)\pi)$$

The first system reduces to the one which we solved earlier. The second system becomes

$$r_1^2 = 4\sin\theta_1 \tag{1}$$
$$-r_1 = 1 - \sin(-\theta_1) = 1 + \sin\theta_1 \tag{2}$$

By replacement, we get

$$r_1^2 = 4(-r_1 - 1)$$

or $r_1^2 + 4r_1 + 4 = 0$
$$(r_1 + 2)^2 = 0$$

Hence, $\qquad r_1 = -2$

and by substitution in equation (1), we get $\theta_1 = \pi/2$. Hence, the point with coordinates $(-2, \pi/2)$ is a point of intersection. Hence, the only points of intersection of the two curves are the pole and the points with coordinates $(-2, \pi/2)$, $(-2 + 2\sqrt{2}, .17278)$, and $(-2 + 2\sqrt{2}, 2.968)$. ∎

In general, to find the points of intersection of two curves whose equations are respectively $f(r, \theta) = 0$ and $g(r, \theta) = 0$, we first check for possible intersection at the pole. To do this, we check whether there is a value of θ for which $f(0, \theta) = 0$ is true and some value of θ (possibly distinct from the first) for which $g(0, \theta) = 0$ is satisfied. If so, both curves pass through the pole and the pole is a point of intersection.

Then we solve both of the following systems of equations.

$$f(r, \theta) = 0$$

$$g(r, \theta + 2n\pi) = 0$$

and
$$f(r, \theta) = 0$$

$$g(-r, \theta + (2n + 1)\pi) = 0$$

The solutions of the two systems yield the coordinates of the points of intersection.

Remark: The reader may find it helpful to interpret the fact that a point of intersection may be obtained for two distinct values of θ by thinking of the two curves as paths followed by two moving particles in the plane. The two paths may very well cross and the particles not collide, provided that they pass through the point of intersection at different times.

Exercises

1. Plot the points whose polar coordinates are
   (a) $(2, 45°)$ (b) $(-3, -\pi/2)$
   (c) $(-2, 3/2 \text{ rev})$ (d) $(2\pi, 45°)$

2. Find an equation in polar coordinates for the curve whose equation in cartesian coordinates is
   (a) $x^2 + y^2 = a^2$
   (b) $x^2 + 9y^2 = 9$
   (c) $x + 3y = 7$

3. Find an equation in cartesian coordinates for the curve whose equation in polar coordinates is
   (a) $r = 4 \sin \theta$
   (b) $r = 3 \cos \theta + 2 \sin \theta$
   (c) $r^2 = 9 \sin 2\theta$

4. By changing to cartesian coordinates, show that the equation $r = 2a \cos \theta$ is the equation of a circle. Find the center and radius of that circle.

5. Derive a formula which gives the distance between the points A and B in terms of their polar coordinates (r_1, θ_1) and (r_2, θ_2). (*Hint:* Use the law of cosines.)

6. Check for symmetry and sketch the graphs of the following equations:
   (a) $r = 9 \cos \theta$
   (b) $r = 2 + 5 \cos \theta$
   (c) $r = 9 \sin 5\theta$

7. Find the points of intersection of the graphs of the following pairs of equations:
   (a) $r = a(1 - \cos \theta)$, $r = a \cos \theta$ $(a > 0)$
   (b) $r^2 = 2a^2 \sin 2\theta$, $r = a$ $(a > 0)$
   (c) $r = 1 + \sin \theta$, $r = 3 \sin \theta$

8. What kind of symmetry does the graph of an equation have if the equation is unaltered when θ is replaced by $\pi/2 - \theta$?

Appendix B: Complex Numbers

B.1. Introduction We have seen that, if we restrict ourselves to the system of real numbers, there are polynomial equations whose solution sets are empty. Motivated by the desire to be able to solve equations such as $x^2 + 1 = 0$, mathematicians invented the number i, which has the property $i^2 = -1$. Because they failed to see any connection between this new number and any "real" application, they called i an *imaginary number* and $a + bi$ was called a *complex number*. We note that even as late as the eighteenth century, an English mathematician, Francis Maseres, published some work on the theory of equations in which he refused to use "impossible" quantities. Today the theory of "functions of complex variables" is one of the most useful theories in applied mathematics.

It has been said many times that the use of the word "imaginary" is a great algebraic calamity and that "imaginary numbers" are just as real as the "real numbers." On the other hand, we perhaps should say that the "real numbers" are just as imaginary as the "imaginary numbers."

The fact remains that the number concept is very abstract indeed. It is, however, very useful for dealing with the concrete. Therefore, we need not be concerned about the "names" given to certain "classes of numbers" but only about their *properties* and their *usefulness*.

In this appendix, we shall describe briefly the system of complex numbers. This system is large enough so that if it is taken as the universe, any polynomial equation of positive degree has at least one root.

B.2. Definitions and properties

Definition B.2.1. The *complex number system* is the set C of ordered pairs of real numbers together with two basic operations, addition and multiplication, which satisfy the following properties:

(a) $(x_1, y_1) = (x_2, y_2)$ if and only if $x_1 = x_2$ and $y_1 = y_2$

(b) $(x_1, y_1) + (x_2, y_2) = (x_1 + x_2, y_1 + y_2)$

(c) $(x_1, y_1) \cdot (x_2, y_2) = (x_1 x_2 - y_1 y_2, x_1 y_2 + x_2 y_1)$

Remark: Since complex numbers are ordered pairs of real numbers, the foregoing property a is automatically satisfied by definition 1.7.1. We stated it again, however, to emphasize the fact that it is indeed a very important property.

Note: If we identify the pair $(x, 0)$ with the real number x and the pair $(0, 1)$ with the imaginary number i,* then we have the following:

* The imaginary number i is often denoted by j in certain branches of engineering.

1. For any real number r, we have

$$r(x, y) = (r, 0)(x, y) = (rx - 0y, ry + 0x)$$
$$= (rx, ry)$$

2. $(x, y) = (x, 0) + (0, y) = (x, 0) + y(0, 1) = x + yi$

Hence (x, y) is identified with $x + yi$.

As a matter of fact, one can formally perform algebraic operations with complex numbers by replacing each complex number (x, y) by $x + yi$, performing all algebraic operations and then replacing each i^2 by -1.

Example 1. $(2, 3)(5, 2) = (2 + 3i)(5 + 2i)$

$$= 10 + 19i + 6i^2$$
$$= 10 + 19i - 6$$
$$= 4 + 19i$$
$$= (4, 19) \ \blacksquare$$

Theorem B.2.2. The system of complex numbers satisfies the eleven field properties.

Proof: See exercise 3.

Theorem B.2.3. The system of complex numbers does not satisfy the order relations O_1, O_2, and O_3 listed in section 1.2.

Proof: We shall assume that the system of complex numbers does satisfy the three properties and arrive at a contradiction.
Suppose that

0.1. There is a non-empty subset P of C such that if we define

$$-P = \{(-x, -y) \,|\, (x, y) \in P\}$$

Then $P \cup \{(0, 0)\} \cup -P = C$ and $-P, \{(0, 0)\}$ and P are mutually disjoint.

0.2. If $(x_1, y_1) \in P$ and $(x_2, y_2) \in P$

then $(x_1, y_1) + (x_2, y_2) \in P$.

0.3. If $(x_1, y_1) \in P$ and $(x_2, y_2) \in P$

then $(x_1, y_1) \cdot (x_2, y_2) \in P$.

Now we know that $(0, 1) \neq (0, 0)$. Hence, we must have $(0, 1) \in P$ or $(0, 1) \in -P$.
Suppose $(0, 1) \in P$. Then $(0, 1) \cdot (0, 1) \in P$ (by property 0.3). That is $(-1, 0) \in P$, since $(0, 1) \cdot (0, 1) = (-1, 0)$. But by property 0.3 $(0, 1) \in P$ and $(-1, 0) \in P$ implies $(0, 1) \cdot (-1, 0) \in P$; that is

$(0, -1) \in P$, which, together with $(0, 1) \in P$, contradicts property 0.1. Hence $(0, 1)$ cannot be an element of P.

Similarly, it can be shown that $(0, 1) \in -P$ leads to a contradiction. Hence, the system C of complex numbers cannot satisfy properties 0.1, 0.2, and 0.3. ∎

Subtraction and division of complex numbers are now defined in terms of addition and multiplication.

Definitions B.2.4. If (x_1, y_1) and (x_2, y_2) are complex numbers, the *difference* $(x_1, y_1) - (x_2, y_2)$ is the complex number (x_3, y_3) which has the property

$$(x_1, y_1) = (x_2, y_2) + (x_3, y_3)$$

Further if $x_2^2 + y_2^2 \neq 0$, the *quotient* $(x_1, y_1)/(x_2, y_2)$ is the complex, number (x_3, y_3) which has the property

$$(x_1, y_1) = (x_2, y_2) \cdot (x_3, y_3)$$

Problem: Find formulations in terms of x_1, y_1, x_2, and y_2 for the complex numbers $(x_1, y_1) - (x_2, y_2)$ and $(x_1, y_1)/(x_2, y_2)$.

The following theorem presents one of the most significant properties of the system of complex numbers.

Theorem B.2.5. Every polynomial equation of positive degree has at least one root, provided that the universe is the system of complex numbers.

The foregoing theorem is known as *the fundamental theorem of algebra*. Gauss, a great German mathematician (1777–1855), thought the theorem so important that he gave four distinct proofs for it, the last one when he was seventy years of age!

The proofs which are known are either too long or make use of techniques which are learned in advanced courses in mathematics. Hence, no proof of the fundamental theorem will be given here.

The reader has undoubtedly noticed that a geometric interpretation of complex numbers can be given. Since a complex number is an ordered pair of real numbers, we can represent it uniquely by a point in a coordinate plane or by a geometric vector with initial point the origin. The distance from the origin to the point (x, y) is $\sqrt{x^2 + y^2}$. It is called the *absolute value* of the complex number (x, y).

$$|(x, y)| = \sqrt{x^2 + y^2}$$

Note: If x is a real number,

$$|x| = |(x, 0)| = \sqrt{x^2 + 0^2} = \sqrt{x^2}$$

This agrees with the remark made in section 1.5, page 24.

The *conjugate* $\overline{(x, y)}$ of the complex number (x, y) is $(x, -y)$.

Note that

$$(x, y) \cdot \overline{(x, y)} = (x, y)(x, -y) = (x^2 + y^2, xy - xy)$$
$$= (x^2 + y^2, 0)$$

Hence, $(x, y) \cdot \overline{(x, y)} = |(x, y)|^2$

Now let (x, y) be a complex number. Let (r, θ) be polar coordinates of the point representing that complex number in the coordinate plane. Then $x = r \cos \theta$ and $y = r \sin \theta$. Therefore,

$$(x, y) = (r \cos \theta, r \sin \theta)$$

$$= r(\cos \theta, \sin \theta)$$

This is called a *polar form* of the complex number (x, y).

Theorem B.2.6. If $r_1(\cos \theta_1, \sin \theta_1)$ and $r_2(\cos \theta_2, \sin \theta_2)$ are polar forms of two complex numbers, then a polar form of their product is

$$r_1 r_2(\cos (\theta_1 + \theta_2), \sin (\theta_1 + \theta_2))$$

Proof: $r_1(\cos \theta_1, \sin \theta_1) \cdot r_2(\cos \theta_2, \sin \theta_2)$

$$= r_1 r_2(\cos \theta_1 \cos \theta_2 - \sin \theta_1 \sin \theta_2, \cos \theta_1 \sin \theta_2 + \sin_1 \theta \cos \theta_2)$$

$$= r_1 r_2(\cos (\theta_1 + \theta_2), \sin (\theta_1 + \theta_2)) \blacksquare$$

A very useful theorem will presently be stated. This theorem is due to De Moivre (1667–1754), a French mathematician who lived most of his life in England.

Theorem B.2.7. For every integer n,

$$(\cos \theta, \sin \theta)^n = (\cos n \theta, \sin n \theta)$$

Proof: The proof consists of four parts.

Part 1. Verify that it is true for $n = 0$.

Part 2. The theorem can easily be proved by induction for all positive integers n.

Part 3. Verify that $(\cos \theta, \sin \theta)^{-1} = (\cos -\theta, \sin -\theta)$.

Part 4. Prove the theorem for all negative integers m, using the fact that if m is negative $(-1)(m)$ is positive and also parts 2 and 3.

The details are left for the reader.

De Moivre's theorem can be used in proving the following:

Theorem B.2.8. If $r(\cos \theta, \sin \theta)$ is a polar form of a complex number with $r > 0$ and if n is a positive integer, then there are exactly n nth roots of that complex number. They are given by

$$r_K = \sqrt[n]{r}\left(\cos \frac{\theta + 2K\pi}{n}, \sin \frac{\theta + 2K\pi}{n}\right)$$

$$K = 0, 1, 2, \ldots, n - 1$$

The proof is left as an exercise for the reader. However, we illustrate the idea of the proof with the following:

Example 2. Find the three cube roots of the number $8i$.

Solution: A polar form of the complex number $8(0, 1)$ is $8(\cos \pi/2, \sin \pi/2)$. Let $r_K(\cos \theta_K, \sin \theta_K)$ be any cube root of the given complex number.

Then $[r_K(\cos \theta_K, \sin \theta_K)]^3 = 8\left(\cos \dfrac{\pi}{2}, \sin \dfrac{\pi}{2}\right)$

or $\quad r_K^3(\cos 3\theta_K, \sin 3\theta_K) = 8\left(\cos \dfrac{\pi}{2}, \sin \dfrac{\pi}{2}\right)$

This equation will be satisfied if and only if

$$r_K^3 = 8 \quad \text{and} \quad 3\theta_K = \frac{\pi}{2} + 2n\pi$$

where n is an integer.

Hence, $r_K = 2$ and $\theta_K = \dfrac{\pi}{6} + \dfrac{2n\pi}{3}$

Letting $n = 0$, we get one possible cube root

$$2\left(\cos \frac{\pi}{6}, \sin \frac{\pi}{6}\right) = 2\left(\frac{\sqrt{3}}{2}, \frac{1}{2}\right) = (\sqrt{3}, 1)$$

With $n = 1$, we get another cube root

$$2\left(\cos \frac{5\pi}{6}, \sin \frac{5\pi}{6}\right) = 2\left(-\frac{\sqrt{3}}{2}, \frac{1}{2}\right) = (-\sqrt{3}, 1)$$

and with $n = 2$, we get a third cube root

$$2\left(\cos \frac{3\pi}{2}, \sin \frac{3\pi}{2}\right) = 2(0, -1) = -2i$$

Because of the periodicity of the sine and cosine functions, for any value of n greater than 2, we obtain one of the three cube roots just given. Hence, there are exactly three distinct cube roots of $8i$.

Exercises   1. Perform the following operations using definitions B.2.1.

      (a) $(2, 3) + (5, -7)$

      (b) $(5, 1) \cdot (2, -8)$

      (c) $(3/2, -1/3) \cdot (2/7, -3/4)$

    2. Perform the operations of exercise 1 by first replacing each (x, y) by $x + yi$.

3. Prove that the system of complex numbers satisfies the eleven field properties.

4. Find formulations in terms of x_1, x_2, y_1, and y_2 for the complex number $(x_1, y_1) - (x_2, y_2)$ and if $(x_2, y_2) \neq (0, 0)$, for $(x_1, y_1)/(x_2, y_2)$.

5. Prove that for any two complex numbers (a, b) and (c, d) it is true that

$$\overline{(a, b) + (e, d)} = \overline{(a, b)} + \overline{(c, d)}$$

and $\quad \overline{(a, b) \cdot (c, d)} = \overline{(a, b)} \cdot \overline{(c, d)}$

6. Prove that a complex number is real if and only if it is equal to its conjugate.

7. Prove De Moivre's theorem.

8. Find the three cube roots of the number 1.

9. Find the 4 fourth roots of $(-8, 8\sqrt{3})$.

10. Prove theorem B.2.8.

11. Show that the four points which represent the 4 fourth roots of $(-8, 8\sqrt{3})$ found in exercise 9 lie on a circle with center at the origin. Also show that these four points divide the circle into four arcs of equal lengths.

12. If $r(\cos \theta, \sin \theta)$ is a polar form of a complex number $(r > 0)$, show that the n points which represent the n nth roots of that number lie on a circle with center the origin and with radius $\sqrt[n]{r}$. Also show that these points divide the circle into n arcs of equal lengths.

13. If P_1, P_2, and P_3 are points which represent the complex numbers (x_1, y_1), (x_2, y_2), and $(x_3, y_3) = (x_1 + x_2, y_1 + y_2)$ respectively and if O is the origin, then $\overrightarrow{OP_3} = \overrightarrow{OP_1} + \overrightarrow{OP_2}$.

    Hence, given the points which represent (x_1, y_1) and (x_2, y_2), it is easy to construct, with a ruler and compass, the point which represents $(x_1, y_1) + (x_2, y_2)$. Given the points which represent (x_1, y_1) and (x_2, y_2) in the plane, give a construction, with ruler and compass, to find the point which represents $(x_1, y_1) \cdot (x_2, y_2)$. (*Hint:* Use theorem B.2.6.)

14. In a basic algebra course, the following problem was given. At a certain instant, two particles are 6 in. apart. If these two particles move on a straight line and in the same direction, the faster one will meet the slower one after covering a distance which is the cube of the distance traveled by the slower particle. What is the distance traveled by each particle?

    A solution of this problem consists of solving a cubic equation. This equation has one real root and two imaginary roots. Solve the equation and show that the two imaginary roots can be interpreted as solutions of the problem which we get by replacing, in the problem just stated, the expression "move on a straight line" with "move on straight lines which lie in the same plane."

Appendix C: Tables

Table 1. COMMON LOGARITHMS OF NUMBERS

1000–1509

N.	L. 0	1	2	3	4	5	6	7	8	9	P. P.
100	00 000	043	087	130	173	217	260	303	346	389	
101	432	475	518	561	604	647	689	732	775	817	
102	860	903	945	988	*030	*072	*115	*157	*199	*242	
103	01 284	326	368	410	452	494	536	578	620	662	

<table>
<tr><td></td><td>44</td><td>43</td><td>42</td></tr>
<tr><td>1</td><td>4.4</td><td>4.3</td><td>4.2</td></tr>
<tr><td>2</td><td>8.8</td><td>8.6</td><td>8.4</td></tr>
<tr><td>3</td><td>13.2</td><td>12.9</td><td>12.6</td></tr>
<tr><td>4</td><td>17.6</td><td>17.2</td><td>16.8</td></tr>
<tr><td>5</td><td>22.0</td><td>21.5</td><td>21.0</td></tr>
<tr><td>6</td><td>26.4</td><td>25.8</td><td>25.2</td></tr>
<tr><td>7</td><td>30.8</td><td>30.1</td><td>29.4</td></tr>
<tr><td>8</td><td>35.2</td><td>34.4</td><td>33.6</td></tr>
<tr><td>9</td><td>39.6</td><td>38.7</td><td>37.8</td></tr>
</table>

N.	L. 0	1	2	3	4	5	6	7	8	9
104	703	745	787	828	870	912	953	995	*036	*078
105	02 119	160	202	243	284	325	366	407	449	490
106	531	572	612	653	694	735	776	816	857	898
107	938	979	*019	*060	*100	*141	*181	*222	*262	*302
108	03 342	383	423	463	503	543	583	623	663	703
109	743	782	822	862	902	941	981	*021	*060	*100
110	04 139	179	218	258	297	336	376	415	454	493
111	532	571	610	650	689	727	766	805	844	883
112	922	961	999	*038	*077	*115	*154	*192	*231	*269
113	05 308	346	385	423	461	500	538	576	614	652

<table>
<tr><td></td><td>41</td><td>40</td><td>39</td></tr>
<tr><td>1</td><td>4.1</td><td>4.0</td><td>3.9</td></tr>
<tr><td>2</td><td>8.2</td><td>8.0</td><td>7.8</td></tr>
<tr><td>3</td><td>12.3</td><td>12.0</td><td>11.7</td></tr>
<tr><td>4</td><td>16.4</td><td>16.0</td><td>15.6</td></tr>
<tr><td>5</td><td>20.5</td><td>20.0</td><td>19.5</td></tr>
<tr><td>6</td><td>24.6</td><td>24.0</td><td>23.4</td></tr>
<tr><td>7</td><td>28.7</td><td>28.0</td><td>27.3</td></tr>
<tr><td>8</td><td>32.8</td><td>32.0</td><td>31.2</td></tr>
<tr><td>9</td><td>36.9</td><td>36.0</td><td>35.1</td></tr>
</table>

N.	L. 0	1	2	3	4	5	6	7	8	9
114	690	729	767	805	843	881	918	956	994	*032
115	06 070	108	145	183	221	258	296	333	371	408
116	446	483	521	558	595	633	670	707	744	781
117	819	856	893	930	967	*004	*041	*078	*115	*151
118	07 188	225	262	298	335	372	408	445	482	518
119	555	591	628	664	700	737	773	809	846	882
120	918	954	990	*027	*063	*099	*135	*171	*207	*243
121	08 279	314	350	386	422	458	493	529	565	600
122	636	672	707	743	778	814	849	884	920	955
123	991	*026	*061	*096	*132	*167	*202	*237	*272	*307

<table>
<tr><td></td><td>38</td><td>37</td><td>36</td></tr>
<tr><td>1</td><td>3.8</td><td>3.7</td><td>3.6</td></tr>
<tr><td>2</td><td>7.6</td><td>7.4</td><td>7.2</td></tr>
<tr><td>3</td><td>11.4</td><td>11.1</td><td>10.8</td></tr>
<tr><td>4</td><td>15.2</td><td>14.8</td><td>14.4</td></tr>
<tr><td>5</td><td>19.0</td><td>18.5</td><td>18.0</td></tr>
<tr><td>6</td><td>22.8</td><td>22.2</td><td>21.6</td></tr>
<tr><td>7</td><td>26.6</td><td>25.9</td><td>25.2</td></tr>
<tr><td>8</td><td>30.4</td><td>29.6</td><td>28.8</td></tr>
<tr><td>9</td><td>34.2</td><td>33.3</td><td>32.4</td></tr>
</table>

N.	L. 0	1	2	3	4	5	6	7	8	9
124	09 342	377	412	447	482	517	552	587	621	656
125	691	726	760	795	830	864	899	934	968	*003
126	10 037	072	106	140	175	209	243	278	312	346
127	380	415	449	483	517	551	585	619	653	687
128	721	755	789	823	857	890	924	958	992	*025
129	11 059	093	126	160	193	227	261	294	327	361
130	394	428	461	494	528	561	594	628	661	694
131	727	760	793	826	860	893	926	959	992	*024
132	12 057	090	123	156	189	222	254	287	320	352
133	385	418	450	483	516	548	581	613	646	678

<table>
<tr><td></td><td>35</td><td>34</td><td>33</td></tr>
<tr><td>1</td><td>3.5</td><td>3.4</td><td>3.3</td></tr>
<tr><td>2</td><td>7.0</td><td>6.8</td><td>6.6</td></tr>
<tr><td>3</td><td>10.5</td><td>10.2</td><td>9.9</td></tr>
<tr><td>4</td><td>14.0</td><td>13.6</td><td>13.2</td></tr>
<tr><td>5</td><td>17.5</td><td>17.0</td><td>16.5</td></tr>
<tr><td>6</td><td>21.0</td><td>20.4</td><td>19.8</td></tr>
<tr><td>7</td><td>24.5</td><td>23.8</td><td>23.1</td></tr>
<tr><td>8</td><td>28.0</td><td>27.2</td><td>26.4</td></tr>
<tr><td>9</td><td>31.5</td><td>30.6</td><td>29.7</td></tr>
</table>

N.	L. 0	1	2	3	4	5	6	7	8	9
134	710	743	775	808	840	872	905	937	969	*001
135	13 033	066	098	130	162	194	226	258	290	322
136	354	386	418	450	481	513	545	577	609	640
137	672	704	735	767	799	830	862	893	925	956
138	988	*019	*051	*082	*114	*145	*176	*208	*239	*270
139	14 301	333	364	395	426	457	489	520	551	582
140	613	644	675	706	737	768	799	829	860	891

<table>
<tr><td></td><td>32</td><td>31</td><td>30</td></tr>
<tr><td>1</td><td>3.2</td><td>3.1</td><td>3.0</td></tr>
<tr><td>2</td><td>6.4</td><td>6.2</td><td>6.0</td></tr>
<tr><td>3</td><td>9.6</td><td>9.3</td><td>9.0</td></tr>
<tr><td>4</td><td>12.8</td><td>12.4</td><td>12.0</td></tr>
<tr><td>5</td><td>16.0</td><td>15.5</td><td>15.0</td></tr>
<tr><td>6</td><td>19.2</td><td>18.6</td><td>18.0</td></tr>
<tr><td>7</td><td>22.4</td><td>21.7</td><td>21.0</td></tr>
<tr><td>8</td><td>25.6</td><td>24.8</td><td>24.0</td></tr>
<tr><td>9</td><td>28.8</td><td>27.9</td><td>27.0</td></tr>
</table>

N.	L. 0	1	2	3	4	5	6	7	8	9
141	922	953	983	*014	*045	*076	*106	*137	*168	*198
142	15 229	259	290	320	351	381	412	442	473	503
143	534	564	594	625	655	685	715	746	776	806
144	836	866	897	927	957	987	*017	*047	*077	*107
145	16 137	167	197	227	256	286	316	346	376	406
146	435	465	495	524	554	584	613	643	673	702
147	732	761	791	820	850	879	909	938	967	997
148	17 026	056	085	114	143	173	202	231	260	289
149	319	348	377	406	435	464	493	522	551	580
150	609	638	667	696	725	754	782	811	840	869

N.	L. 0	1	2	3	4	5	6	7	8	9	P. P.

1500–2009

N.	L. 0	1	2	3	4	5	6	7	8	9
150	17 609	638	667	696	725	754	782	811	840	869
151	898	926	955	984	*013	*041	*070	*099	*127	*156
152	18 184	213	241	270	298	327	355	384	412	441
153	469	498	526	554	583	611	639	667	696	724
154	752	780	808	837	865	893	921	949	977	*005
155	19 033	061	089	117	145	173	201	229	257	285
156	312	340	368	396	424	451	479	507	535	562
157	590	618	645	673	700	728	756	783	811	838
158	866	893	921	948	976	*003	*030	*058	*085	*112
159	20 140	167	194	222	249	276	303	330	358	385
160	412	439	466	493	520	548	575	602	629	656
161	683	710	737	763	790	817	844	871	898	925
162	952	978	*005	*032	*059	*085	*112	*139	*165	*192
163	21 219	245	272	299	325	352	378	405	431	458
164	484	511	537	564	590	617	643	669	696	722
165	748	775	801	827	854	880	906	932	958	985
166	22 011	037	063	089	115	141	167	194	220	246
167	272	298	324	350	376	401	427	453	479	505
168	531	557	583	608	634	660	686	712	737	763
169	789	814	840	866	891	917	943	968	994	*019
170	23 045	070	096	121	147	172	198	223	249	274
171	300	325	350	376	401	426	452	477	502	528
172	553	578	603	629	654	679	704	729	754	779
173	805	830	855	880	905	930	955	980	*005	*030
174	24 055	080	105	130	155	180	204	229	254	279
175	304	329	353	378	403	428	452	477	502	527
176	551	576	601	625	650	674	699	724	748	773
177	797	822	846	871	895	920	944	969	993	*018
178	25 042	066	091	115	139	164	188	212	237	261
179	285	310	334	358	382	406	431	455	479	503
180	527	551	575	600	624	648	672	696	720	744
181	768	792	816	840	864	888	912	935	959	983
182	26 007	031	055	079	102	126	150	174	198	221
183	245	269	293	316	340	364	387	411	435	458
184	482	505	529	553	576	600	623	647	670	694
185	717	741	764	788	811	834	858	881	905	928
186	951	975	998	*021	*045	*068	*091	*114	*138	*161
187	27 184	207	231	254	277	300	323	346	370	393
188	416	439	462	485	508	531	554	577	600	623
189	646	669	692	715	738	761	784	807	830	852
190	875	898	921	944	967	989	*012	*035	*058	*081
191	28 103	126	149	171	194	217	240	262	285	307
192	330	353	375	398	421	443	466	488	511	533
193	556	578	601	623	646	668	091	713	735	758
194	780	803	825	847	870	892	914	937	959	981
195	29 003	026	048	070	092	115	137	159	181	203
196	226	248	270	292	314	336	358	380	403	425
197	447	469	491	513	535	557	579	601	623	645
198	667	688	710	732	754	776	798	820	842	863
199	885	907	929	951	973	994	*016	*038	*060	*081
200	30 103	125	146	168	190	211	233	255	276	298
N.	L. 0	1	2	3	4	5	6	7	8	9

P. P.

	29	28
1	2.9	2.8
2	5.8	5.6
3	8.7	8.4
4	11.6	11.2
5	14.5	14.0
6	17.4	16.8
7	20.3	19.6
8	23.2	22.4
9	26.1	25.2

	27	26
1	2.7	2.6
2	5.4	5.2
3	8.1	7.8
4	10.8	10.4
5	13.5	13.0
6	16.2	15.6
7	18.9	18.2
8	21.6	20.8
9	24.3	23.4

	25
1	2.5
2	5.0
3	7.5
4	10.0
5	12.5
6	15.0
7	17.5
8	20.0
9	22.5

	24	23
1	2.4	2.3
2	4.8	4.6
3	7.2	6.9
4	9.6	9.2
5	12.0	11.5
6	14.4	13.8
7	16.8	16.1
8	19.2	18.4
9	21.6	20.7

	22	21
1	2.2	2.1
2	4.4	4.2
3	6.6	6.3
4	8.8	8.4
5	11.0	10.5
6	13.2	12.6
7	15.4	14.7
8	17.6	16.8
9	19.8	18.9

Table I. COMMON LOGARITHMS OF NUMBERS (CON'T)

2000–2509

N.	L.0	1	2	3	4	5	6	7	8	9
200	30 103	125	146	168	190	211	233	255	276	298
201	320	341	363	384	406	428	449	471	492	514
202	535	557	578	600	621	643	664	685	707	728
203	750	771	792	814	835	856	878	899	920	942
204	963	984	*006	*027	*048	*069	*091	*112	*133	*154
205	31 175	197	218	239	260	281	302	323	345	366
206	387	408	429	450	471	492	513	534	555	576
207	597	618	639	660	681	702	723	744	765	785
208	806	827	848	869	890	911	931	952	973	994
209	32 015	035	056	077	098	118	139	160	181	201
210	222	243	263	284	305	325	346	366	387	408
211	428	449	469	490	510	531	552	572	593	613
212	634	654	675	695	715	736	756	777	797	818
213	838	858	879	899	919	940	960	980	*001	*021
214	33 041	062	082	102	122	143	163	183	203	224
215	244	264	284	304	325	345	365	385	405	425
216	445	465	486	506	526	546	566	586	606	626
217	646	666	686	706	726	746	766	786	806	826
218	846	866	885	905	925	945	965	985	*005	*025
219	34 044	064	084	104	124	143	163	183	203	223
220	242	262	282	301	321	341	361	380	400	420
221	439	459	479	498	518	537	557	577	596	616
222	635	655	674	694	713	733	753	772	792	811
223	830	850	869	889	908	928	947	967	986	*005
224	35 025	044	064	083	102	122	141	160	180	199
225	218	238	257	276	295	315	334	353	372	392
226	411	430	449	468	488	507	526	545	564	583
227	603	622	641	660	679	698	717	736	755	774
228	793	813	832	851	870	889	908	927	946	965
229	984	*003	*021	*040	*059	*078	*097	*116	*135	*154
230	36 173	192	211	229	248	267	286	305	324	342
231	361	380	399	418	436	455	474	493	511	530
232	5'9	568	586	605	624	642	661	680	698	717
233	736	754	773	791	810	829	847	866	884	903
234	922	940	959	977	996	*014	*033	*051	*070	*088
235	37 107	125	144	162	181	199	218	236	254	273
236	291	310	328	346	365	383	401	420	438	457
237	475	493	511	530	548	566	585	603	621	639
238	658	676	694	712	731	749	767	785	803	822
239	840	858	876	894	912	931	949	967	985	*003
240	38 021	039	057	075	093	112	130	148	166	184
241	202	220	238	256	274	292	310	328	346	364
242	382	399	417	435	453	471	489	507	525	543
243	561	578	596	614	632	650	668	686	703	721
244	739	757	775	792	810	828	846	863	881	899
245	917	934	952	970	987	*005	*023	*041	*058	*076
246	39 094	111	129	146	164	182	199	217	235	252
247	270	287	305	322	340	358	375	393	410	428
248	445	463	480	498	515	533	550	568	585	602
249	620	637	655	672	690	707	724	742	759	777
250	794	811	829	846	863	881	898	915	933	950

P. P.

	22	21
1	2.2	2.1
2	4.4	4.2
3	6.6	6.3
4	8.8	8.4
5	11.0	10.5
6	13.2	12.6
7	15.4	14.7
8	17.6	16.8
9	19.8	18.9

	20
1	2.0
2	4.0
3	6.0
4	8.0
5	10.0
6	12.0
7	14.0
8	16.0
9	18.0

	19
1	1.9
2	3.8
3	5.7
4	7.6
5	9.5
6	11.4
7	13.3
8	15.2
9	17.1

	18
1	1.8
2	3.6
3	5.4
4	7.2
5	9.0
6	10.8
7	12.6
8	14.4
9	16.2

	17
1	1.7
2	3.4
3	5.1
4	6.8
5	8.5
6	10.2
7	11.9
8	13.6
9	15.3

N.	L.0	1	2	3	4	5	6	7	8	9	P. P.

2500–3009

N.	L. 0	1	2	3	4	5	6	7	8	9
250	39 794	811	829	846	863	881	898	915	933	950
251	967	985	*002	*019	*037	*054	*071	*088	*106	*123
252	40 140	157	175	192	209	226	243	261	278	295
253	312	329	346	364	381	398	415	432	449	466
254	483	500	518	535	552	569	586	603	620	637
255	654	671	688	705	722	739	756	773	790	807
256	824	841	858	875	892	909	926	943	960	976
257	993	*010	*027	*044	*061	*078	*095	*111	*128	*145
258	41 162	179	196	212	229	246	263	280	296	313
259	330	347	363	380	397	414	430	447	464	481
260	497	514	531	547	564	581	597	614	631	647
261	664	681	697	714	731	747	764	780	797	814
262	830	847	863	880	896	913	929	946	963	979
263	996	*012	*029	*045	*062	*078	*095	*111	*127	*144
264	42 160	177	193	210	226	243	259	275	292	308
265	325	341	357	374	390	406	423	439	455	472
266	488	504	521	537	553	570	586	602	619	635
267	651	667	684	700	716	732	749	765	781	797
268	813	830	846	862	878	894	911	927	943	959
269	975	991	*008	*024	*040	*056	*072	*088	*104	*120
270	43 136	152	169	185	201	217	233	249	265	281
271	297	313	329	345	361	377	393	409	425	441
272	457	473	489	505	521	537	553	569	584	600
273	616	632	648	664	680	696	712	727	743	759
274	775	791	807	823	838	854	870	886	902	917
275	933	949	965	981	996	*012	*028	*044	*059	*075
276	44 091	107	122	138	154	170	185	201	217	232
277	248	264	279	295	311	326	342	358	373	389
278	404	420	436	451	467	483	498	514	529	545
279	560	576	592	607	623	638	654	669	685	700
280	716	731	747	762	778	793	809	824	840	855
281	871	886	902	917	932	948	963	979	994	*010
282	45 025	040	056	071	086	102	117	133	148	163
283	179	194	209	225	240	255	271	286	301	317
284	332	347	362	378	393	408	423	439	454	469
285	484	500	515	530	545	561	576	591	606	621
286	637	652	667	682	697	712	728	743	758	773
287	788	803	818	834	849	864	879	894	909	924
288	939	954	969	984	*000	*015	*030	*045	*060	*075
289	46 090	105	120	135	150	165	180	195	210	225
290	240	255	270	285	300	315	330	345	359	374
291	389	404	419	434	449	464	479	494	509	523
292	538	553	568	583	598	613	627	642	657	672
293	687	702	716	731	746	761	776	790	805	820
294	835	850	864	879	894	909	923	938	953	967
295	982	997	*012	*026	*041	*056	*070	*085	*100	*114
296	47 129	144	159	173	188	202	217	232	246	261
297	276	290	305	319	334	349	363	378	392	407
298	422	436	451	465	480	494	509	524	538	553
299	567	582	596	611	625	640	654	669	683	698
300	712	727	741	756	770	784	799	813	828	842

P. P.

18
1	1.8
2	3.6
3	5.4
4	7.2
5	9.0
6	10.8
7	12.6
8	14.4
9	16.2

17
1	1.7
2	3.4
3	5.1
4	6.8
5	8.5
6	10.2
7	11.9
8	13.6
9	15.3

16
1	1.6
2	3.2
3	4.8
4	6.4
5	8.0
6	9.6
7	11.2
8	12.8
9	14.4

15
1	1.5
2	3.0
3	4.5
4	6.0
5	7.5
6	9.0
7	10.5
8	12.0
9	13.5

14
1	1.4
2	2.8
3	4.2
4	5.6
5	7.0
6	8.4
7	9.8
8	11.2
9	12.6

Table I. COMMON LOGARITHMS OF NUMBERS (CON'T)

3000–3509

N.	L. 0	1	2	3	4	5	6	7	8	9
300	47 712	727	741	756	770	784	799	813	828	842
301	857	871	885	900	914	929	943	958	972	986
302	48 001	015	029	044	058	073	087	101	116	130
303	144	159	173	187	202	216	230	244	259	273
304	287	302	316	330	344	359	373	387	401	416
305	430	444	458	473	487	501	515	530	544	558
306	572	586	601	615	629	643	657	671	686	700
307	714	728	742	756	770	785	799	813	827	841
308	855	869	883	897	911	926	940	954	968	982
309	996	*010	*024	*038	*052	*066	*080	*094	*108	*122
310	49 136	150	164	178	192	206	220	234	248	262
311	276	290	304	318	332	346	360	374	388	402
312	415	429	443	457	471	485	499	513	527	541
313	554	568	582	596	610	624	638	651	665	679
314	693	707	721	734	748	762	776	790	803	817
315	831	845	859	872	886	900	914	927	941	955
316	969	982	996	*010	*024	*037	*051	*065	*079	*092
317	50 106	120	133	147	161	174	188	202	215	229
318	243	256	270	284	297	311	325	338	352	365
319	379	393	406	420	433	447	461	474	488	501
320	515	529	542	556	569	583	596	610	623	637
321	651	664	678	691	705	718	732	745	759	772
322	786	799	813	826	840	853	866	880	893	907
323	920	934	947	961	974	987	*001	*014	*028	*041
324	51 055	068	081	095	108	121	135	148	162	175
325	188	202	215	228	242	255	268	282	295	308
326	322	335	348	362	375	388	402	415	428	441
327	455	468	481	495	508	521	534	548	561	574
328	587	601	614	627	640	654	667	680	693	706
329	720	733	746	759	772	786	799	812	825	838
330	851	865	878	891	904	917	930	943	957	970
331	983	996	*009	*022	*035	*048	*061	*075	*088	*101
332	52 114	127	140	153	166	179	192	205	218	231
333	244	257	270	284	297	310	323	336	349	362
334	375	388	401	414	427	440	453	466	479	492
335	504	517	530	543	556	569	582	595	608	621
336	634	647	660	673	686	699	711	724	737	750
337	763	776	789	802	815	827	840	853	866	879
338	892	905	917	930	943	956	969	982	994	*007
339	53 020	033	046	058	071	084	097	110	122	135
340	148	161	173	186	199	212	224	237	250	263
341	275	288	301	314	326	339	352	364	377	390
342	403	415	428	441	453	466	479	491	504	517
343	529	542	555	567	580	593	605	618	631	643
344	656	668	681	694	706	719	732	744	757	769
345	782	794	807	820	832	845	857	870	882	895
346	908	920	933	945	958	970	983	995	*008	*020
347	54 033	045	058	070	083	095	108	120	133	145
348	158	170	183	195	208	220	233	245	258	270
349	283	295	307	320	332	345	357	370	382	394
350	407	419	432	444	456	469	481	494	506	518

P. P.

	15
1	1.5
2	3.0
3	4.5
4	6.0
5	7.5
6	9.0
7	10.5
8	12.0
9	13.5

	14
1	1.4
2	2.8
3	4.2
4	5.6
5	7.0
6	8.4
7	9.8
8	11.2
9	12.6

	13
1	1.3
2	2.6
3	3.9
4	5.2
5	6.5
6	7.8
7	9.1
8	10.4
9	11.7

	12
1	1.2
2	2.4
3	3.6
4	4.8
5	6.0
6	7.2
7	8.4
8	9.6
9	10.8

$\text{Log } \pi = .49715$

3500–4009

N.	L. 0	1	2	3	4	5	6	7	8	9
350	54 407	419	432	444	456	469	481	494	506	518
351	531	543	555	568	580	593	605	617	630	642
352	654	667	679	691	704	716	728	741	753	765
353	777	790	802	814	827	839	851	864	876	888
354	900	913	925	937	949	962	974	986	998	*011
355	55 023	035	047	060	072	084	096	108	121	133
356	145	157	169	182	194	206	218	230	242	255
357	267	279	291	303	315	328	340	352	364	376
358	388	400	413	425	437	449	461	473	485	497
359	509	522	534	546	558	570	582	594	606	618
360	630	642	654	666	678	691	703	715	727	739
361	751	763	775	787	799	811	823	835	847	859
362	871	883	895	907	919	931	943	955	967	979
363	991	*003	*015	*027	*038	*050	*062	*074	*086	*098
364	56 110	122	134	146	158	170	182	194	205	217
365	229	241	253	265	277	289	301	312	324	336
366	348	360	372	384	396	407	419	431	443	455
367	467	478	490	502	514	526	538	549	561	573
368	585	597	608	620	632	644	656	667	679	691
369	703	714	726	738	750	761	773	785	797	808
370	820	832	844	855	867	879	891	902	914	926
371	937	949	961	972	984	996	*008	*019	*031	*043
372	57 054	066	078	089	101	113	124	136	148	159
373	171	183	194	206	217	229	241	252	264	276
374	287	299	310	322	334	345	357	368	380	392
375	403	415	426	438	449	461	473	484	496	507
376	519	530	542	553	565	576	588	600	611	623
377	634	646	657	669	680	692	703	715	726	738
378	749	761	772	784	795	807	818	830	841	852
379	864	875	887	898	910	921	933	944	955	967
380	978	990	*001	*013	*024	*035	*047	*058	*070	*081
381	58 092	104	115	127	138	149	161	172	184	195
382	206	218	229	240	252	263	274	286	297	309
383	320	331	343	354	365	377	388	399	410	422
384	433	444	456	467	478	490	501	512	524	535
385	546	557	569	580	591	602	614	625	636	647
386	659	670	681	692	704	715	726	737	749	760
387	771	782	794	805	816	827	838	850	861	872
388	883	894	906	917	928	939	950	961	973	984
389	995	*006	*017	*028	*040	*051	*062	*073	*084	*095
390	59 106	118	129	140	151	162	173	184	195	207
391	218	229	240	251	262	273	284	295	306	318
392	329	340	351	362	373	384	395	406	417	428
393	439	450	461	472	483	494	506	517	528	539
394	550	561	572	583	594	605	616	627	638	649
395	660	671	682	693	704	715	726	737	748	759
396	770	780	791	802	813	824	835	846	857	868
397	879	890	901	912	923	934	945	956	966	977
398	988	999	*010	*021	*032	*043	*054	*065	*076	*086
399	60 097	108	119	130	141	152	163	173	184	195
400	206	217	228	239	249	260	271	282	293	304
N.	L. 0	1	2	3	4	5	6	7	8	9

P. P.

13		12		11		10	
1	1.3	1	1.2	1	1.1	1	1.0
2	2.6	2	2.4	2	2.2	2	2.0
3	3.9	3	3.6	3	3.3	3	3.0
4	5.2	4	4.8	4	4.4	4	4.0
5	6.5	5	6.0	5	5.5	5	5.0
6	7.8	6	7.2	6	6.6	6	6.0
7	9.1	7	8.4	7	7.7	7	7.0
8	10.4	8	9.6	8	8.8	8	8.0
9	11.7	9	10.8	9	9.9	9	9.0

Table I. COMMON LOGARITHMS OF NUMBERS (CON'T)

4000–4509

N.	L. 0	1	2	3	4	5	6	7	8	9	P. P.
400	60 206	217	228	239	249	260	271	282	293	304	
401	314	325	336	347	358	369	379	390	401	412	
402	423	433	444	455	466	477	487	498	509	520	
403	531	541	552	563	574	584	595	606	617	627	
404	638	649	660	670	681	692	703	713	724	735	
405	746	756	767	778	788	799	810	821	831	842	
406	853	863	874	885	895	906	917	927	938	949	
407	959	970	981	991	*002	*013	*023	*034	*045	*055	
408	61 066	077	087	098	109	119	130	140	151	162	
409	172	183	194	204	215	225	236	247	257	268	
410	278	289	300	310	321	331	342	352	363	374	
411	384	395	405	416	426	437	448	458	469	479	
412	490	500	511	521	532	542	553	563	574	584	
413	595	606	616	627	637	648	658	669	679	690	
414	700	711	721	731	742	752	763	773	784	794	
415	805	815	826	836	847	857	868	878	888	899	
416	909	920	930	941	951	962	972	982	993	*003	
417	62 014	024	034	045	055	066	076	086	097	107	
418	118	128	138	149	159	170	180	190	201	211	
419	221	232	242	252	263	273	284	294	304	315	
420	325	335	346	356	366	377	387	397	408	418	
421	428	439	449	459	469	480	490	500	511	521	
422	531	542	552	562	572	583	593	603	613	624	
423	634	644	655	665	675	685	696	706	716	726	
424	737	747	757	767	778	788	798	808	818	829	
425	839	849	859	870	880	890	900	910	921	931	
426	941	951	961	972	982	992	*002	*012	*022	*033	
427	63 043	053	063	073	083	094	104	114	124	134	
428	144	155	165	175	185	195	205	215	225	236	
429	246	256	266	276	286	296	306	317	327	337	
430	347	357	367	377	387	397	407	417	428	438	
431	448	458	468	478	488	498	508	518	528	538	
432	548	558	568	579	589	599	609	619	629	639	
433	649	659	669	679	689	699	709	719	729	739	
434	749	759	769	779	789	799	809	819	829	839	
435	849	859	869	879	889	899	909	919	929	939	
436	949	959	969	979	988	998	*008	*018	*028	*038	
437	64 048	058	068	078	088	098	108	118	128	137	
438	147	157	167	177	187	197	207	217	227	237	
439	246	256	266	276	286	296	306	316	326	335	
440	345	355	365	375	385	395	404	414	424	434	
441	444	454	464	473	483	493	503	513	523	532	
442	542	552	562	572	582	591	601	611	621	631	
443	640	650	660	670	680	689	699	709	719	729	
444	738	748	758	768	777	787	797	807	816	826	
445	836	846	856	865	875	885	895	904	914	924	
446	933	943	953	963	972	982	992	*002	*011	*021	
447	65 031	040	050	060	070	079	089	099	108	118	
448	128	137	147	157	167	176	186	196	205	215	
449	225	234	244	254	263	273	283	292	302	312	
450	321	331	341	350	360	369	379	389	398	408	
N.	L. 0	1	2	3	4	5	6	7	8	9	P. P.

P. P. column:

11
1 | 1.1
2 | 2.2
3 | 3.3
4 | 4.4
5 | 5.5
6 | 6.6
7 | 7.7
8 | 8.8
9 | 9.9

10
1 | 1.0
2 | 2.0
3 | 3.0
4 | 4.0
5 | 5.0
6 | 6.0
7 | 7.0
8 | 8.0
9 | 9.0

9
1 | 0.9
2 | 1.8
3 | 2.7
4 | 3.6
5 | 4.5
6 | 5.4
7 | 6.3
8 | 7.2
9 | 8.1

4500–5009

N.	L. 0	1	2	3	4	5	6	7	8	9
450	65 321	331	341	350	360	369	379	389	398	408
451	418	427	437	447	456	466	475	485	495	504
452	514	523	533	543	552	562	571	581	591	600
453	610	619	629	639	648	658	667	677	686	696
454	706	715	725	734	744	753	763	772	782	792
455	801	811	820	830	839	849	858	868	877	887
456	896	906	916	925	935	944	954	963	973	982,
457	992	*001	*011	*020	*030	*039	*049	*058	*068	*077
458	66 087	096	106	115	124	134	143	153	162	172
459	181	191	200	210	219	229	238	247	257	266
460	276	285	295	304	314	323	332	342	351	361
461	370	380	389	398	408	417	427	436	445	455
462	464	474	483	492	502	511	521	530	539	549
463	558	567	577	586	596	605	614	624	633	642
464	652	661	671	680	689	699	708	717	727	736
465	745	755	764	773	783	792	801	811	820	829
466	839	848	857	867	876	885	894	904	913	922
467	932	941	950	960	969	978	987	997	*006	*015
468	67 025	034	043	052	062	071	080	089	099	108
469	117	127	136	145	154	164	173	182	191	201
470	210	219	228	237	247	256	265	274	284	293
471	302	311	321	330	339	348	357	367	376	385
472	394	403	413	422	431	440	449	459	468	477
473	486	495	504	514	523	532	541	550	560	569
474	578	587	596	605	614	624	633	642	651	660
475	669	679	688	697	706	715	724	733	742	752
476	761	770	779	788	797	806	815	825	834	843
477	852	861	870	879	888	897	906	916	925	934
478	943	952	961	970	979	988	997	*006	*015	*024
479	68 034	043	052	061	070	079	088	097	106	115
480	124	133	142	151	160	169	178	187	196	205
481	215	224	233	242	251	260	269	278	287	296
482	305	314	323	332	341	350	359	368	377	386
483	395	404	413	422	431	440	449	458	467	476
484	485	494	502	511	520	529	538	547	556	565
485	574	583	592	601	610	619	628	637	646	655
486	664	673	681	690	699	708	717	726	735	744
487	753	762	771	780	789	797	806	815	824	833
488	842	851	860	869	878	886	895	904	913	922
489	931	940	949	958	966	975	984	993	*002	*011
490	69 020	028	037	046	055	064	073	082	090	099
491	108	117	126	135	144	152	161	170	179	188
492	197	205	214	223	232	241	249	258	267	276
493	285	294	302	311	320	329	338	346	355	364
494	373	381	390	399	408	417	425	434	443	452
495	461	469	478	487	496	504	513	522	531	539
496	548	557	566	574	583	592	601	609	618	627
497	636	644	653	662	671	679	688	697	705	714
498	723	732	740	749	758	767	775	784	793	801
499	810	819	827	836	845	854	862	871	880	888
500	897	906	914	923	932	940	949	958	966	975

N.	L. 0	1	2	3	4	5	6	7	8	9

P. P.

10		9		8	
1	1.0	1	0.9	1	0.8
2	2.0	2	1.8	2	1.6
3	3.0	3	2.7	3	2.4
4	4.0	4	3.6	4	3.2
5	5.0	5	4.5	5	4.0
6	6.0	6	5.4	6	4.8
7	7.0	7	6.3	7	5.6
8	8.0	8	7.2	8	6.4
9	9.0	9	8.1	9	7.2

Table 1. COMMON LOGARITHMS OF NUMBERS (CON'T)

5000–5509	N.	L. 0	1	2	3	4	5	6	7	8	9	P. P.
	500	69 897	906	914	923	932	940	949	958	966	975	
	501	984	992	*001	*010	*018	*027	*036	*044	*053	*062	
	502	70 070	079	088	096	105	114	122	131	140	148	
	503	157	165	174	183	191	200	209	217	226	234	
	504	243	252	260	269	278	286	295	303	312	321	
	505	329	338	346	355	364	372	381	389	398	406	
	506	415	424	432	441	449	458	467	475	484	492	
	507	501	509	518	526	535	544	552	561	569	578	**9**
	508	586	595	603	612	621	629	638	646	655	663	1 0.9
	509	672	680	689	697	706	714	723	731	740	749	2 1.8
	510	757	766	774	783	791	800	808	817	825	834	3 2.7 / 4 3.6
	511	842	851	859	868	876	885	893	902	910	919	5 4.5 / 6 5.4
	512	927	935	944	952	961	969	978	986	995	*003	7 6.3 / 8 7.2
	513	71 012	020	029	037	046	054	063	071	079	088	9 8.1
	514	096	105	113	122	130	139	147	155	164	172	
	515	181	189	198	206	214	223	231	240	248	257	
	516	265	273	282	290	299	307	315	324	332	341	
	517	349	357	366	374	383	391	399	408	416	425	
	518	433	441	450	458	466	475	483	492	500	508	
	519	517	525	533	542	550	559	567	575	584	592	
	520	600	609	617	625	634	642	650	659	667	675	
	521	684	692	700	709	717	725	734	742	750	759	**8**
	522	767	775	784	792	800	809	817	825	834	842	1 0.8
	523	850	858	867	875	883	892	900	908	917	925	2 1.6 / 3 2.4
	524	933	941	950	958	966	975	983	991	999	*008	4 3.2 / 5 4.0
	525	72 016	024	032	041	049	057	066	074	082	090	6 4.8
	526	099	107	115	123	132	140	148	156	165	173	7 5.6 / 8 6.4
	527	181	189	198	206	214	222	230	239	247	255	9 7.2
	528	263	272	280	288	296	304	313	321	329	337	
	529	346	354	362	370	378	387	395	403	411	419	
	530	428	436	444	452	460	469	477	485	493	501	
	531	509	518	526	534	542	550	558	567	575	583	
	532	591	599	607	616	624	632	640	648	656	665	
	533	673	681	689	697	705	713	722	730	738	746	
	534	754	762	770	779	787	795	803	811	819	827	
	535	835	843	852	860	868	876	884	892	900	908	
	536	916	925	933	941	949	957	965	973	981	989	**7**
	537	997	*006	*014	*022	*030	*038	*046	*054	*062	*070	1 0.7 / 2 1.4
	538	73 078	086	094	102	111	119	127	135	143	151	3 2.1
	539	159	167	175	183	191	199	207	215	223	231	4 2.8 / 5 3.5
	540	239	247	255	263	272	280	288	296	304	312	6 4.2 / 7 4.9
	541	320	328	336	344	352	360	368	376	384	392	8 5.6
	542	400	408	416	424	432	440	448	456	464	472	9 6.3
	543	480	488	496	504	512	520	528	536	544	552	
	544	560	568	576	584	592	600	608	616	624	632	
	545	640	648	656	664	672	679	687	695	703	711	
	546	719	727	735	743	751	759	767	775	783	791	
	547	799	807	815	823	830	838	846	854	862	870	
	548	878	886	894	902	910	918	926	933	941	949	
	549	957	965	973	981	989	997	*005	*013	*020	*028	
	550	74 036	044	052	060	068	076	084	092	099	107	
	N.	L. 0	1	2	3	4	5	6	7	8	9	P. P.

5500–6009

N.	L. 0	1	2	3	4	5	6	7	8	9
550	74 036	044	052	060	068	076	084	092	099	107
551	115	123	131	139	147	155	162	170	178	186
552	194	202	210	218	225	233	241	249	257	265
553	273	280	288	296	304	312	320	327	335	343
554	351	359	367	374	382	390	398	406	414	421
555	429	437	445	453	461	468	476	484	492	500
556	507	515	523	531	539	547	554	562	570	578
557	586	593	601	609	617	624	632	640	648	656
558	663	671	679	687	695	702	710	718	726	733
559	741	749	757	764	772	780	788	796	803	811
560	819	827	834	842	850	858	865	873	881	889
561	896	904	912	920	927	935	943	950	958	966
562	974	981	989	997	*005	*012	*020	*028	*035	*043
563	75 051	059	066	074	082	089	097	105	113	120
564	128	136	143	151	159	166	174	182	189	197
565	205	213	220	228	236	243	251	259	266	274
566	282	289	297	305	312	320	328	335	343	351
567	358	366	374	381	389	397	404	412	420	427
568	435	442	450	458	465	473	481	488	496	504
569	511	519	526	534	542	549	557	565	572	580
570	587	595	603	610	618	626	633	641	648	656
571	664	671	679	686	694	702	709	717	724	732
572	740	747	755	762	770	778	785	793	800	808
573	815	823	831	838	846	853	861	868	876	884
574	891	899	906	914	921	929	937	944	952	959
575	967	974	982	989	997	*005	*012	*020	*027	035
576	76 042	050	057	065	072	080	087	095	103	110
577	118	125	133	140	148	155	163	170	178	185
578	193	200	208	215	223	230	238	245	253	260
579	268	275	283	290	298	305	313	320	328	335
580	343	350	358	365	373	380	388	395	403	410
581	418	425	433	440	448	455	462	470	477	485
582	492	500	507	515	522	530	537	545	552	559
583	567	574	582	589	597	604	612	619	626	634
584	641	649	656	664	671	678	686	693	701	708
585	716	723	730	738	745	753	760	768	775	782
586	790	797	805	812	819	827	834	842	849	856
587	864	871	879	886	893	901	908	916	923	930
588	938	945	953	960	967	975	982	989	997	*004
589	77 012	019	026	034	041	048	056	063	070	078
590	085	093	100	107	115	122	129	137	144	151
591	159	166	173	181	188	195	203	210	217	225
592	232	240	247	254	262	269	276	283	291	298
593	305	313	320	327	335	342	349	357	364	371
594	379	386	393	401	408	415	422	430	437	444
595	452	459	466	474	481	488	495	503	510	517
596	525	532	539	546	554	561	568	576	583	590
597	597	605	612	619	627	634	641	648	656	663
598	670	677	685	692	699	706	714	721	728	735
599	743	750	757	764	772	779	786	793	801	808
600	815	822	830	837	844	851	859	866	873	880
N.	L. 0	1	2	3	4	5	6	7	8	9

P. P.

8
1	0.8
2	1.6
3	2.4
4	3.2
5	4.0
6	4.8
7	5.6
8	6.4
9	7.2

7
1	0.7
2	1.4
3	2.1
4	2.8
5	3.5
6	4.2
7	4.9
8	5.6
9	6.3

Table 1. COMMON LOGARITHMS OF NUMBERS (CON'T)

6000–6509

N.	L. 0	1	2	3	4	5	6	7	8	9	P. P.
600	77 815	822	830	837	844	851	859	866	873	880	
601	887	895	902	909	916	924	931	938	945	952	
602	960	967	974	981	988	996	*003	*010	*017	*025	
603	78 032	039	046	053	061	068	075	082	089	097	
604	104	111	118	125	132	140	147	154	161	168	
605	176	183	190	197	204	211	219	226	233	240	
606	247	254	262	269	276	283	290	297	305	312	
607	319	326	333	340	347	355	362	369	376	383	
608	390	398	405	412	419	426	433	440	447	455	
609	462	469	476	483	490	497	504	512	519	526	
610	533	540	547	554	561	569	576	583	590	597	
611	604	611	618	625	633	640	647	654	661	668	
612	675	682	689	696	704	711	718	725	732	739	
613	746	753	760	767	774	781	789	796	803	810	
614	817	824	831	838	845	852	859	866	873	880	
615	888	895	902	909	916	923	930	937	944	951	
616	958	965	972	979	986	993	*000	*007	*014	*021	
617	79 029	036	043	050	057	064	071	078	085	092	
618	099	106	113	120	127	134	141	148	155	162	
619	169	176	183	190	197	204	211	218	225	232	
620	239	246	253	260	267	274	281	288	295	302	
621	309	316	323	330	337	344	351	358	365	372	
622	379	386	393	400	407	414	421	428	435	442	
623	449	456	463	470	477	484	491	498	505	511	
624	518	525	532	539	546	553	560	567	574	581	
625	588	595	602	609	616	623	630	637	644	650	
626	657	664	671	678	685	692	699	706	713	720	
627	727	734	741	748	754	761	768	775	782	789	
628	796	803	810	817	824	831	837	844	851	858	
629	865	872	879	886	893	900	906	913	920	927	
630	934	941	948	955	962	969	975	982	989	996	
631	80 003	010	017	024	030	037	044	051	058	065	
632	072	079	085	092	099	106	113	120	127	134	
633	140	147	154	161	168	175	182	188	195	202	
634	209	216	223	229	236	243	250	257	264	271	
635	277	284	291	298	305	312	318	325	332	339	
636	346	353	359	366	373	380	387	393	400	407	
637	414	421	428	434	441	448	455	462	468	475	
638	482	489	496	502	509	516	523	530	536	543	
639	550	557	564	570	577	584	591	598	604	611	
640	618	625	632	638	645	652	659	665	672	679	
641	686	693	699	706	713	720	726	733	740	747	
642	754	760	767	774	781	787	794	801	808	814	
643	821	828	835	841	848	855	862	868	875	882	
644	889	895	902	909	916	922	929	936	943	949	
645	956	963	969	976	983	990	996	*003	*010	*017	
646	81 023	030	037	043	050	057	064	070	077	084	
647	090	097	104	111	117	124	131	137	144	151	
648	158	164	171	178	184	191	198	204	211	218	
649	224	231	238	245	251	258	265	271	278	285	
650	291	298	305	311	318	325	331	338	345	351	
N.	L. 0	1	2	3	4	5	6	7	8	9	P. P.

P. P.

8
1 | 0.8
2 | 1.6
3 | 2.4
4 | 3.2
5 | 4.0
6 | 4.8
7 | 5.6
8 | 6.4
9 | 7.2

7
1 | 0.7
2 | 1.4
3 | 2.1
4 | 2.8
5 | 3.5
6 | 4.2
7 | 4.9
8 | 5.6
9 | 6.3

6
1 | 0.6
2 | 1.2
3 | 1.8
4 | 2.4
5 | 3.0
6 | 3.6
7 | 4.2
8 | 4.8
9 | 5.4

6500–7009

N.	L. 0	1	2	3	4	5	6	7	8	9
650	81 291	298	305	311	318	325	331	338	345	351
651	358	365	371	378	385	391	398	405	411	418
652	425	431	438	445	451	458	465	471	478	485
653	491	498	505	511	518	525	531	538	544	551
654	558	564	571	578	584	591	598	604	611	617
655	624	631	637	644	651	657	664	671	677	684
656	690	697	704	710	717	723	730	737	743	750
657	757	763	770	776	783	790	796	803	809	816
658	823	829	836	842	849	856	862	869	875	882
659	889	895	902	908	915	921	928	935	941	948
660	954	961	968	974	981	987	994	*000	*007	*014
661	82 020	027	033	040	046	053	060	066	073	079
662	086	092	099	105	112	119	125	132	138	145
663	151	158	164	171	178	184	191	197	204	210
664	217	223	230	236	243	249	256	263	269	276
665	282	289	295	302	308	315	321	328	334	341
666	347	354	360	367	373	380	387	393	400	406
667	413	419	426	432	439	445	452	458	465	471
668	478	484	491	497	504	510	517	523	530	536
669	543	549	556	562	569	575	582	588	595	601
670	607	614	620	627	633	640	646	653	659	666
671	672	679	685	692	698	705	711	718	724	730
672	737	743	750	756	763	769	776	782	789	795
673	802	808	814	821	827	834	840	847	853	860
674	866	872	879	885	892	898	905	911	918	924
675	930	937	943	950	956	963	969	975	982	988
676	995	*001	*008	*014	*020	*027	*033	*040	*046	*052
677	83 059	065	072	078	085	091	097	104	110	117
678	123	129	136	142	149	155	161	168	174	181
679	187	193	200	206	213	219	225	232	238	245
680	251	257	264	270	276	283	289	296	302	308
681	315	321	327	334	340	347	353	359	366	372
682	378	385	391	398	404	410	417	423	429	436
683	442	448	455	461	467	474	480	487	493	499
684	506	512	518	525	531	537	544	550	556	563
685	569	575	582	588	594	601	607	613	620	626
686	632	639	645	651	658	664	670	677	683	689
687	696	702	708	715	721	727	734	740	746	753
688	759	765	771	778	784	790	797	803	809	816
689	822	828	835	841	847	853	860	866	872	879
690	885	891	897	904	910	916	923	929	935	942
691	948	954	960	967	973	979	985	992	998	*004
692	84 011	017	023	029	036	042	048	055	061	067
693	073	080	086	092	098	105	111	117	123	130
694	136	142	148	155	161	167	173	180	186	192
695	198	205	211	217	223	230	236	242	248	255
696	261	267	273	280	286	292	298	305	311	317
697	323	330	336	342	348	354	361	367	373	379
698	386	392	398	404	410	417	423	429	435	442
699	448	454	460	466	473	479	485	491	497	504
700	510	516	522	528	535	541	547	553	559	566
N.	L. 0	1	2	3	4	5	6	7	8	9

P. P.

7

1	0.7
2	1.4
3	2.1
4	2.8
5	3.5
6	4.2
7	4.9
8	5.6
9	6.3

6

1	0.6
2	1.2
3	1.8
4	2.4
5	3.0
6	3.6
7	4.2
8	4.8
9	5.4

Table 1. COMMON LOGARITHMS OF NUMBERS (CON'T)

7000–7509

N.	L. 0	1	2	3	4	5	6	7	8	9	P. P.
700	84 510	516	522	528	535	541	547	553	559	566	
701	572	578	584	590	597	603	609	615	621	628	
702	634	640	646	652	658	665	671	677	683	689	
703	696	702	708	714	720	726	733	739	745	751	
704	757	763	770	776	782	788	794	800	807	813	
705	819	825	831	837	844	850	856	862	868	874	
706	880	887	893	899	905	911	917	924	930	936	
707	942	948	954	960	967	973	979	985	991	997	
708	85 003	009	016	022	028	034	040	046	052	058	
709	065	071	077	083	089	095	101	107	114	120	
710	126	132	138	144	150	156	163	169	175	181	
711	187	193	199	205	211	217	224	230	236	242	
712	248	254	260	266	272	278	285	291	297	303	
713	309	315	321	327	333	339	345	352	358	364	
714	370	376	382	388	394	400	406	412	418	425	
715	431	437	443	449	455	461	467	473	479	485	
716	491	497	503	509	516	522	528	534	540	546	
717	552	558	564	570	576	582	588	594	600	606	
718	612	618	625	631	637	643	649	655	661	667	
719	673	679	685	691	697	703	709	715	721	727	
720	733	739	745	751	757	763	769	775	781	788	
721	794	800	806	812	818	824	830	836	842	848	
722	854	860	866	872	878	884	890	896	902	908	
723	914	920	926	932	938	944	950	956	962	968	
724	974	980	986	992	998	*004	*010	*016	*022	*028	
725	86 034	040	046	052	058	064	070	076	082	088	
726	094	100	106	112	118	124	130	136	141	147	
727	153	159	165	171	177	183	189	195	201	207	
728	213	219	225	231	237	243	249	255	261	267	
729	273	279	285	291	297	303	308	314	320	326	
730	332	338	344	350	356	362	368	374	380	386	
731	392	398	404	410	415	421	427	433	439	445	
732	451	457	463	469	475	481	487	493	499	504	
733	510	516	522	528	534	540	546	552	558	564	
734	570	576	581	587	593	599	605	611	617	623	
735	629	635	641	646	652	658	664	670	676	682	
736	688	694	700	705	711	717	723	729	735	741	
737	747	753	759	764	770	776	782	788	794	800	
738	806	812	817	823	829	835	841	847	853	859	
739	864	870	876	882	888	894	900	906	911	917	
740	923	929	935	941	947	953	958	964	970	976	
741	982	988	994	999	*005	*011	*017	*023	*029	*035	
742	87 040	046	052	058	064	070	075	081	087	093	
743	099	105	111	116	122	128	134	140	146	151	
744	157	163	169	175	181	186	192	198	204	210	
745	216	221	227	233	239	245	251	256	262	268	
746	274	280	286	291	297	303	309	315	320	326	
747	332	338	344	349	355	361	367	373	379	384	
748	390	396	402	408	413	419	425	431	437	442	
749	448	454	460	466	471	477	483	489	495	500	
750	506	512	518	523	529	535	541	547	552	558	
N.	L. 0	1	2	3	4	5	6	7	8	9	P. P.

P. P.

7
1 | 0.7
2 | 1.4
3 | 2.1
4 | 2.8
5 | 3.5
6 | 4.2
7 | 4.9
8 | 5.6
9 | 6.3

6
1 | 0.6
2 | 1.2
3 | 1.8
4 | 2.4
5 | 3.0
6 | 3.6
7 | 4.2
8 | 4.8
9 | 5.4

5
1 | 0.5
2 | 1.0
3 | 1.5
4 | 2.0
5 | 2.5
6 | 3.0
7 | 3.5
8 | 4.0
9 | 4.5

7500–8009

N.	L. 0	1	2	3	4	5	6	7	8	9
750	87 506	512	518	523	529	535	541	547	552	558
751	564	570	576	581	587	593	599	604	610	616
752	622	628	633	639	645	651	656	662	668	674
753	679	685	691	697	703	708	714	720	726	731
754	737	743	749	754	760	766	772	777	783	789
755	795	800	806	812	818	823	829	835	841	846
756	852	858	864	869	875	881	887	892	898	904
757	910	915	921	927	933	938	944	950	955	961
758	967	973	978	984	990	996	*001	*007	*013	*018
759	88 024	030	036	041	047	053	058	064	070	076
760	081	087	093	098	104	110	116	121	127	133
761	138	144	150	156	161	167	173	178	184	190
762	195	201	207	213	218	224	230	235	241	247
763	252	258	264	270	275	281	287	292	298	304
764	309	315	321	326	332	338	343	349	355	360
765	366	372	377	383	389	395	400	406	412	417
766	423	429	434	440	446	451	457	463	468	474
767	480	485	491	497	502	508	513	519	525	530
768	536	542	547	553	559	564	570	576	581	587
769	593	598	604	610	615	621	627	632	638	643
770	649	655	660	666	672	677	683	689	694	700
771	705	711	717	722	728	734	739	745	750	756
772	762	767	773	779	784	790	795	801	807	812
773	818	824	829	835	840	846	852	857	863	868
774	874	880	885	891	897	902	908	913	919	925
775	930	936	941	947	953	958	964	969	975	981
776	986	992	997	*003	*009	*014	*020	*025	*031	*037
777	89 042	048	053	059	064	070	076	081	087	092
778	098	104	109	115	120	126	131	137	143	148
779	154	159	165	170	176	182	187	193	198	204
780	209	215	221	226	232	237	243	248	254	260
781	265	271	276	282	287	293	298	304	310	315
782	321	326	332	337	343	348	354	360	365	371
783	376	382	387	393	398	404	409	415	421	426
784	432	437	443	448	454	459	465	470	476	481
785	487	492	498	504	509	515	520	526	531	537
786	542	548	553	559	564	570	575	581	586	592
787	597	603	609	614	620	625	631	636	642	647
788	653	658	664	669	675	680	686	691	697	702
789	708	713	719	724	730	735	741	746	752	757
790	763	768	774	779	785	790	796	801	807	812
791	818	823	829	834	840	845	851	856	862	867
792	873	878	883	889	894	900	905	911	916	922
793	927	933	938	944	949	955	960	966	971	977
794	982	988	993	998	*004	*009	*015	*020	*026	*031
795	90 037	042	048	053	059	064	069	075	080	086
796	091	097	102	108	113	119	124	129	135	140
797	146	151	157	162	168	173	179	184	189	195
798	200	206	211	217	222	227	233	238	244	249
799	255	260	266	271	276	282	287	293	298	304
800	309	314	320	325	331	336	342	347	352	358

| N. | L. 0 | 1 | 2 | 3 | 4 | 5 | 6 | 7 | 8 | 9 |

P. P.

6
1 | 0.6
2 | 1.2
3 | 1.8
4 | 2.4
5 | 3.0
6 | 3.6
7 | 4.2
8 | 4.8
9 | 5.4

5
1 | 0.5
2 | 1.0
3 | 1.5
4 | 2.0
5 | 2.5
6 | 3.0
7 | 3.5
8 | 4.0
9 | 4.5

Table I. COMMON LOGARITHMS OF NUMBERS (CON'T)

8000–8509

N.	L. 0	1	2	3	4	5	6	7	8	9	P. P.
800	90 309	314	320	325	331	336	342	347	352	358	
801	363	369	374	380	385	390	396	401	407	412	
802	417	423	428	434	439	445	450	455	461	466	
803	472	477	482	488	493	499	504	509	515	520	
804	526	531	536	542	547	553	558	563	569	574	
805	580	585	590	596	601	607	612	617	623	628	
806	634	639	644	650	655	660	666	671	677	682	
807	687	693	698	703	709	714	720	725	730	736	
808	741	747	752	757	763	768	773	779	784	789	
809	795	800	806	811	816	822	827	832	838	843	
810	849	854	859	865	870	875	881	886	891	897	
811	902	907	913	918	924	939	934	940	945	950	
812	956	961	966	972	977	982	988	993	998	*004	
813	91 009	014	020	025	030	036	041	046	052	057	
814	062	068	073	078	084	089	094	100	105	110	**6**
815	116	121	126	132	137	142	148	153	158	164	1 0.6
816	169	174	180	185	190	196	201	206	212	217	2 1.2
817	222	228	233	238	243	249	254	259	265	270	3 1.8 / 4 2.4 / 5 3.0 / 6 3.6
818	275	281	286	291	297	302	307	312	318	323	7 4.2
819	328	334	339	344	350	355	360	365	371	376	8 4.8 / 9 5.4
820	381	387	392	397	403	408	413	418	424	429	
821	434	440	445	450	455	461	466	471	477	482	
822	487	492	498	503	508	514	519	524	529	535	
823	540	545	551	556	561	566	572	577	582	587	
824	593	598	603	609	614	619	624	630	635	640	
825	645	651	656	661	666	672	677	682	687	693	
826	698	703	709	714	719	724	730	735	740	745	
827	751	756	761	766	772	777	782	787	793	798	
828	803	808	814	819	824	829	834	840	845	850	
829	855	861	866	871	876	882	887	892	897	903	
830	908	913	918	924	929	934	939	944	950	955	
831	960	965	971	976	981	986	991	997	*002	*007	**5**
832	92 012	018	023	028	033	038	044	049	054	059	1 0.5
833	065	070	075	080	085	091	096	101	106	111	2 1.0 / 3 1.5
834	117	122	127	132	137	143	148	153	158	163	4 2.0 / 5 2.5
835	169	174	179	184	189	195	200	205	210	215	6 3.0
836	221	226	231	236	241	247	252	257	262	267	7 3.5 / 8 4.0
837	273	278	283	288	293	298	304	309	314	319	9 4.5
838	324	330	335	340	345	350	355	361	366	371	
839	376	381	387	392	397	402	407	412	418	423	
840	428	433	438	443	449	454	459	464	469	474	
841	480	485	490	495	500	505	511	516	521	526	
842	531	536	542	547	552	557	562	567	572	578	
843	583	588	593	598	603	609	614	619	624	629	
844	634	639	645	650	655	660	665	670	675	681	
845	686	691	696	701	706	711	716	722	727	732	
846	737	742	747	752	758	763	768	773	778	783	
847	788	793	799	804	809	814	819	824	829	834	
848	840	845	850	855	860	865	870	875	881	886	
849	891	896	901	906	911	916	921	927	932	937	
850	942	947	952	957	962	967	973	978	983	988	

| N. | L. 0 | 1 | 2 | 3 | 4 | 5 | 6 | 7 | 8 | 9 | P. P. |

8500–9009

N.	L. 0	1	2	3	4	5	6	7	8	9	P. P.
850	92 942	947	952	957	962	967	973	978	983	988	
851	993	998	*003	*008	*013	*018	*024	*029	*034	*039	
852	93 044	049	054	059	064	069	075	080	085	090	
853	095	100	105	110	115	120	125	131	136	141	
854	146	151	156	161	166	171	176	181	186	192	
855	197	202	207	212	217	222	227	232	237	242	
856	247	252	258	263	268	273	278	283	288	293	
857	298	303	308	313	318	323	328	334	339	344	
858	349	354	359	364	369	374	379	384	389	394	
859	399	404	409	414	420	425	430	435	440	445	
860	450	455	460	465	470	475	480	485	490	495	
861	500	505	510	515	520	526	531	536	541	546	
862	551	556	561	566	571	576	581	586	591	596	
863	601	606	611	616	621	626	631	636	641	646	
864	651	656	661	666	671	676	682	687	692	697	
865	702	707	712	717	722	727	732	737	742	747	
866	752	757	762	767	772	777	782	787	792	797	
867	802	807	812	817	822	827	832	837	842	847	
868	852	857	862	867	872	877	882	887	892	897	
869	902	907	912	917	922	927	932	937	942	947	
870	952	957	962	967	972	977	982	987	992	997	
871	94 002	007	012	017	022	027	032	037	042	047	
872	052	057	062	067	072	077	082	086	091	096	
873	101	106	111	116	121	126	131	136	141	146	
874	151	156	161	166	171	176	181	186	191	196	
875	201	206	211	216	221	226	231	236	240	245	
876	250	255	260	265	270	275	280	285	290	295	
877	300	305	310	315	320	325	330	335	340	345	
878	349	354	359	364	369	374	379	384	389	394	
879	399	404	409	414	419	424	429	433	438	443	
880	448	453	458	463	468	473	478	483	488	493	
881	498	503	507	512	517	522	527	532	537	542	
882	547	552	557	562	567	571	576	581	586	591	
883	596	601	606	611	616	621	626	630	635	640	
884	645	650	655	660	665	670	675	680	685	689	
885	694	699	704	709	714	719	724	729	734	738	
886	743	748	753	758	763	768	773	778	783	787	
887	792	797	802	807	812	817	822	827	832	836	
888	841	846	851	856	861	866	871	876	880	885	
889	890	895	900	905	910	915	919	924	929	934	
890	939	944	949	954	959	963	968	973	978	983	
891	988	993	998	*002	*007	*012	*017	*022	*027	*032	
892	95 036	041	046	051	056	061	066	071	075	080	
893	085	090	095	100	105	109	114	119	124	129	
894	134	139	143	148	153	158	163	168	173	177	
895	182	187	192	197	202	207	211	216	221	226	
896	231	236	240	245	250	255	260	265	270	274	
897	279	284	289	294	299	303	308	313	318	323	
898	328	332	337	342	347	352	357	361	366	371	
899	376	381	386	390	395	400	405	410	415	419	
900	424	429	434	439	444	448	453	458	463	468	
N.	L. 0	1	2	3	4	5	6	7	8	9	P. P.

P. P.

6
1	0.6
2	1.2
3	1.8
4	2.4
5	3.0
6	3.6
7	4.2
8	4.8
9	5.4

5
1	0.5
2	1.0
3	1.5
4	2.0
5	2.5
6	3.0
7	3.5
8	4.0
9	4.5

4
1	0.4
2	0.8
3	1.2
4	1.6
5	2.0
6	2.4
7	2.8
8	3.2
9	3.6

Table I. COMMON LOGARITHMS OF NUMBERS (CON'T)

9000–9509

N.	L. 0	1	2	3	4	5	6	7	8	9	P. P.
900	95 424	429	434	439	444	448	453	458	463	468	
901	472	477	482	487	492	497	501	506	511	516	
902	521	525	530	535	540	545	550	554	559	564	
903	569	574	578	583	588	593	598	602	607	612	
904	617	622	626	631	636	641	646	650	655	660	
905	665	670	674	679	684	689	694	698	703	708	
906	713	718	722	727	732	737	742	746	751	756	
907	761	766	770	775	780	785	789	794	799	804	
908	809	813	818	823	828	832	837	842	847	852	
909	856	861	866	871	875	880	885	890	895	899	
910	904	909	914	918	923	928	933	938	942	947	
911	952	957	961	966	971	976	980	985	990	995	
912	999	*004	*009	*014	*019	*023	*028	*033	*038	*042	
913	96 047	052	057	061	066	071	076	080	085	090	
914	095	099	104	109	114	118	123	128	133	137	
915	142	147	152	156	161	166	171	175	180	185	
916	190	194	199	204	209	213	218	223	227	232	
917	237	242	246	251	256	261	265	270	275	280	
918	284	289	294	298	303	308	313	317	322	327	
919	332	336	341	346	350	355	360	365	369	374	
920	379	384	388	393	398	402	407	412	417	421	
921	426	431	435	440	445	450	454	459	464	468	
922	473	478	483	487	492	497	501	506	511	515	
923	520	525	530	534	539	544	548	553	558	562	
924	567	572	577	581	586	591	595	600	605	609	
925	614	619	624	628	633	638	642	647	652	656	
926	661	666	670	675	680	685	689	694	699	703	
927	708	713	717	722	727	731	736	741	745	750	
928	755	759	764	769	774	778	783	788	792	797	
929	802	806	811	816	820	825	830	834	839	844	
930	848	853	858	862	867	872	876	881	886	890	
931	895	900	904	909	914	918	923	928	932	937	
932	942	946	951	956	960	965	970	974	979	984	
933	988	993	997	*002	*007	*011	*016	*021	*025	*030	
934	97 035	039	044	049	053	058	063	067	072	077	
935	081	086	090	095	100	104	109	114	118	123	
936	128	132	137	142	146	151	155	160	165	169	
937	174	179	183	188	192	197	202	206	211	216	
938	220	225	230	234	239	243	248	253	257	262	
939	267	271	276	280	285	290	294	299	304	308	
940	313	317	322	327	331	336	340	345	350	354	
941	359	364	368	373	377	382	387	391	396	400	
942	405	410	414	419	424	428	433	437	442	447	
943	451	456	460	465	470	474	479	483	488	493	
944	497	502	506	511	516	520	525	529	534	539	
945	543	548	552	557	562	566	571	575	580	585	
946	589	594	598	603	607	612	617	621	626	630	
947	635	640	644	649	653	658	663	667	672	676	
948	681	685	690	695	699	704	708	713	717	722	
949	727	731	736	740	745	749	754	759	763	768	
950	772	777	782	786	791	795	800	804	809	813	
N.	L. 0	1	2	3	4	5	6	7	8	9	P. P.

P. P.

5
1	0.5
2	1.0
3	1.5
4	2.0
5	2.5
6	3.0
7	3.5
8	4.0
9	4.5

4
1	0.4
2	0.8
3	1.2
4	1.6
5	2.0
6	2.4
7	2.8
8	3.2
9	3.6

9500–10009

N.	L. 0	1	2	3	4	5	6	7	8	9	P. P.
950	97 772	777	782	786	791	795	800	804	809	813	
951	818	823	827	832	836	841	845	850	855	859	
952	864	868	873	877	882	886	891	896	900	905	
953	909	914	918	923	928	932	937	941	946	950	
954	955	959	964	968	973	978	982	987	991	996	
955	98 000	005	009	014	019	023	028	032	037	041	
956	046	050	055	059	064	068	073	078	082	087	
957	091	096	100	105	109	114	118	123	127	132	
958	137	141	146	150	155	159	164	168	173	177	
959	182	186	191	195	200	204	209	214	218	223	
960	227	232	236	241	245	250	254	259	263	268	
961	272	277	281	286	290	295	299	304	308	313	
962	318	322	327	331	336	340	345	349	354	358	
963	363	367	372	376	381	385	390	394	399	403	
964	408	412	417	421	426	430	435	439	444	448	
965	453	457	462	466	471	475	480	484	489	493	
966	498	502	507	511	516	520	525	529	534	538	
967	543	547	552	556	561	565	570	574	579	583	
968	588	592	597	601	605	610	614	619	623	628	
969	632	637	641	646	650	655	659	664	668	673	
970	677	682	686	691	695	700	704	709	713	717	
971	722	726	731	735	740	744	749	753	758	762	
972	767	771	776	780	784	789	793	798	802	807	
973	811	816	820	825	829	834	838	843	847	851	
974	856	860	865	869	874	878	883	887	892	896	
975	900	905	909	914	918	923	927	932	936	941	
976	945	949	954	958	963	967	972	976	981	985	
977	989	994	998	*003	*007	*012	*016	*021	*025	*029	
978	99 034	038	043	047	052	056	061	065	069	074	
979	078	083	087	092	096	100	105	109	114	118	
980	123	127	131	136	140	145	149	154	158	162	
981	167	171	176	180	185	189	193	198	202	207	
982	211	216	220	224	229	233	238	242	247	251	
983	255	260	264	269	273	277	282	286	291	295	
984	300	304	308	313	317	322	326	330	335	339	
985	344	348	352	357	361	366	370	374	379	383	
986	388	392	396	401	405	410	414	419	423	427	
987	432	436	441	445	449	454	458	463	467	471	
988	476	480	484	489	493	498	502	506	511	515	
989	520	524	528	533	537	542	546	550	555	559	
990	564	568	572	577	581	585	590	594	599	603	
991	607	612	616	621	625	629	634	638	642	647	
992	651	656	660	664	669	673	677	682	686	691	
993	695	699	704	708	712	717	721	726	730	734	
994	739	743	747	752	756	760	765	769	774	778	
995	782	787	791	795	800	804	808	813	817	822	
996	826	830	835	839	843	848	852	856	861	865	
997	870	874	878	883	887	891	896	900	904	909	
998	913	917	922	926	930	935	939	944	948	952	
999	957	961	965	970	974	978	983	987	991	996	
1000	00 000	004	009	013	017	022	026	030	035	039	
N.	**L. 0**	**1**	**2**	**3**	**4**	**5**	**6**	**7**	**8**	**9**	**P. P.**

P. P.

	5
1	0.5
2	1.0
3	1.5
4	2.0
5	2.5
6	3.0
7	3.5
8	4.0
9	4.5

	4
1	0.4
2	0.8
3	1.2
4	1.6
5	2.0
6	2.4
7	2.8
8	3.2
9	3.6

238 Appendix C   *Tables*

Table 2. VALUES OF TRIGONOMETRIC FUNCTIONS

α	sin α	cos α	tan α	cot α	α	sin α	cos α	tan α	cot α
.00	.0000	1.000	.0000	......	.40	.3894	.9211	.4228	2.365
.01	.0100	1.000	.0100	100.0	.41	.3986	.9171	.4346	2.301
.02	.0200	.9998	.0200	49.99	.42	.4078	.9131	.4466	2.239
.03	.0300	.9996	.0300	33.32	.43	.4169	.9090	.4586	2.180
.04	.0400	.9992	.0400	24.99	.44	.4259	.9048	.4708	2.124
.05	.0500	.9988	.0500	19.98	.45	.4350	.9004	.4831	2.070
.06	.0600	.9982	.0601	16.65	.46	.4439	.8961	.4954	2.018
.07	.0699	.9976	.0701	14.26	.47	.4529	.8916	.5080	1.969
.08	.0799	.9968	.0802	12.47	.48	.4618	.8870	.5206	1.921
.09	.0899	.9960	.0902	11.08	.49	.4706	.8823	.5334	1.875
.10	.0998	.9950	.1003	9.967	.50	.4794	.8776	.5463	1.830
.11	.1098	.9940	.1104	9.054	.51	.4882	.8727	.5594	1.788
.12	.1197	.9928	.1206	8.293	.52	.4969	.8678	.5726	1.747
.13	.1296	.9916	.1307	7.649	.53	.5055	.8628	.5859	1.707
.14	.1395	.9902	.1409	7.096	.54	.5141	.8577	.5994	1.668
.15	.1494	.9888	.1511	6.617	.55	.5227	.8525	.6131	1.631
.16	.1593	.9872	.1614	6.197	.56	.5312	.8473	.6269	1.595
.17	.1692	.9856	.1717	5.826	.57	.5396	.8419	.6410	1.560
.18	.1790	.9838	.1820	5.495	.58	.5480	.8365	.6552	1.526
.19	.1889	.9820	.1923	5.200	.59	.5564	.8309	.6696	1.494
.20	.1987	.9801	.2027	4.933	.60	.5646	.8253	.6841	1.462
.21	.2085	.9780	.2131	4.692	.61	.5729	.8196	.6989	1.431
.22	.2182	.9759	.2236	4.472	.62	.5810	.8139	.7139	1.401
.23	.2280	.9737	.2341	4.271	.63	.5891	.8080	.7291	1.372
.24	.2377	.9713	.2447	4.086	.64	.5972	.8021	.7445	1.343
.25	.2474	.9689	.2553	3.916	.65	.6052	.7961	.7602	1.315
.26	.2571	.9664	.2660	3.759	.66	.6131	.7900	.7761	1.288
.27	.2667	.9638	.2768	3.613	.67	.6210	.7838	.7923	1.262
.28	.2764	.9611	.2876	3.478	.68	.6288	.7776	.8087	1.237
.29	.2860	.9582	.2984	3.351	.69	.6365	.7712	.8253	1.212
.30	.2955	.9553	.3093	3.233	.70	.6442	.7648	.8423	1.187
.31	.3051	.9523	.3203	3.122	.71	.6518	.7584	.8595	1.163
.32	.3146	.9492	.3314	3.018	.72	.6594	.7518	.8771	1.140
.33	.3240	.9460	.3425	2.920	.73	.6669	.7452	.8949	1.117
.34	.3335	.9428	.3537	2.827	.74	.6743	.7385	.9131	1.095
.35	.3429	.9394	.3650	2.740	.75	.6816	.7317	.9316	1.073
.36	.3523	.9359	.3764	2.657	.76	.6889	.7248	.9505	1.052
.37	.3616	.9323	.3879	2.578	.77	.6961	.7179	.9697	1.031
.38	.3709	.9287	.3994	2.504	.78	.7033	.7109	.9893	1.011
.39	.3802	.9249	.4111	2.433	.79	.7104	.7038	1.009	.9908

α	$\sin \alpha$	$\cos \alpha$	$\tan \alpha$	$\cot \alpha$	α	$\sin \alpha$	$\cos \alpha$	$\tan \alpha$	$\cot \alpha$
.80	.7174	.6967	1.030	.9712	1.20	.9320	.3624	2.572	.3888
.81	.7243	.6895	1.050	.9520	1.21	.9356	.3530	2.650	.3773
.82	.7311	.6822	1.072	.9331	1.22	.9391	.3436	2.733	.3659
.83	.7379	.6749	1.093	.9146	1.23	.9425	.3342	2.820	.3546
.84	.7446	.6675	1.116	.8964	1.24	.9458	.3248	2.912	.3434
.85	.7513	.6600	1.138	.8785	1.25	.9490	.3153	3.010	.3323
.86	.7578	.6524	1.162	.8609	1.26	.9521	.3058	3.113	.3212
.87	.7643	.6448	1.185	.8437	1.27	.9551	.2963	3.224	.3102
.88	.7707	.6372	1.210	.8267	1.28	.9580	.2867	3.341	.2993
.89	.7771	.6294	1.235	.8100	1.29	.9608	.2771	3.467	.2884
.90	.7833	.6216	1.260	.7936	1.30	.9636	.2675	3.602	.2776
.91	.7895	.6137	1.286	.7774	1.31	.9662	.2579	3.747	.2669
.92	.7956	.6058	1.313	.7615	1.32	.9687	.2482	3.903	.2562
.93	.8016	.5978	1.341	.7458	1.33	.9711	.2385	4.072	.2456
.94	.8076	.5898	1.369	.7303	1.34	.9735	.2288	4.256	.2350
.95	.8134	.5817	1.398	.7151	1.35	.9757	.2190	4.455	.2245
.96	.8192	.5735	1.428	.7001	1.36	.9779	.2092	4.673	.2140
.97	.8249	.5653	1.459	.6853	1.37	.9799	.1994	4.913	.2035
.98	.8305	.5570	1.491	.6707	1.38	.9819	.1896	5.177	.1931
.99	.8360	.5487	1.524	.6563	1.39	.9837	.1798	5.471	.1828
1.00	.8415	.5403	1.557	.6421	1.40	.9854	.1700	5.798	.1725
1.01	.8468	.5319	1.592	.6281	1.41	.9871	.1601	6.165	.1622
1.02	.8521	.5234	1.628	.6142	1.42	.9887	.1502	6.581	.1519
1.03	.8573	.5148	1.665	.6005	1.43	.9901	.1403	7.055	.1417
1.04	.8624	.5062	1.704	.5870	1.44	.9915	.1304	7.602	.1315
1.05	.8674	.4976	1.743	.5736	1.45	.9927	.1205	8.238	.1214
1.06	.8724	.4889	1.784	.5604	1.46	.9939	.1106	8.989	.1113
1.07	.8772	.4801	1.827	.5473	1.47	.9949	.1006	9.887	.1011
1.08	.8820	.4713	1.871	.5344	1.48	.9959	.0907	10.98	.0910
1.09	.8866	.4625	1.917	.5216	1.49	.9967	.0807	12.35	.0810
1.10	.8912	.4536	1.965	.5090	1.50	.9975	.0707	14.10	.0709
1.11	.8957	.4447	2.014	.4964	1.51	.9982	.0608	16.43	.0609
1.12	.9001	.4357	2.066	.4840	1.52	.9987	.0508	19.67	.0508
1.13	.9044	.4267	2.120	.4718	1.53	.9992	.0408	24.50	.0408
1.14	.9086	.4176	2.176	.4596	1.54	.9995	.0308	32.46	.0308
1.15	.9128	.4085	2.234	.4475	1.55	.9998	.0208	48.08	.0208
1.16	.9168	.3993	2.296	.4356	1.56	.9999	.0108	92.62	.0108
1.17	.9208	.3902	2.360	.4237	1.57	1.000	.0008	1256.	.0008
1.18	.9246	.3809	2.427	.4120	$\pi/2$	1.000	.0000	....	.0000
1.19	.9284	.3717	2.498	.4003					
					1.58	1.000	−.0092	−108.6	−.0092
					1.59	.9998	−.0192	− 52.07	−.0192
					1.60	.9996	−.0292	− 34.23	−.0292

Table 3. LOGARITHMS OF FUNCTIONAL VALUES

For each logarithm use value listed minus 10.

α	log sin α	log cos α	log tan α	log cot α	α	log sin α	log cos α	log tan α	log cot α
.00	......	10.0000	......	....	.40	9.5904	9.9643	9.6261	10.3739
.01	8.0000	.0000	8.0000	12.0000	.41	.6005	.9624	.6381	.3619
.02	.3010	9.9999	.3011	11.6989	.42	.6104	.9605	.6499	.3501
.03	.4771	.9998	.4773	.5227	.43	.6200	.9585	.6615	.3385
.04	.6019	.9997	.6023	.3977	.44	.6293	.9565	.6728	.3272
.05	8.6988	9.9995	8.6993	11.3007	.45	9.6385	9.9545	9.3840	10.3160
.06	.7779	.9992	.7787	.2213	.46	.6473	.9523	.6950	.3050
.07	.8447	.9989	.8458	.1542	.47	.6560	.9502	.7058	.2942
.08	.9026	.9986	.9040	.0960	.48	.6644	.9479	.7165	.2835
.09	.9537	.9982	.9554	.0446	.49	.6727	.9456	.7270	.2730
.10	8.9993	9.9978	9.0015	10.9985	.50	9.6807	9.9433	9.7374	10.2626
.11	9.0405	.9974	.0431	.9569	.51	.6886	.9409	.7477	.2523
.12	.0781	.9969	.0813	.9187	.52	.6963	.9384	.7578	.2422
.13	.1127	.9963	.1164	.8836	.53	.7037	.9359	.7678	.2322
.14	.1447	.9957	.1490	.8510	.54	.7111	.9333	.7777	.2223
.15	9.1745	9.9951	9.1794	10.8206	.55	9.7182	9.9307	9.7875	10.2125
.16	.2023	.9944	.2078	.7922	.56	.7252	.9280	.7972	.2028
.17	.2284	.9937	.2347	.7653	.57	.7321	.9253	.8068	.1932
.18	.2529	.9929	.2600	.7400	.58	.7388	.9224	.8164	.1836
.19	.2761	.9921	.2840	.7160	.59	.7454	.9196	.8258	.1742
.20	9.2981	9.9913	9.3069	10.6931	.60	9.7518	9.9166	9.8351	10.1649
.21	.3190	.9904	.3287	.6713	.61	.7581	.9136	.8444	.1556
.22	.3389	.9894	.3495	.6505	.62	.7642	.9106	.8536	.1464
.23	.3579	.9884	.3695	.6305	.63	.7702	.9074	.8628	.1372
.24	.3760	.9874	.3887	.6113	.64	.7761	.9042	.8719	.1281
.25	9.3934	9.9863	9.4071	10.5929	.65	9.7819	9.9010	9.8809	10.1191
.26	.4101	.9852	.4249	.5751	.66	.7875	.8976	.8899	.1101
.27	.4261	.9840	.4421	.5579	.67	.7931	.8942	.8989	.1011
.28	.4415	.9827	.4587	.5413	.68	.7985	.8907	.9078	.0922
.29	.4563	.9815	.4748	.5252	.69	.8038	.8872	.9166	.0834
.30	9.4706	9.9802	9.4904	10.5096	.70	9.8090	9.8836	9.9255	10.0745
.31	.4844	.9788	.5056	.4944	.71	.8141	.8799	.9343	.0657
.32	.4977	.9774	.5203	.4797	.72	.8191	.8761	.9430	.0570
.33	.5106	.9759	.5347	.4653	.73	.8240	.8723	.9518	.0482
.34	.5231	.9744	.5487	.4513	.74	.8288	.8683	.9605	.0395
.35	9.5352	9.9728	9.5623	10.4377	.75	9.8336	9.8643	9.9692	10.0308
.36	.5469	.9712	.5757	.4243	.76	.8382	.8602	.9779	.0221
.37	.5582	.9696	.5887	.4113	.77	.8427	.8561	.9866	.0134
.38	.5693	.9679	.6014	.3986	.78	.8471	.8518	.9953	.0047
.39	.5800	.9661	.6139	.3861	.79	.8515	.8475	10.0040	9.9960

α	log sin α	log cos α	log tan α	log cot α	α	log sin α	log cos α	log tan α	log cot α
.80	9.8557	9.8431	10.0127	9.9873	1.20	9.9694	9.5591	10.4103	9.5897
.81	.8599	.8385	.0214	.9786	.21	.9711	.5478	.4233	.5767
.82	.8640	.8339	.0301	.9699	.22	.9727	.5361	.4366	.5634
.83	.8680	.8292	.0388	.9612	.23	.9743	.5241	.4502	.5498
.84	.8719	.8244	.0475	.9525	.24	.9758	.5116	.4642	.5358
.85	9.8758	9.8195	10.0563	9.9437	1.25	9.9773	9.4988	10.4785	9.5215
.86	.8796	.8145	.0650	.9350	.26	.9787	.4855	.4932	.5068
.87	.8833	.8094	.0738	.9262	.27	.9800	.4717	.5083	.4917
.88	.8869	.8042	.0827	.9173	.28	.9814	.4575	.5239	.4761
.89	.8905	.7989	.0915	.9085	.29	.9826	.4427	.5400	.4600
.90	9.8939	9.7935	10.1004	9.8996	1.30	9.9839	9.4273	10.5566	9.4434
.91	.8974	.7880	.1094	.8906	.31	.9851	.4114	.5737	.4263
.92	.9007	.7823	.1184	.8816	.32	.9862	.3948	.5914	.4086
.93	.9040	.7766	.1274	.8726	.33	.9873	.3774	.6098	.3902
.94	.9072	.7707	.1365	.8635	.34	.9883	.3594	.6290	.3710
.95	9.9103	9.7647	10.1456	9.8544	1.35	9.9893	9.3405	10.6489	9.3511
.96	.9134	.7585	.1548	.8452	.36	.9903	.3206	.6696	.3304
.97	.9164	.7523	.1641	.8359	.37	.9912	.2998	.6914	.3086
.98	.9193	.7459	.1735	.8265	.38	.9920	.2779	.7141	.2859
.99	.9222	.7393	.1829	.8171	.39	.9929	.2548	.7380	.2620
1.00	9.9250	9.7326	10.1924	9.8076	1.40	9.9936	9.2304	10.7633	9.2367
.01	.9278	.7258	.2020	.7980	.41	.9944	.2044	.7900	.2100
.02	.9305	.7188	.2117	.7883	.42	.9950	.1767	.8183	.1817
.03	.9331	.7117	.2215	.7785	.43	.9957	.1472	.8485	.1515
.04	.9357	.7043	.2314	.7686	.44	.9963	.1154	.8809	.1191
1.05	9.9382	9.6969	10.2414	9.7586	1.45	9.9968	9.0810	10.9158	9.0842
.06	.9407	.6892	.2515	.7485	.46	.9973	.0436	.9537	.0463
.07	.9431	.6814	.2617	.7383	.47	.9978	.0027	.9951	.0049
.08	.9454	.6733	.2721	.7279	.48	.9982	8.9575	11.0407	8.9593
.09	.9477	.6651	.2826	.7174	.49	.9986	.9069	.0917	.9083
1.10	9.9500	9.6567	10.2933	9.7067	1.50	9.9989	8.8496	11.1493	8.8507
.11	.9522	.6480	.3041	.6959	.51	.9992	.7836	.2156	.7844
.12	.9543	.6392	.3151	.6849	.52	.9994	.7056	.2938	.7062
.13	.9564	.6301	.3263	.6737	.53	.9996	.6105	.3891	.6109
.14	.9584	.6208	.3376	.6624	.54	.9998	.4884	.5114	.4886
1.15	9.9604	9.6112	10.3492	9.6508	1.55	9.9999	8.3180	11.6820	8.3180
.16	.9623	.6013	.3609	.6391	.56	10.0000	.0333	.9667	.0333
.17	.9641	.5912	.3729	.6271	.57	10.0000	6.9011	13.0989	6.9011
.18	.9660	.5808	.3851	.6149	π/2	10.0000	......	....	......
.19	.9677	.5701	.3976	.6024					

Table 4. DEGREES, MINUTES, AND SECONDS, TO RADIANS

Deg.	Radians	Deg.	Radians	Min.	Radians	Sec.	Radians
0	0.00000	60	1.04720	0	0.00000	0	0.00000
1	0.01745	61	1.06465	1	0.00029	1	0.00000
2	0.03491	62	1.08210	2	0.00058	2	0.00001
3	0.05236	63	1.09956	3	0.00087	3	0.00001
4	0.06981	64	1.11701	4	0.00116	4	0.00002
5	0.08727	65	1.13446	5	0.00145	5	0.00002
6	0.10472	66	1.15192	6	0.00175	6	0.00003
7	0.12217	67	1.16937	7	0.00204	7	0.00003
8	0.13963	68	1.18682	8	0.00233	8	0.00004
9	0.15708	69	1.20428	9	0.00262	9	0.00004
10	0.17453	70	1.22173	10	0.00291	10	0.00005
11	0.19199	71	1.23918	11	0.00320	11	0.00005
12	0.20944	72	1.25664	12	0.00349	12	0.00006
13	0.22689	73	1.27409	13	0.00378	13	0.00006
14	0.24435	74	1.29154	14	0.00407	14	0.00007
15	0.26180	75	1.30900	15	0.00436	15	0.00007
16	0.27925	76	1.32645	16	0.00465	16	0.00008
17	0.29671	77	1.34390	17	0.00495	17	0.00008
18	0.31416	78	1.36136	18	0.00524	18	0.00009
19	0.33161	79	1.37881	19	0.00553	19	0.00009
20	0.34907	80	1.39626	20	0.00582	20	0.00010
21	0.36652	81	1.41372	21	0.00611	21	0.00010
22	0.38397	82	1.43117	22	0.00640	22	0.00011
23	0.40143	83	1.44862	23	0.00669	23	0.00011
24	0.41888	84	1.46608	24	0.00698	24	0.00012
25	0.43633	85	1.48353	25	0.00727	25	0.00012
26	0.45379	86	1.50098	26	0.00756	26	0.00013
27	0.47124	87	1.51844	27	0.00785	27	0.00013
28	0.48869	88	1.53589	28	0.00814	28	0.00014
29	0.50615	89	1.55334	29	0.00844	29	0.00014
30	0.52360	90	1.57080	30	0.00873	30	0.00015
31	0.54105	91	1.58825	31	0.00902	31	0.00015
32	0.55851	92	1.60570	32	0.00931	32	0.00016
33	0.57596	93	1.62316	33	0.00960	33	0.00016
34	0.59341	94	1.64061	34	0.00989	34	0.00016
35	0.61087	95	1.65806	35	0.01018	35	0.00017
36	0.62832	96	1.67552	36	0.01047	36	0.00017
37	0.64577	97	1.69297	37	0.01076	37	0.00018
38	0.66323	98	1.71042	38	0.01105	38	0.00018
39	0.68068	99	1.72788	39	0.01134	39	0.00019
40	0.69813	100	1.74533	40	0.01164	40	0.00019
41	0.71558	101	1.76278	41	0.01193	41	0.00020
42	0.73304	102	1.78024	42	0.01222	42	0.00020
43	0.75049	103	1.79769	43	0.01251	43	0.00021
44	0.76794	104	1.81514	44	0.01280	44	0.00021
45	0.78540	105	1.83260	45	0.01309	45	0.00022
46	0.80285	106	1.85004	46	0.01338	46	0.00022
47	0.82030	107	1.86750	47	0.01367	47	0.00023
48	0.83776	108	1.88496	48	0.01396	48	0.00023
49	0.85521	109	1.90241	49	0.01425	49	0.00024
50	0.87266	110	1.91986	50	0.01454	50	0.00024
51	0.89012	111	1.93732	51	0.01484	51	0.00025
52	0.90757	112	1.95477	52	0.01513	52	0.00025
53	0.92502	113	1.97222	53	0.01542	53	0.00026
54	0.94248	114	1.98968	54	0.01571	54	0.00026
55	0.95993	115	2.00713	55	0.01600	55	0.00027
56	0.97738	116	2.02458	56	0.01629	56	0.00027
57	0.99484	117	2.04204	57	0.01658	57	0.00028
58	1.01229	118	2.05949	58	0.01687	58	0.00028
59	1.02974	119	2.07694	59	0.01716	59	0.00029
60	1.04720	120	2.09440	60	0.01745	60	0.00029

Table 5. RADIANS TO DEGREES AND MINUTES

Rad.		Rad.		Rad.		Rad.	
1	57°18′	.1	5°44′	.01	0°34′	.001	0°03′
2	114°35′	.2	11°28′	.02	1°09′	.002	0°07′
3	171°53′	.3	17°11′	.03	1°43′	.003	0°10′
4	229°11′	.4	22°55′	.04	2°18′	.004	0°14′
5	286°29′	.5	28°39′	.05	2°52′	.005	0°17′
6	343°46′	.6	34°23′	.06	3°26′	.006	0°21′
7	401°04′	.7	40°06′	.07	4°01′	.007	0°24′
8	458°22′	.8	45°50′	.08	4°35′	.008	0°28′
9	515°40′	.9	51°34′	.09	5°09′	.009	0°31′
10	572°57′	1.0	57°18′	.10	5°44′	.010	0°34′

Table 6. IMPORTANT CONSTANTS

N	Value to 8 Places	Log N to 6 Places
e	2.71828183	0.434294
$\pi/6$	0.52359878	9.718999 − 10
$\pi/4$	0.78539816	9.895090 − 10
$\pi/3$	1.04719755	0.020029
$\pi/2$	1.57079633	0.196120
π	3.14159265	0.497150
2π	6.28318531	0.798180
3π	9.42477796	0.974271
4π	12.56637061	1.099210
5π	15.70796327	1.196120
6π	18.84955592	1.275301
7π	21.99114858	1.342248
8π	25.13274123	1.400240
9π	28.27433388	1.451392
$180/\pi$	57.29577951	1.758123
$\pi/180$	0.01745329	8.241877 − 10

Table 7. FUNCTIONS FOR ANGLES

For each logarithm use value listed minus 10.

Angle	Sin	Log Sin	Tan	Log Tan	Cot	Log Cot	Cos	Log Cos	
0°00′	.0000	———	.0000	———		———	1.0000	.0000	90°00′
10	.0029	7.4637	.0029	7.4637	343.77	12.5363	1.0000	.0000	50
20	.0058	7.7648	.0058	7.7648	171.89	12.2352	1.0000	.0000	40
30	.0087	7.9408	.0087	7.9409	114.59	12.0591	1.0000	.0000	30
40	.0116	8.0658	.0116	8.0658	85.940	11.9342	.9999	.0000	20
50	.0145	8.1627	.0145	8.1627	68.750	11.8373	.9999	.0000	10
1°00′	.0175	8.2419	.0175	8.2419	57.290	11.7581	.9998	9.9999	89°00′
10	.0204	8.3088	.0204	8.3089	49.104	11.6911	.9998	9.9999	50
20	.0233	8.3668	.0233	8.3669	42.964	11.6331	.9997	9.9999	40
30	.0262	8.4179	.0262	8.4181	38.188	11.5819	.9997	9.9999	30
40	.0291	8.4637	.0291	8.4638	34.368	11.5362	.9996	9.9998	20
50	.0320	8.5050	.0320	8.5053	31.242	11.4947	.9995	9.9998	10
2°00′	.0349	8.5428	.0349	8.5431	28.636	11.4569	.9994	9.9997	88°00′
10	.0378	8.5776	.0378	8.5779	26.432	11.4221	.9993	9.9997	50
20	.0407	8.6097	.0407	8.6101	24.542	11.3899	.9992	9.9996	40
30	.0436	8.6397	.0437	8.6401	22.904	11.3599	.9990	9.9996	30
40	.0465	8.6677	.0466	8.6682	21.470	11.3318	.9989	9.9995	20
50	.0494	8.6940	.0495	8.6945	20.206	11.3055	.9988	9.9995	10
3°00′	.0523	8.7188	.0524	8.7194	19.081	11.2806	.9986	9.9994	87°00′
10	.0552	8.7423	.0553	8.7429	18.075	11.2571	.9985	9.9993	50
20	.0581	8.7645	.0582	8.7652	17.169	11.2348	.9983	9.9993	40
30	.0610	8.7857	.0612	8.7865	16.350	11.2135	.9981	9.9992	30
40	.0640	8.8059	.0641	8.8067	15.605	11.1933	.9980	9.9991	20
50	.0669	8.8251	.0670	8.8261	14.924	11.1739	.9978	9.9990	10
4°00′	.0698	8.8436	.0699	8.8446	14.301	11.1554	.9976	9.9989	86°00′
10	.0727	8.8613	.0729	8.8624	13.727	11.1376	.9974	9.9989	50
20	.0756	8.8783	.0758	8.8795	13.197	11.1205	.9971	9.9988	40
30	.0785	8.8946	.0787	8.8960	12.706	11.1040	.9959	9.9987	30
40	.0814	8.9104	.0816	8.9118	12.251	11.0882	.9967	9.9986	20
50	.0843	8.9256	.0846	8.9272	11.826	11.0728	.9964	9.9985	10
5°00′	.0872	8.9403	.0875	8.9420	11.430	11.0580	.9962	9.9983	85°00′
10	.0901	8.9545	.0904	8.9563	11.059	11.0437	.9959	9.9982	50
20	.0929	8.9682	.0934	8.9701	10.712	11.0299	.9957	9.9981	40
30	.0958	8.9816	.0963	8.9836	10.385	11.0164	.9954	9.9980	30
40	.0987	8.9945	.0992	8.9966	10.078	11.0034	.9951	9.9979	20
50	.1016	9.0070	.1022	9.0093	9.7882	10.9907	.9948	9.9977	10
6°00′	.1045	9.0192	.1051	9.0216	9.5144	10.9784	.9945	9.9976	84°00′
10	.1074	9.0311	.1080	9.0336	9.2553	10.9664	.9942	9.9975	50
20	.1103	9.0426	.1110	9.0453	9.0098	10.9547	.9939	9.9973	40
30	.1132	9.0539	.1139	9.0567	8.7769	10.9433	.9936	9.9972	30
40	.1161	9.0648	.1169	9.0678	8.5555	10.9322	.9932	9.9971	20
50	.1190	9.0755	.1198	9.0786	8.3450	10.9214	.9929	9.9969	10
7°00′	.1219	9.0859	.1228	9.0891	8.1443	10.9109	.9925	9.9968	83°00′
10	.1248	9.0961	.1257	9.0995	7.9530	10.9005	.9922	9.9966	50
20	.1276	9.1060	.1287	9.1096	7.7704	10.8904	.9918	9.9964	40
30	.1305	9.1157	.1317	9.1194	7.5958	10.8806	.9914	9.9963	30
40	.1334	9.1252	.1346	9.1291	7.4287	10.8709	.9911	9.9961	20
50	.1363	9.1345	.1376	9.1385	7.2687	10.8615	.9907	9.9959	10
8°00′	.1392	9.1436	.1405	9.1478	7.1154	10.8522	.9903	9.9958	82°00′
10	.1421	9.1525	.1435	9.1569	6.9682	10.8431	.9899	9.9956	50
20	.1449	9.1612	.1465	9.1658	6.8269	10.8342	.9894	9.9954	40
30	.1478	9.1697	.1495	9.1745	6.6912	10.8255	.9890	9.9952	30
40	.1507	9.1781	.1524	9.1831	6.5606	10.8169	.9886	9.9950	20
50	.1536	9.1863	.1554	9.1915	6.4348	10.8085	.9881	9.9948	10
9°00′	.1564	9.1943	.1584	9.1997	6.3138	10.8003	.9877	9.9946	81°00′
	Cos	Log Cos	Cot	Log Cot	Tan	Log Tan	Sin	Log Sin	Angle

Angle	Sin	Log Sin	Tan	Log Tan	Cot	Log Cot	Cos	Log Cos	
9°00′	.1564	9.1943	.1584	9.1997	6.3138	10.8003	.9877	9.9946	**81°00′**
10	.1593	9.2022	.1614	9.2078	6.1970	10.7922	.9872	9.9944	50
20	.1622	9.2100	.1644	9.2158	6.0844	10.7842	.9868	9.9942	40
30	.1650	9.2176	.1673	9.2236	5.9758	10.7764	.9863	9.9940	30
40	.1679	9.2251	.1703	9.2313	5.8708	10.7687	.9858	9.9938	20
50	.1708	9.2324	.1733	9.2389	5.7694	10.7611	.9853	9.9936	10
10°00′	.1736	9.2397	.1763	9.2463	5.6713	10.7537	.9848	9.9934	**80°00′**
10	.1765	9.2468	.1793	9.2536	5.5764	10.7464	.9843	9.9931	50
20	.1794	9.2538	.1823	9.2609	5.4845	10.7391	.9838	9.9929	40
30	.1822	9.2606	.1853	9.2680	5.3955	10.7320	.9833	9.9927	30
40	.1851	9.2674	.1883	9.2750	5.3093	10.7250	.9827	9.9924	20
50	.1880	9.2740	.1914	9.2819	5.2257	10.7181	.9822	9.9922	10
11°00′	.1908	9.2806	.1944	9.2887	5.1446	10.7113	.9816	9.9919	**79°00′**
10	.1937	9.2870	.1974	9.2953	5.0658	10.7047	.9811	9.9917	50
20	.1965	9.2934	.2004	9.3020	4.9894	10.6980	.9805	9.9914	40
30	.1994	9.2997	.2035	9.3085	4.9152	10.6915	.9799	9.9912	30
40	.2022	9.3058	.2065	9.3149	4.8430	10.6851	.9793	9.9909	20
50	.2051	9.3119	.2095	9.3212	4.7729	10.6788	.9787	9.9907	10
12°00′	.2079	9.3179	.2126	9.3275	4.7046	10.6725	.9781	9.9904	**78°00′**
10	.2108	9.3238	.2156	9.3336	4.6382	10.6664	.9775	9.9901	50
20	.2136	9.3296	.2186	9.3397	4.5736	10.6603	.9769	9.9899	40
30	.2164	9.3353	.2217	9.3458	4.5107	10.6542	.9763	9.9896	30
40	.2193	9.3410	.2247	9.3517	4.4494	10.6483	.9757	9.9893	20
50	.2221	9.3466	.2278	9.3576	4.3897	10.6424	.9750	9.9890	10
13°00′	.2250	9.3521	.2309	9.3634	4.3315	10.6366	.9744	9.9887	**77°00′**
10	.2278	9.3575	.2339	9.3691	4.2747	10.6309	.9737	9.9884	50
20	.2306	9.3629	.2370	9.3748	4.2193	10.6252	.9730	9.9881	40
30	.2334	9.3682	.2401	9.3804	4.1653	10.6196	.9724	9.9878	30
40	.2363	9.3734	.2432	9.3859	4.1126	10.6141	.9717	9.9875	20
50	.2391	9.3786	.2462	9.3914	4.0611	10.6086	.9710	9.9872	10
14°00′	.2419	9.3837	.2493	9.3968	4.0108	10.6032	.9703	9.9869	**76°00′**
10	.2447	9.3887	.2524	9.4021	3.9617	10.5979	.9696	9.9866	50
20	.2476	9.3937	.2555	9.4074	3.9136	10.5926	.9689	9.9863	40
30	.2504	9.3986	.2586	9.4127	3.8667	10.5873	.9681	9.9859	30
40	.2532	9.4035	.2617	9.4178	3.8208	10.5822	.9674	9.9856	20
50	.2560	9.4083	.2648	9.4230	3.7760	10.5770	.9667	9.9853	10
15°00′	.2588	9.4130	.2679	9.4281	3.7321	10.5719	.9659	9.9849	**75°00′**
10	.2616	9.4177	.2711	9.4331	3.6891	10.5669	.9652	9.9846	50
20	.2644	9.4223	.2742	9.4381	3.6470	10.5619	.9644	9.9843	40
30	.2672	9.4269	.2773	9.4430	3.6059	10.5570	.9636	9.9839	30
40	.2700	9.4314	.2805	9.4479	3.5656	10.5521	.9628	9.9836	20
50	.2728	9.4359	.2836	9.4527	3.5261	10.5473	.9621	9.9832	10
16°00′	.2756	9.4403	.2867	9.4575	3.4874	10.5425	.9613	9.9828	**74°00′**
10	.2784	9.4447	.2899	9.4622	3.4495	10.5378	.9605	9.9825	50
20	.2812	9.4491	.2931	9.4669	3.4124	10.5331	.9596	9.9821	40
30	.2840	9.4533	.2962	9.4716	3.3759	10.5824	.9588	9.9817	30
40	.2868	9.4576	.2994	9.4762	3.3402	10.5238	.9580	9.9814	20
50	.2896	9.4618	.3026	9.4808	3.3052	10.5192	.9572	9.9810	10
17°00′	.2924	9.4659	.3057	9.4853	3.2709	10.5147	.9563	9.9806	**73°00′**
10	.2952	9.4700	.3089	9.4898	3.2371	10.5102	.9555	9.9802	50
20	.2979	9.4741	.3121	9.4943	3.2041	10.5057	.9546	9.9798	40
30	.3007	9.4781	.3153	9.4987	3.1716	10.5013	.9537	9.9794	30
40	.3035	9.4821	.3185	9.5031	3.1397	10.4969	.9528	9.9790	20
50	.3062	9.4861	.3217	9.5075	3.1084	10.4925	.9520	9.9786	10
18°00′	.3090	9.4900	.3249	9.5118	3.0777	10.4882	.9511	9.9782	**72°00′**
	Cos	Log Cos	Cot	Log Cot	Tan	Log Tan	Sin	Log Sin	Angle

Table 1. FUNCTIONS FOR ANGLES (CON'T)

For each logarithm use value listed minus 10.

Angle	Sin	Log Sin	Tan	Log Tan	Cot	Log Cot	Cos	Log Cos	
18°00′	.3090	9.4900	.3249	9.5118	3.0777	10.4882	.9511	9.9782	**72°00′**
10	.3118	9.4939	.3281	9.5161	3.0475	10.4839	.9502	9.9778	50
20	.3145	9.4977	.3314	9.5203	3.0178	10.4797	.9492	9.9774	40
30	.3173	9.5015	.3346	9.5245	2.9887	10.4755	.9483	9.9770	30
40	.3201	9.5052	.3378	9.5287	2.9600	10.4713	.9474	9.9765	20
50	.3228	9.5090	.3411	9.5329	2.9319	10.4671	.9465	9.9761	10
19°00′	.3256	9.5126	.3443	9.5370	2.9042	10.4630	.9455	9.9757	**71°00′**
10	.3283	9.5163	.3476	9.5411	2.8770	10.4589	.9446	9.9752	50
20	.3311	9.5199	.3508	9.5451	2.8502	10.4549	.9436	9.9748	40
30	.3338	9.5235	.3541	9.5491	2.8239	10.4509	.9426	9.9743	30
40	.3365	9.5270	.3574	9.5531	2.7980	10.4469	.9417	9.9739	20
50	.3393	9.5306	.3607	9.5571	2.7725	10.4429	.9407	9.9734	10
20°00′	.3420	9.5341	.3640	9.5611	2.7475	10.4389	.9397	9.9730	**70°00′**
10	.3448	9.5375	.3673	9.5650	2.7228	10.4350	.9387	9.9725	50
20	.3475	9.5409	.3706	9.5689	2.6985	10.4311	.9377	9.9721	40
30	.3502	9.5443	.3739	9.5727	2.6746	10.4273	.9367	9.9716	30
40	.3529	9.5477	.3772	9.5766	2.6511	10.4234	.9356	9.9711	20
50	.3557	9.5510	.3805	9.5804	2.6279	10.4196	.9346	9.9706	10
21°00′	.3584	9.5543	.3839	9.5842	2.6051	10.4158	.9336	9.9702	**69°00′**
10	.3611	9.5576	.3872	9.5879	2.5826	10.4121	.9325	9.9697	50
20	.3638	9.5609	.3906	9.5917	2.5605	10.4083	.9315	9.9692	40
30	.3665	9.5641	.3939	9.5954	2.5386	10.4046	.9304	9.9687	30
40	.3692	9.5673	.3973	9.5991	2.5172	10.4009	.9293	9.9682	20
50	.3719	9.5704	.4006	9.6028	2.4960	10.3972	.9283	9.9677	10
22°00′	.3746	9.5736	.4040	9.6064	2.4751	10.3936	.9272	9.9672	**68°00′**
10	.3773	9.5767	.4074	9.6100	2.4545	10.3900	.9261	9.9667	50
20	.3800	9.5798	.4108	9.6136	2.4342	10.3864	.9250	9.9661	40
30	.3827	9.5828	.4142	9.6172	2.3145	10.3828	.9239	9.9656	30
40	.3854	9.5859	.4176	9.6208	2.3945	10.3792	.9228	9.9651	20
50	.3881	9.5889	.4210	9.6243	2.3750	10.3757	.9216	9.9646	10
23°00′	.3907	9.5919	.4245	9.6279	2.3559	10.3721	.9205	9.9640	**67°00′**
10	.3934	9.5948	.4279	9.6314	2.3369	10.3686	.9194	9.9635	50
20	.3961	9.5978	.4314	9.6348	2.3183	10.3652	.9182	9.9629	40
30	.3987	9.6007	.4348	9.6383	2.2998	10.3617	.9171	9.9624	30
40	.4014	9.6036	.4383	9.6417	2.2817	10.3583	.9159	9.9618	20
50	.4041	9.6065	.4417	9.6452	2.2637	10.3548	.9147	9.9613	10
24°00′	.4067	9.6093	.4452	9.6486	2.2460	10.3514	.9135	9.9607	**66°00′**
10	.4094	9.6121	.4487	9.6520	2.2286	10.3480	.9124	9.9602	50
20	.4120	9.6149	.4522	9.6553	2.2113	10.3447	.9112	9.9596	40
30	.4147	9.6177	.4557	9.6587	2.1943	10.3413	.9100	9.9590	30
40	.4173	9.6205	.4592	9.6620	2.1775	10.3380	.9088	9.9584	20
50	.4200	9.6232	.4628	9.6654	2.1609	10.3346	.9075	9.9579	10
25°00′	.4226	9.6259	.4663	9.6687	2.1445	10.3313	.9063	9.9573	**65°00′**
10	.4253	9.6286	.4699	9.6720	2.1283	10.3280	.9051	9.9567	50
20	.4279	9.6313	.4734	9.6752	2.1123	10.3248	.9038	9.9561	40
30	.4305	9.6340	.4770	9.6785	2.0965	10.3215	.9026	9.9555	30
40	.4331	9.6366	.4806	9.6817	2.0809	10.3183	.9013	9.9549	20
50	.4358	9.6392	.4841	9.6850	2.0655	10.3150	.9001	9.9543	10
26°00′	.4384	9.6418	.4877	9.6882	2.0503	10.3118	.8988	9.9537	**64°00′**
10	.4410	9.6444	.4913	9.6914	2.0353	10.3086	.8975	9.9530	50
20	.4436	9.6470	.4950	9.6946	2.0204	10.3054	.8962	9.9524	40
30	.4462	9.6495	.4986	9.6977	2.0057	10.3023	.8949	9.9518	30
40	.4488	9.6521	.5022	9.7009	1.9912	10.2991	.8936	9.9512	20
50	.4514	9.6546	.5059	9.7040	1.9768	10.2960	.8923	9.9505	10
27°00′	.4540	9.6570	.5095	9.7072	1.9626	10.2928	.8910	9.9499	**63°00′**
	Cos	Log Cos	Cot	Log Cot	Tan	Log Tan	Sin	Log Sin	Angle

Angle	Sin	Log Sin	Tan	Log Tan	Cot	Log Cot	Cos	Log Cos	
27°00′	.4540	9.6570	.5095	9.7072	1.9626	10.2928	.8910	9.9499	**63°00′**
10	.4566	9.6595	.5132	9.7103	1.9486	10.2897	.8897	9.9492	50
20	.4592	9.6620	.5169	9.7134	1.9347	10.2866	.8884	9.9486	40
30	.4617	9.6644	.5206	9.7165	1.9210	10.2835	.8870	9.9479	30
40	.4643	9.6668	.5243	9.7196	1.9074	10.2804	.8857	9.9473	20
50	.4669	9.6692	.5280	9.7226	1.8940	10.2774	.8843	9.9466	10
28°00′	.4695	9.6716	.5317	9.7257	1.8807	10.2743	.8829	9.9459	**62°00′**
10	.4720	9.6740	.5354	9.7287	1.8676	10.2713	.8816	9.9453	50
20	.4746	9.6763	.5392	9.7317	1.8546	10.2683	.8802	9.9446	40
30	.4772	9.6787	.5430	9.7348	1.8418	10.2652	.8788	9.9439	30
40	.4797	9.6810	.5467	9.7378	1.8291	10.2622	.8774	9.9432	20
50	.4823	9.6833	.5505	9.7408	1.8165	10.2592	.8760	9.9425	10
29°00′	.4848	9.6856	.5543	9.7438	1.8040	10.2562	.8746	9.9418	**61°00′**
10	.4874	9.6878	.5581	9.7467	1.7917	10.2533	.8732	9.9411	50
20	.4899	9.6901	.5619	9.7497	1.7796	10.2503	.8718	9.9404	40
30	.4924	9.6923	.5658	9.7526	1.7675	10.2474	.8704	9.9397	30
40	.4950	9.6946	.5696	9.7556	1.7556	10.2444	.8689	9.9390	20
50	.4975	9.6968	.5735	9.7585	1.7437	10.2415	.8675	9.9383	10
30°00′	.5000	9.6990	.5774	9.7614	1.7321	10.2386	.8660	9.9375	**60°00′**
10	.5025	9.7012	.5812	9.7644	1.7205	10.2356	.8646	9.9368	50
20	.5050	9.7033	.5851	9.7673	1.7090	10.2327	.8631	9.9361	40
30	.5075	9.7055	.5890	9.7701	1.6977	10.2299	.8616	9.9353	30
40	.5100	9.7076	.5930	9.7730	1.6864	10.2270	.8601	9.9346	20
50	.5125	9.7097	.5969	9.7759	1.6753	10.2241	.8587	9.9338	10
31°00′	.5150	9.7118	.6009	9.7788	1.6643	10.2212	.8572	9.9331	**59°00′**
10	.5175	9.7139	.6048	9.7816	1.6534	10.2184	.8557	9.9323	50
20	.5200	9.7160	.6088	9.7845	1.6426	10.2155	.8542	9.9315	40
30	.5225	9.7181	.6128	9.7873	1.6319	10.2127	.8526	9.9308	30
40	.5250	9.7201	.6168	9.7902	1.6212	10.2098	.8511	9.9300	20
50	.5275	9.7222	.6208	9.7930	1.6107	10.2070	.8496	9.9292	10
32°00′	.5299	9.7242	.6249	9.7958	1.6003	10.2042	.8480	9.9284	**58°00′**
10	.5324	9.7262	.6289	9.7986	1.5900	10.2014	.8465	9.9276	50
20	.5348	9.7282	.6330	9.8014	1.5798	10.1986	.8450	9.9268	40
30	.5373	9.7302	.6371	9.8042	1.5697	10.1958	.8434	9.9260	30
40	.5398	9.7322	.6412	9.8070	1.5597	10.1930	.8418	9.9252	20
50	.5422	9.7342	.6453	9.8097	1.5497	10.1903	.8403	9.9244	10
33°00′	.5446	9.7361	.6494	9.8125	1.5399	10.1875	.8387	9.9236	**57°00′**
10	.5471	9.7380	.6536	9.8153	1.5301	10.1847	.8371	9.9228	50
20	.5495	9.7400	.6577	9.8180	1.5204	10.1820	.8355	9.9219	40
30	.5519	9.7419	.6619	9.8208	1.5108	10.1792	.8339	9.9211	30
40	.5544	9.7438	.6661	9.8235	1.5013	10.1765	.8323	9.9203	20
50	.5568	9.7457	.6703	9.8263	1.4919	10.1737	.8307	9.9194	10
34°00′	.5592	9.7476	.6745	9.8290	1.4826	10.1710	.8290	9.9186	**56°00′**
10	.5616	9.7494	.6787	9.8317	1.4733	10.1683	.8274	9.9177	50
20	.5640	9.7513	.6830	9.8344	1.4641	10.1656	.8258	9.9169	40
30	.5664	9.7531	.6873	9.8371	1.4550	10.1629	.8241	9.9160	30
40	.5688	9.7550	.6916	9.8398	1.4460	10.1602	.8225	9.9151	20
50	.5712	9.7568	.6959	9.8425	1.4370	10.1575	.8208	9.9142	10
35°00′	.5736	9.7586	.7002	9.8452	1.4281	10.1548	.8192	9.9134	**55°00′**
10	.5760	9.7604	.7046	9.8479	1.4193	10.1521	.8175	9.9125	50
20	.5783	9.7622	.7089	9.8506	1.4106	10.1494	.8158	9.9116	40
30	.5807	9.7640	.7133	9.8533	1.4019	10.1467	.8141	9.9107	30
40	.5831	9.7657	.7177	9.8559	1.3934	10.1441	.8124	9.9098	20
50	.5854	9.7675	.7221	9.8586	1.3848	10.1414	.8107	9.9089	10
36°00′	.5878	9.7692	.7265	9.8613	1.3764	10.1387	.8090	9.9080	**54°00′**
	Cos	Log Cos	Cot	Log Cot	Tan	Log Tan	Sin	Log Sin	Angle

Table 7. FUNCTIONS FOR ANGLES (CON'T)

For each logarithm use value listed minus 10.

Angle	Sin	Log Sin	Tan	Log Tan	Cot	Log Cot	Cos	Log Cos	
36°00′	.5878	9.7692	.7265	9.8613	1.3764	10.1387	.8090	9.9080	54°00′
10	.5901	9.7710	.7310	9.8639	1.3680	10.1361	.8073	9.9070	50
20	.5925	9.7727	.7355	9.8666	1.3597	10.1334	.8056	9.9061	40
30	.5948	9.7744	.7400	9.8692	1.3514	10.1308	.8039	9.9052	30
40	.5972	9.7761	.7445	9.8718	1.3432	10.1282	.8021	9.9042	20
50	.5995	9.7778	.7490	9.8745	1.3351	10.1255	.8004	9.9033	10
37°00′	.6018	9.7795	.7536	9.8771	1.3270	10.1229	.7986	9.9023	53°00′
10	.6041	9.7811	.7581	9.8797	1.3190	10.1203	.7969	9.9014	50
20	.6065	9.7828	.7627	9.8824	1.3111	10.1176	.7951	9.9004	40
30	.6088	9.7844	.7673	9.8850	1.3032	10.1150	.7934	9.8995	30
40	.6111	9.7861	.7720	9.8876	1.2954	10.1124	.7916	9.8985	20
50	.6134	9.7877	.7766	9.8902	1.2876	10.1098	.7898	9.8975	10
38°00′	.6157	9.7893	.7813	9.8928	1.2799	10.1072	.7880	9.8965	52°00′
10	.6180	9.7910	.7860	9.8954	1.2723	10.1046	.7862	9.8955	50
20	.6202	9.7926	.7907	9.8980	1.2647	10.1020	.7844	9.8945	40
30	.6225	9.7941	.7954	9.9006	1.2572	10.0994	.7826	9.8935	30
40	.6248	9.7957	.8002	9.9032	1.2497	10.0968	.7808	9.8925	20
50	.6271	9.7973	.8050	9.9058	1.2423	10.0942	.7790	9.8915	10
39°00′	.6293	9.7989	.8098	9.9084	1.2349	10.0916	.7771	9.8905	51°00′
10	.6316	9.8004	.8146	9.9110	1.2276	10.0890	.7753	9.8895	50
20	.6338	9.8020	.8195	9.9135	1.2203	10.0865	.7735	9.8884	40
30	.6361	9.8035	.8243	9.9161	1.2131	10.0839	.7716	9.8874	30
40	.6383	9.8050	.8292	9.9187	1.2059	10.0813	.7698	9.8864	20
50	.6406	9.8066	.8342	9.9212	1.1988	10.0788	.7679	9.8853	10
40°00′	.6428	9.8081	.8391	9.9238	1.1918	10.0762	.7660	9.8843	50°00′
10	.6450	9.8096	.8441	9.9264	1.1847	10.0736	.7642	9.8832	50
20	.6472	9.8111	.8491	9.9289	1.1778	10.0711	.7623	9.8821	40
30	.6494	9.8125	.8541	9.9315	1.1708	10.0685	.7604	9.8810	30
40	.6517	9.8140	.8591	9.9341	1.1640	10.0659	.7585	9.8800	20
50	.6539	9.8155	.8642	9.9366	1.1571	10.0634	.7566	9.8789	10
41°00′	.6561	9.8169	.8693	9.9392	1.1504	10.0608	.7547	9.8778	49°00′
10	.6583	9.8184	.8744	9.9417	1.1436	10.0583	.7528	9.8767	50
20	.6604	9.8198	.8796	9.9443	1.1369	10.0557	.7509	9.8756	40
30	.6626	9.8213	.8847	9.9468	1.1303	10.0532	.7490	9.8745	30
40	.6648	9.8227	.8899	9.9494	1.1237	10.0506	.7470	9.8733	20
50	.6670	9.8241	.8952	9.9519	1.1171	10.0481	.7451	9.8722	10
42°00′	.6691	9.8255	.9004	9.9544	1.1106	10.0456	.7431	9.8711	48°00′
10	.6713	9.8269	.9057	9.9570	1.1041	10.0430	.7412	9.8699	50
20	.6734	9.8283	.9110	9.9595	1.0977	10.0405	.7392	9.8688	40
30	.6756	9.8297	.9163	9.9621	1.0913	10.0379	.7373	9.8676	30
40	.6777	9.8311	.9217	9.9646	1.0850	10.0354	.7353	9.8665	20
50	.6799	9.8324	.9271	9.9671	1.0786	10.0329	.7333	9.8653	10
43°00′	.6820	9.8338	.9325	9.9697	1.0724	10.0303	.7314	9.8641	47°00′
10	.6841	9.8351	.9380	9.9722	1.0661	10.0278	.7294	9.8629	50
20	.6862	9.8365	.9435	9.9747	1.0599	10.0253	.7274	9.8618	40
30	.6884	9.8378	.9490	9.9772	1.0538	10.0228	.7254	9.8606	30
40	.6905	9.8391	.9545	9.9798	1.0477	10.0202	.7234	9.8594	20
50	.6926	9.8405	.9601	9.9823	1.0416	10.0177	.7214	9.8582	10
44°00′	.6947	9.8418	.9657	9.9848	1.0355	10.0152	.7193	9.8569	46°00′
10	.6967	9.8431	.9713	9.9874	1.0295	10.0126	.7173	9.8557	50
20	.6988	9.8444	.9770	9.9899	1.0235	10.0101	.7153	9.8545	40
30	.7009	9.8457	.9827	9.9924	1.0176	10.0076	.7133	9.8532	30
40	.7030	9.8469	.9884	9.9949	1.0117	10.0051	.7112	9.8520	20
50	.7050	9.8482	.9942	9.9975	1.0058	10.0025	.7092	9.8507	10
45°00′	.7071	9.8495	1.0000	10.0000	1.0000	10.0000	.7071	9.8495	45°00′
	Cos	Log Cos	Cot	Log Cot	Tan	Log Tan	Sin	Log Sin	Angle

Answers to Odd-Numbered Exercises

Section 1.1. 1. $A \cup B = \{1, 2, 3, 4, 5, 6, 7, 9\}$, $A \cap B = \{7\}$

3. (a) $\{x \mid x$ is a vowel of the English alphabet$\}$
   (b) $\{x \mid x$ is one of the first two Americans who accomplished space travel$\}$
   (c) $\{x \mid x$ is the company publishing this text$\}$

5. To each $x \in A$ corresponds $x + 1 \in B$

7. (a) $A \cup B = \{-7, 1, 2\}$;   (b) $(A \cup B) \cap (C \cup D) = \{-7, 1, 2\}$
   (c) $(A \cap B) \cup (C \cap D) = \{1, 2\}$; (d) $(A \cup C) \setminus D = \{-7, 1, 3\}$
   (e) $(A \cup B) \cap C = \{-7, 1\}$ and $(A \cap C) \cup (B \cap C) = \{-7, 1\}$
   (f) $(A \cup D) \cup C = \{-7, 1, 2, 3, 4\}$ and
       $A \cup (D \cup C) = \{-7, 1, 2, 3, 4\}$
   (g) $(A \cap B) \cup C = \{-7, 1, 2, 3\}$ and
       $(A \cup C) \cap (B \cup C) = \{-7, 1, 2, 3\}$

Section 1.2. 1. Add $-x$ to both sides.

3. If x, y, z are in R, $xy = xz$, and $x \neq 0$, then $y = z$.

5. Suppose $x^{-1} = y_1$ and $x^{-1} = y_2$. Then $xy_1 = 1$ and $xy_2 = 1$. Hence, $xy_1 = xy_2$. Now use the left cancellation law.

9. First prove that $(-x)y = -xy$ starting with $x + (-x) = 0$ and multiplying both sides by y. Then multiply both sides of $y + (-y) = 0$ by $-x$, etc.

11. Note that $(y - z) - (x - z) = y - x$.

13. Prove that either of the assumptions $1/x = 0$ or $1/x \in -P$ leads to a contradiction.

15. Note that $y - x \in P$ and $z \in P$ implies $(y - x)z \in P$.

17. Note that $xy \in P$, hence $1/xy \in P$. Also $y - x \in P$. Hence, $(1/xy)(y - x) \in P$, etc.

19. First get $xz < yz$ and $yz < yw$ and use the result of example 4.

21. Note that $y^2 - x^2 = (y - x)(y + x)$.

23. By exercise 21, we first get $0 < \sqrt{x} < \sqrt{y}$. Then, multiply successively by $\sqrt{x}$ and $\sqrt{y}$.

Section 1.3. 3. If x and y are rational, there exist integers a, b, c, and d such that $x = a/b$ and $y = c/d$. Then $x + y = (a/b) + (c/d) = (ad + bc)/bd$ which is rational.

5. Yes. For example, $\sqrt{2} + (-\sqrt{2})$. (See exercise 20.)

Section 1.4. 1. (a) 10, 15, and 35 are upper bounds; 0, -5, and 2 are lower bounds; 9 is the l.u.b., and 5 is the g.l.b.
   (b) 7, 9, 50 are upper bounds; -5, -25, -6 are lower bounds; 7 is the l.u.b.; and -2 is the g.l.b.

(c) 25, 50, 1000 are upper bounds; -50, $1/2$, 0 are lower bounds; 25 is the l.u.b.; and 1 is the g.l.b.

(d) 26, 30, 50 are upper bounds; 0, 1, 5 are lower bounds; 25 is the l.u.b.; and 10 is the g.l.b.

3. Let $A = \{x \mid x$ is a positive rational number and $x^2 < 2\}$. A has a rational upper bound but there is no rational least upper bound.

Section 1.5. 1. $|x - y| = |x + (-y)| \leq |x| + |-y| = |x| + |y|$

3. $x = (x - y) + y$. Hence, $|x| = |(x - y) + y| \leq |x - y| + |y|$, etc.

5. $1/6 < x < 1/2$

7. Start with $|(1/x) - 4| < 2$ if and only if $-2 < (1/x) - 4 < 2$. Add 4 to each member, etc.

Section 1.6. 1. (a) $S + T = \{x \mid x$ is an odd positive integer and $3 \leq x\}$.
$S \cdot T = \{x \mid x$ is a positive even integer$\}$.

(b) g.l.b. $S = 1$; g.l.b. $T = 2$; g.l.b. $(S + T) = 3$; and g.l.b. $(S \cdot T) = 2$.

(c) Yes.

3. If $A \subset B$, $A \neq \varnothing$ and B has a lower bound, then g.l.b. $B \leq$ g.l.b. A. Also see the proof of theorem 1.6.2.

5. $2.\underline{56} = 254/99$

9. In the process of dividing a by b, at each step of the division, the remainder can be 0, 1, 2, ..., $b - 1$. Hence, after a certain number of steps, the remainders must cease to be distinct.

Section 1.7. 1. (a) a function, (b) not a function, (c) a function, (d) not a function, (e) a function.

3. (a) a function, (b) a function, (c) not a function.

5. Show that the sets $\{(x, y) \mid y = (x^2 - 1)/5x\}$ and $\{(u, v) \mid v = (u^2 - 1)/5u\}$ are equal.

9. Use definition 1.7.1.

Section 1.8. 1. (a) $D_f = R$ (the set of real numbers); $R_f = \{y \mid y \geq -2\}$; $D_g = R \setminus \{3\}$; and $R_g = R \setminus \{0\}$

(b) $f(1) = -1$, $f(-3) = 7$, $g(2) = -1$, $g(7) = 1/4$, $f \circ g(7) = -31/16$

(c) $S(x) = (x^3 - 3x^2 - 2x + 7)/(x - 3)$, $D(x) = (x^3 - 3x^2 - 2x + 5)/(x - 3)$, or $(-x^3 + 3x^2 + 2x - 5)/(x - 3)$, depending on whether we let $D(x) = f(x) - g(x)$ or $D(x) = g(x) - f(x)$; $P(x) = (x^2 - 2)/(x - 3)$, $Q(x) = (x^2 - 2)(x - 3)$, or $Q(x) = 1/(x^2 - 2)(x - 3)$

3. $D_f = R_f = D_g = R_g$, since each set is the set of all real numbers.
$g \circ f(x) = g[f(x)] = 2x + 5$ and $f \circ g(x) = f[g(x)] = 2x + 7$

Section 1.9. 3. (a) $\sqrt{41}$, (b) $\sqrt{26}$, (c) $\sqrt{34}$.

5. $100 = 80 + 20$.

7. Show that $[(5 + 1)^2 + (3 - 1)^2]^{1/2} = [(5 - 3)^2 + (3 + 3)^2]^{1/2}$.

11. For (a) use the fact that, if r and s are real numbers, then $r^2 + s^2 = 0$ if and only if $r = s = 0$. For (b) use the fact that for any real numbers u and v, $(u - v)^2 = (v - u)^2$. For (c), note that for any four real numbers a, b, c, and d we have $(ad - cb)^2 \geqq 0$.

Then, $$0 \leqq a^2d^2 - 2abcd + c^2b^2$$
$$2abcd \leqq a^2d^2 + c^2b^2$$
and, $$a^2b^2 + 2abcd + c^2d^2 \leqq a^2b^2 + a^2d^2 + c^2b^2 + c^2d^2$$
$$(ab + cd)^2 \leqq (a^2 + c^2)(b^2 + d^2)$$
$$2(ab + cd) \leqq 2\sqrt{(a^2 + c^2)(b^2 + d^2)}$$
Add $a^2 + b^2 + c^2 + d^2$ to both sides and conclude that
$$\sqrt{(a + b)^2 + (c + d)^2} \leqq \sqrt{a^2 + c^2} + \sqrt{b^2 + d^2}$$
Now use the preceding inequality and the distance formula to complete the proof.

13. Use the fact that, if p, q, p', and q' are integers, p/q is in its lowest terms, and $p/q = p'/q'$, then there exists an integer n such that $p' = np$ and $q' = nq$. Then use similar triangles.

15. Set the parallelogram in a coordinate plane so that the vertices are the points $(0, 0)$, $(a, 0)$, $(b + a, c)$, and (b, c) where a, b, c are positive real numbers. Using theorem 1.9.4 find the midpoint of each diagonal and show that the two points coincide.

Section 1.10. 5. Each graph is a semicircle.

7. $8y = x^2$

9. Show that the segment with end points (x_1, ax_1) and $(x_1, ax_1 + b)$ is parallel and congruent to the segment with end points $(0, 0)$ and $(0, b)$. The conclusion follows.

Section 1.11. 1. (a) $(x_1/3) - 1 = (x_2/3) - 1$ implies $x_1 = x_2$.
(b) $f^{-1}: x \rightarrow 3(x + 1)$

3. $g^{-1}(x) = \sqrt{9 - x^2}$; $0 \leqq x \leqq 3$.

5. $f \circ g(x) = f[g(x)] = [x + (1/2)] = x$, since x is an integer. On the other hand, $g \circ f(1.3) = g([1.3]) = g(1) = 1 + (1/2) = 3/2$.

Section 1.12. 3. $f^{-1}(x) = (x - 1)/x$

Section 1.13. 1. $S(x + p) = f(x + p) + g(x + p) = f(x) + g(x) = S(x)$; similarly for D, P, and Q.

Section 1.14. 1. Imitate the proof of theorem 1.14.2, using the fact that the points (a, b) and (c, d) are symmetric with respect to the origin if and only if $a = -c$ and $b = -d$.

3. $f(1) = -2$, $f(-1) = 8$, $-f(1) = 2$; hence, $f(-1) \neq f(1)$ and $f(-1) \neq -f(1)$.

5. Suppose f is both even and odd. Then, by definition, $x \in D_f$ implies $-x \in D_f$, $f(-x) = f(x)$, and $f(-x) = -f(x)$. It follows that $f(x) = -f(x)$ for all $x \in D_f$. Hence, $2f(x) = 0$ and $f(x) = 0$.

Section 2.3. 3. If min $\{s_1, s_2\} > \pi r$, then we have $s_1 > \pi r$ and $s_2 > \pi r$ so that $s_1 + s_2 > 2\pi r$, which is a contradiction.

7. Reduce the problem to theorem 2.3.3 by dividing α_1 and α_2 by $2\pi r$ and noting that the remainders must be equal.

Section 2.4. 1. $g_+ \circ S(t) = g_+[S(t)] = g_+[\alpha t / 2\pi r]$, $g \circ S(1) = g_+(\alpha/2\pi r)$. Using condition 5, we have $s_{\alpha/2\pi r}/s_1 = (\alpha/2\pi r)/1$. But $s_1 = 2\pi r$. Hence $s_{\alpha/2\pi r} = (\alpha/2\pi r)2\pi r = \alpha$.

3. If $t = (u/4) + nu$, then $nu \leq t < (n+1)u$. Hence, $n = k$ and

$$F\left(\frac{u}{4} + nu\right) = \frac{(u/4) + nu}{u} - n = \frac{1}{4}$$

It follows that $g_+ \circ F\left(\frac{u}{4} + nu\right) = g_+\left(\frac{1}{4}\right) = P_+.$

Section 2.5. 1. (a) $\sin(-3\pi/2) = 1$; $\cos(-3\pi/2) = 0$; $\cot(-3\pi/2) = 0$; $\csc(-3\pi/2) = 1$.
(b) Same as part a.
(c) $\sin(-2,251\pi) = 0$; $\cos(-2,251\pi) = -1$; $\tan(-2,251\pi) = 0$; and $\sec(-2,251\pi) = -1$.

3. $\sin(29\pi/4) = -\sin(\pi/4)$; $\quad\cos(29\pi/4) = -\cos(\pi/4)$;
$\tan(29\pi/4) = \tan(\pi/4)$; $\quad\cot(29\pi/4) = \cot(\pi/4)$;
$\sec(29\pi/4) = -\sec(\pi/4)$; and $\csc(29\pi/4) = -\csc(\pi/4)$.

Section 2.6. 1. (a) $(0, 0)$; (b) $(\sqrt{3}/2, 1/2)$; (c) $(\sqrt{2}/2, \sqrt{2}/2)$; (d) $(1/2, \sqrt{3}/2)$; (e) $(0, 1)$; (f) $(-1/2, \sqrt{3}/2)$; (g) $(-\sqrt{2}/2, \sqrt{2}/2)$; (h) $(-\sqrt{3}/2, 1/2)$; (i) $(-1, 0)$; (j) $(-\sqrt{3}/2, -1/2)$; (k) $(-\sqrt{2}/2, -\sqrt{2}/2)$; (l) $(-1/2, -\sqrt{3}/2)$; (m) $(0, -1)$; (n) $(1/2, -\sqrt{3}/2)$; (o) $(\sqrt{2}/2, -\sqrt{2}/2)$; (p) $(\sqrt{3}/2, -1/2)$

3. (a) $\sin(14\pi/3) = \sqrt{3}/2$; (b) $\cos(-29\pi/4) = -\sqrt{2}/2$; (c) $\tan(11\pi/6) = -1/\sqrt{3}$; (d) $\cot(-5\pi/2) = 0$; (e) $\sec(13\pi/2)$ is not defined; (f) $\csc(-23\pi/4) = \sqrt{2}$

Section 2.7. 1. See the proof of part a of theorem 2.7.1.

3. See the proof of part a of theorem 2.7.1.

5. (a) Odd because the function is the sum of two odd functions.
   (b) Even because the function is the product of two odd functions.
   (c) Odd because the function is a product of an even function by an odd function.
   (d) Even because the function is the quotient of two odd functions.

Section 2.8. 1. $\cos \alpha = -12/13$; $\tan \alpha = 5/12$; $\cot \alpha = 12/5$; $\sec \alpha = -13/12$; $\csc \alpha = -13/5$

3. $\sin (5\pi/6) = 1/2$; $\cos (5\pi/6) = -\sqrt{3}/2$; $\tan (5\pi/6) = -1/\sqrt{3}$; $\cot(5\pi/6) = -\sqrt{3}$; $\sec (5\pi/6) = -2/\sqrt{3}$; $\csc (5\pi/6) = 2$

5. $[(2 \sin \alpha + 3)/\cos \alpha] - [5 \cos \alpha/\sin^2 \alpha]$

Section 2.9. 1. (a) $\sin (5\pi/12) = (\sqrt{3} + 1)/2\sqrt{2}$
   (b) $\cos (11\pi/12) = -(\sqrt{3} + 1)/2\sqrt{2}$
   (c) $\tan (7\pi/12) = (1 + \sqrt{3})/(1 - \sqrt{3})$
   (d) $\sin (-13\pi/12) = (\sqrt{3} - 1)/2\sqrt{2}$

3. $\sin \left(\dfrac{\pi}{2} + \alpha \right) = \cos \alpha$

5. $\tan \left(\dfrac{\pi}{2} + \alpha \right) = -\cot \alpha$

7. $\sec \left(\alpha - \dfrac{\pi}{2} \right) = \csc \alpha$

9. $(\cos \alpha - \sqrt{3} \sin \alpha)/2$

11. $(\tan \alpha + \sqrt{3})/(\sqrt{3} \tan \alpha - 1)$

13. $2/(\sqrt{3} \cos \alpha - \sin \alpha)$

19. From the identity obtain $8 \sin^3 (\pi/18) - 6 \sin (\pi/18) + 1 = 0$. Now, if $\sin (\pi/18) = m/n$ where m and n are integers, then m is a factor of 1 and n is a factor of 8. So the only possible rational values for $\sin (\pi/18)$ are ± 1, $\pm 1/2$, $\pm 1/4$ and $\pm 1/8$. Show that each of these values is not a solution of the equation above.

Section 2.10. 1. (a) $\sin (-\pi/8) = -\sqrt{(2 - \sqrt{2})}/2$
   (b) $\cos (7\pi/12) = (1 - \sqrt{3})/2\sqrt{2}$
   (c) $\tan (9\pi/8) = \sqrt{(2 - \sqrt{2})/(2 + \sqrt{2})}$
   (d) $\cot (-\pi/8) = -\sqrt{(2 + \sqrt{2})/(2 - \sqrt{2})}$

3. $\sin 2\alpha = 24/25$, $\quad \cos 2\alpha = 7/25$

5. $\sin \dfrac{\pi}{5} \cdot \cos \dfrac{\pi}{3} = \dfrac{1}{2} \cdot \sin \dfrac{8\pi}{15} + \dfrac{1}{2} \cdot \sin \left(\dfrac{-2\pi}{15} \right)$

7. $\cos \dfrac{7\pi}{12} \cdot \cos \dfrac{3\pi}{5} = \dfrac{1}{2} \cdot \cos \dfrac{71\pi}{60} + \dfrac{1}{2} \cdot \cos \dfrac{\pi}{60}$

9. (a) $x = \pi/72$ and $x = 19\pi/48$
   (b) $x = 13\pi/108$ and $x = 17\pi/60$
   (c) $x = 17\pi/60$ and $x = 23\pi/120$
   (d) $x = 17\pi/40$ and $x = 7\pi/20$

Section 2.12. 1. (a) $\mathrm{Sin}^{-1}(1/2) = \pi/6$ (b) $\mathrm{Cos}^{-1}(1/\sqrt{2}) = \pi/4$
   (c) $\mathrm{Tan}^{-1} 1 = \pi/4$ (d) $\mathrm{Cot}^{-1}(-1) = 3\pi/4$
   (e) $\mathrm{Sec}^{-1} 2 = \pi/3$ (f) $\mathrm{Csc}^{-1}(2/\sqrt{3}) = \pi/3$

3. (a) $\arcsin(-1/2) = \left\{ (-1)^{k+1} \cdot \dfrac{\pi}{6} + k\pi \mid k \text{ an integer} \right\}$

   (b) $\arccos \dfrac{\sqrt{3}}{2} = \left\{ \pm \dfrac{\pi}{6} + 2n\pi \mid n \text{ an integer} \right\}$
   (c) $\arctan 3 = \{ (\mathrm{Tan}^{-1} 3) + n\pi \mid n \text{ an integer} \}$
   (d) $\mathrm{arccot}(-5) = \{ [\mathrm{Cot}^{-1}(-5)] + n\pi \mid n \text{ an integer} \}$
   (e) $\mathrm{arcsec}\, 7 = \{ (\pm \mathrm{Sec}^{-1} 7) + 2n\pi \mid n \text{ an integer} \}$
   (f) $\mathrm{arccsc}(-2) = \left\{ (-1)^{k+1} \cdot \dfrac{\pi}{6} + k\pi \mid k \text{ an integer} \right\}$

5. (a) $\mathrm{Sin}^{-1}\left(\sin \dfrac{\pi}{4} \right) = \dfrac{\pi}{4}$ (b) $\mathrm{Cos}^{-1}\left(\sin \dfrac{\pi}{6} \right) = \dfrac{\pi}{3}$

   (c) $\mathrm{Tan}^{-1}\left(\sin \dfrac{\pi}{2} \right) = \dfrac{\pi}{4}$ (d) $\mathrm{Cot}^{-1}\left(\sec \dfrac{7\pi}{6} \right) = \mathrm{Cot}^{-1} \dfrac{-2}{\sqrt{3}}$

   (e) $\mathrm{Sec}^{-1}\left(\sec \dfrac{3\pi}{4} \right) = \dfrac{5\pi}{4}$ (f) $\mathrm{Csc}^{-1}\left(\sin \dfrac{-\pi}{2} \right) = \dfrac{3\pi}{2}$

7. Note that $b/a = d/c$ if and only if there is a number k such that $b = kd$ and $a = kc$. Since we also have $a^2 + b^2 = 1$ and $c^2 + d^2 = 1$, we obtain $(kc)^2 + (kd)^2 = 1$. That is, $k^2(c^2 + d^2) = 1$. We conclude that $k^2 = 1$ and that $k = \pm 1$. The required result follows.

Section 2.14. 1. $x = k\pi \pm \pi/4$

3. $x = \mathrm{Tan}^{-1} 3 + k\pi$

5. $x = \arcsin [(1 - \sqrt{5})/2]$

7. $x = k\pi \pm \pi/3$

9. No solution.

11. $x = (-\pi/2) + 2n\pi$ or $x = \mathrm{Sin}^{-1}(\frac{4}{5}) + 2n\pi$

13. $x = (-1)^k \cdot \dfrac{\pi}{6} + k\pi$

15. $x = (-1)^k \cdot \dfrac{\pi}{6} + k\pi$

17. $x = (-\pi/6) + (2n\pi/3)$

19. $x = (-\pi/12) + k\pi$

21. $x = 2n\pi$ or $x = 2a + (2n+1)\pi$ where $a = \text{Sin}^{-1}(1/\sqrt{10})$

23. $x = 0$

25. $x = 1$

27. $x = 0$ and approximately $x = \pm 1.8; x = \pm 4.8; x = \pm \left(\dfrac{\pi}{2} + n\pi\right)$

29. Approximately $x = \pm.82$

Section 2.15. 7. $x = 2/3$

9. $x = -1$

11. $x = 1,$ or $x = -6$

Section 2.17. 3. (a) $3^4 = 81$ (b) $81^{1/4} = 3$ (c) $4^{-1/2} = \frac{1}{2}$ (d) $10^{-2} = .01$

5. (a) $x = 5$ (b) $x = 16$ (c) $x = 1$ (d) $x = 8$

(e) $x = .001$ (f) $x = 1/2$ (g) $x = 3/2;$ (h) $x = 2$

Section 3.1. 1. $\log(2.561) \doteq 0.40841$

3. $\log(.0023) \doteq 7.36173 - 10$

5. $x \doteq 1{,}435.8$

7. $x \doteq 0.0000000010028$

9. $x = 216{,}080$

11. $x = 35.473$

13. $x = 309{,}190{,}000$

Section 3.2. 1. (a) $(OP, 1/2 \text{ rev}), (OP, \pi), (OP, 180°)$

(b) $(OP, 1/6\sqrt{2} \text{ rev}), (OP, \pi/3\sqrt{2}), (OP, 60°/\sqrt{2})$

(c) $(OP, -1/2\sqrt{2} \text{ rev}), (OP, -\pi/\sqrt{2}), (OP, -180°/\sqrt{2})$

(d) $(OP, -3/14\sqrt{2} \text{ rev}), (OP, -3\pi/7\sqrt{2}), (OP, -540°/7\sqrt{2})$

3. (a) $900°;\ 5/2 \text{ rev}$ (b) $-135°;\ -3/8 \text{ rev}$

(c) $-4{,}140°/\pi;\ -23/2\pi \text{ rev}$ (d) $180°/\pi^2;\ 1/2\pi^2 \text{ rev}$

Section 3.3. 1. (a) $\sin(-51°) = -.77715$ (b) $\cos(5\pi/6) = -\sqrt{3}/2$

(c) $\tan(-395°) = -.70021$ (d) $\cot(2/3 \text{ rev}) = 1/\sqrt{3}$

(e) $\sec(7\pi/3) = 2$ (f) $\csc(-275°) = 1/.99619$

3. (a) $\sin(-51°22'35'') = -.78126$ (b) $\cos(253°21'37'') = -.28635$

(c) $\tan(-27°21') = -.51724$ (d) $\cot(523°48') = -3.4420$

(e) $\sec(-357°2') = \sec(2°58') = 1/.99866$

(f) $\csc(275°5'25'') = -\sec(5°5'25'') = -1/.9960$

5. 167.2 ft

7. $74°3'17''$

Section 3.4. 1. $a = 2.9394$

3. $\beta° = 51°46'$

Section 3.5. 1. $\gamma° = 85°$; $b = 7.64$; $c = 9.29$

3. $\beta° = 58°4'$; $c = 127.3$; $a = 159.5$

5. No solution.

7. $\beta° = 65°11'35''$; $\gamma° = 81°48'25''$,   and $c = 10.9$,   or
    $\beta° = 114°48'25''$; $\gamma° = 32°11'35''$;   and $c = 5.87$

9. $\beta° = 61°17'$; $\gamma° = 76°33'$;   and $c = 8.982$,   or
    $\beta° = 118°43'$; $\gamma° = 19°7'$;   and $c = 3.02$

15. 539.274 yd

Section 3.6. 9. Equality, congruence of triangles, similarity between triangles.

11. The terminal point is (a) $(8, 1)$, (b) $(-4, -6)$, (c) $(-4, 5)$.

Section 3.7. 1. Approximately 495 mph, $39°34'$ south of east

3. 1,200 ft

5. 172.7 lb and 230.6 lb

7. 102.606 lb and 281.907 lb respectively

Section 3.8. 1. Approximately $57,600\sqrt[3]{5}$ in 1965   and $22,500\sqrt[3]{5}$ in 1935

3. (a) \$31,184;   (b) \$31,455

5. 14.5 years

7. $6 + 2 \tan \alpha - 6 \sec \alpha$ where $\alpha = \text{Sec}^{-1} \left(\dfrac{x + 2}{2} \right)$

Appendix A 3. (a) $x^2 + y^2 = 4y$;   (b) $x^2 + y^2 = 3x + 2y$;   (c) $(x^2 + y^2)^2 = 18xy$

5. $d = \sqrt{r_1^2 + r_2^2 - 2r_1r_2 \cos(\theta_2 - \theta_1)}$

7. (a) $(a/2, \pi/3), (a/2, -\pi/3)$, and the pole
   (b) $(a, \pi/12), (-a, \pi/12), (a, 5\pi/12), (-a, 5\pi/12)$
   (c) $(3/2, \pi/6), (3/2, 5\pi/6)$, and the pole

Appendix B 1. (a) $(7, -4)$;   (b) $(18, -38)$;   (c) $(5/28, -205/168)$

9. $(\sqrt{3}, 1), (-1, \sqrt{3}), (-\sqrt{3}, -1)$, and $(1, -\sqrt{3})$

Index

A

Abscissa, 44
Absolute values, 21–24, 214
Acceleration, 186
Addition:
  associative law, 8, 11
  closure under, 8
  commutative law, 9, 11, 78
  complex numbers, 214
  formulas, 104–116, 120–121
  of paths, 78–80
Additive property, of arc length, 75–77
Algebra, fundamental theorem of, 214
Amplitude, 200
Analytic geometry, 41
Angles:
  image of, 168
  initial side of, 168
  law of cosines, 178–180
  law of sines, 180–185
  logarithms, 182
  measuring, 168–174
  revolutions, 168–170, 186
  rotation, 168–170, 172
  solution of right triangles, 175–177
  standard path, 170–174
  standard position, 170–174
  terminal side of, 168
  trigonometric, 167–174
  trigonometric function of, 171–172, 174
  vectors, 186–197
  vertex of, 168
Arbitrary member, of a set, 26
Arc:
  chord of, 78
  inscripture of, 68–77
  major, 68
  minor, 68
Arc length, 68–77
  additive property, 75–77
Archimedean principle, 19, 20
Area function, 154–160
Associative law:
  for addition, 8, 11
  for multiplication, 8
Axiom of completeness, 155–157

Axis:
  polar, 204, 206
  x axis, 41–44, 51
  y axis, 41–44

B

Briggs, Henry, 164
Briggs logarithm, 164

C

Cardinality:
  of the domain of a function, 48
  of functions, 35, 48
  of sets, 6–7
Cardioid, 206
Cartesian coordinate system, 41–46, 85, 204–205, 207
"Chain rule of logarithms," 152
Chord, of the arc, 78
Circle:
  arc length, 68–77
  circumference of, 75
  measuring angles, 168–170
  paths, 77–84
  ratio of the circumference, 75
Circular functions, 85–89, 98–99, 124–125, 170, 174. *See also* Trigonometric functions.
Circumference of a circle, 75
Closed interval, 155
Closure, under addition and multiplication, 8
Cofunction, 98–99, 106
Common logarithm function, 164
Commutative law:
  for addition, 9, 11, 78
  for multiplication, 9
Complements, 99–100
Completeness properties, of real numbers, 8, 9, 13, 18–19, 21, 23–30, 71, 73, 75, 142–149, 155–159
  axiom of completeness, 155–157
  connection with decimal expansion, 24, 29–30
  greatest lower bound, 18–19, 21
  least upper bound, 18–19, 21, 24–28, 30, 73, 75, 142–149, 158–159